THE GRAMPIAN BOOK

Publications edited by Donald Omand:

THE CAITHNESS BOOK	Inverness	1972
THE MORAY BOOK	Edinburgh	1976
RED DEER MANAGEMENT	Edinburgh	1981
THE SUTHERLAND BOOK	Golspie	1982
THE ROSS AND CROMARTY BOOK	Golspie	1984

Other publications:

THE CAITHNESS FLAGSTONE INDUSTRY (with J. Porter)	Aberdeen	1981
A KAITNESS KIST (with J. P. Campbell)	Thurso	1984

THE GRAMPIAN BOOK

Edited by
DONALD OMAND

ESTABLISHED
1899

THE NORTHERN TIMES LIMITED

Published and printed by
The Northern Times Limited,
Golspie, Sutherland, Scotland

ISBN 0 9501718 8 3

Acknowledgements

We wish to acknowledge, with gratitude, the help given by Mr T. Sprott, Department of Physical Planning, Grampian Regional Council; Dr Alan and Ann-Marie Knox for comments on the "Bird Life" chapter; Mr D. Welch for comments on the "Plant Life" chapter; to Mr D. Adams for assistance with the material for Kincardineshire shown in Figure 32.

We are indebted to the following persons and institutions for permission to reproduce illustrations:
Plate 9, Aerofilms Ltd.; Plate 27, The National Trust for Scotland; Plate 28, (Ref RHP 2487), reproduced with the approval of the Keeper of the Records of Scotland; Plate 51, City of Dundee District Council; Plate 52, Aberdeen Journals Ltd.; Plate 53, Mrs R. Martin.

Rainfall data was provided courtesy of the Meteorological Office, Edinburgh.

The figures were drawn by Dr Con Gillen, University of Aberdeen. The index was compiled by Mr Stewart Angus, Stornoway.

We are indebted to Mrs J. Mowat, Halkirk, for her invaluable secretarial assistance.

The Authors

Professor W. RITCHIE	Department of Geography, University of Aberdeen.
Dr. C. GILLEN	Tutor-Organiser, Department of Adult Education and Extra-Mural Studies, University of Aberdeen.
Professor D. SUGDEN	Department of Geography, University of Edinburgh.
Dr. J. STONE	Senior Lecturer, Department of Geography, University of Aberdeen.
Dr. G. MILLER	Institute of Terrestrial Ecology, Banchory.
Mr N. PICOZZI	Institute of Terrestrial Ecology, Banchory.
Dr. M. YOUNG	Lecturer, Department of Zoology, University of Aberdeen.
Dr. B. STAINES	Institute of Terrestrial Ecology, Banchory.
Professor P. RACEY	Department of Zoology, University of Aberdeen.
Dr. P. MAITLAND	Institute of Terrestrial Ecology, Edinburgh.
Mr I. SHEPHERD	Archaeologist, Grampian Regional Council.
Dr. I. RALSTON	Lecturer, Department of Archaeology, University of Edinburgh.
Dr. J. S. SMITH	Senior Lecturer, Department of Geography, University of Aberdeen.
Dr. C. GRAHAM	Writer, Aberdeen.
Dr. D. TURNOCK	Senior Lecturer, Department of Geography, University of Leicester.
Dr. G. DALTON	Senior Lecturer in Agricultural Economics, University of Aberdeen.
Mr D. CUMMING	Senior Lecturer, Department of Forestry, University of Aberdeen.
Dr. J. COULL	Senior Lecturer, Department of Geography, University of Aberdeen.
Dr. S. BAIN	Department of Geography, University of Aberdeen.

Dr. K. CHAPMAN	Senior Lecturer, Department of Geography, University of Aberdeen.
Dr. A. FENTON	Director, Royal Museum of Scotland, Edinburgh.
Mr W. BROOKER	Director, Department of Adult Education and Extra-Mural Studies, University of Aberdeen.
Mr D. MacAULAY	Head of Celtic Studies, University of Aberdeen.
Mr J. D. McCLURE	Lecturer, Department of English, University of Aberdeen.
Dr. D. YOUNG	Lecturer, Aberdeen College of Education.
Dr. P. DUKES	Reader, Department of History, University of Aberdeen.

Contents

Part Three — **GENERAL**

List of Tables

List of Figures

List of Plates

41. **The Crown Tower at King's College, University of Aberdeen. The building was completed in 1506** — *G. Stables*

42. **The Town House, Old Aberdeen. It was built in 1788 of hewn granite. It signified the civic independence of Old Aberdeen from 1489 to 1891, when the small burgh of barony was finally absorbed by its royal burgh neighbour** — *G. Stables*

43. **The Shetland ferry, St. Clair, in Aberdeen harbour** — *J. Livingstone*

44. **Provost Skene's House in Broad Street, Aberdeen. With Provost Ross's house in the nearby Shiprow, it forms two surviving 17th century houses in the centre of the city** — *J. Livingstone*

45. **The planned settlement of Charlestown of Aboyne, on Deeside** — *J. S. Smith*

46. **Strathisla Distillery** — *G. Stables*

Following page 320

47. **The coastal settlements of Findochty, Portknockie and Cullen (background)** — *J. S. Smith*

48. **Elgin, in the productive Laich o' Moray, with the cathedral in the centre of the picture** — *Moray Aerial Archaeology Group*

49. **In Forres (like Elgin) the late medieval layout of the town is still distinguishable** — *Moray Aerial Archaeology Group*

50. **The planned village of Burghead** — *Moray Aerial Archaeology Group*

51. **The Strathspey King: James Scott Skinner** — *Painted in 1913 by J. Young Hunter, City of Dundee District Council*

52. **The first Labour Prime Minister: James Ramsay Macdonald** — *Aberdeen Journals Limited*

53. **The distinguished novelist James Leslie Mitchell, alias Lewis Grassic Gibbon** — *Mrs R. Martin*

Introduction

Prof. W. Ritchie

THE GRAMPIAN REGION

As the shoulder of Scotland is approached from the North-east, a distant view produces an impression of symmetry. Beaches and dunes at Kinnaird Head stretch away to chequered coastal lowlands and, towards the interior, the land rises in a series of lightly dissected broad ridges to the highest point in the extreme south-west limit, the Cairngorm high tops (Plate 2). From the high divide of the Cairngorm plateau area two major rivers flow to the Moray Firth (the Spey and the Deveron) and two to the North Sea (the Dee and the Don). From Kinnaird Head the distances to the west and south limits of the region are approximately equal (c. 90 km; 56 miles). Initially, the pattern of field and forest, farms and towns gives an impression of broad similarity as the eye moves upwards and landwards from the flat coastal lowlands to rounded foothills, and beyond to the deer and grouse moors and occasional snow patches on the rounded summits [more than 1200 m (3940 ft) above sea level], but, on closer approach, these generalisations begin to disappear and subtle differences become increasingly apparent. Viewed from a point above Fraserburgh, the more rugged coast lies to the west and contrasts with the sweep of dunes and beaches between Rattray and Peterhead. The greater area of forest to the west has no parallel southwards. Prominent local hills based on resistant areas of durable rock such as Mormond, Binn of Cullen, Tap O' Noth and Bennachie loom large, and, in the extreme distance, a grey haze marks the eccentric position of the dominant city hub of Aberdeen.

Historically, this approach to the Grampian Region was confined to steamers from Orkney and Shetland or fleets of fishing boats heading south; both epitomising two traditional aspects of its regional identity. Today, helicopters and pipelines make similar approaches and symbolise what appears to the outsider to characterise the modern identity of the Grampian Region — North Sea oil, from which derives growth, expanding service industries, low unemployment (relative to the U.K. average), accelerated urban spread, improved transport and infrastructure. But is this an impression of the economy of Aberdeen and its local hinterland, or is it valid for the entire Grampian Region? One of the more important aspects of this area is the need to recognise that Grampian Region may be dominated by the greater Aberdeen urban area, but that is not to deny the importance of distinctive regional centres such as Peterhead, Stonehaven, Inverurie, Huntly, Buckie, Elgin and many more. Just as the functional hierarchy has more than a dozen second order communities (Aberdeen being first order), there is an almost equal number of areas with unique characteristics and personalities. Where, for example, is the equivalent of the group of fishing towns between Buckie and Macduff, or the whisky villages centred on Grantown? In more general terms, the Laich of Moray, the high unpopulated glens radiating out from the Cairngorm plateau, the gravel terraces of the Lower Spey and several other areas have a palpable identity that is more than just the form of the land, the pattern of settlement or the cover of vegetation. History, cultural associations and the day to day ways of life are the unseen but essential ingredients of these richly varied local landscapes.

Although one should not equate the Grampian Region with Aberdeenshire, an old gazetteer entry for this county might have read "famous for granite, fishing, agriculture, forestry, whisky and holiday-making." Castles, golf, Royal Deeside, skiing and hill climbing could be added as supplementary details. Clearly, it is not possible to encapsulate the rich diversity of any region in a few nouns and adjectives, especially for an area which ranges in climate from the near Alpine (in the Cairngorms) to one of the driest and sunniest in Scotland (near Fraserburgh); in geology, from recent glacial deposits to ancient granites and schists; in cultural antiquity, from flint chipping sites to the magnificent baronial castles and the Victorian splendour of town and country houses; in transport, from steam railways to NATO airfields and radar installations. And what of the unseen landscape of literature, oral tradition, political and religious attitudes?

Like any sizeable area in Britain, Grampian is a palimpsest. There is always farming, industry, antiquities, tourist attractions, literary associations and so on, most of which contain both old and recent elements. Similarly, the nature of any area cannot be summarised in a few glib phrases like "Wordsworth Country" or "Celtic Fringe", or as a catalogue of places, populations and products; regional insight requires some level of systematic description and explanation under a series of headings, so that the reader can judge the relative importance of causal factors and evaluate the validity of sub-regional differences and, in the end, synthesise his or her own image of this ill-defined concept, a regional landscape.

In the 24 succeeding chapters, different writers give their views on one or more facets of the geography, history, economy and culture of the Grampian Region. Some chapters are contemporary descriptive records; some are essentially explanatory or contextual. This book is not a tourist guide, and should not be compared with the numerous books that can be found in the 'travel section' of bookshops and libraries. It is a book in the tradition of the Statistical Accounts or British Association Handbooks; a scholarly record that seeks not only to describe but also to explain. It is a timely book in that it is written at precisely the moment when the price of oil has slumped and the question that has been on everyone's mind for the last 20 years — what happens when the oil runs out? — begins to move into sharper, more persistent focus. Yet, it is timeless, in that the writers have produced expert accounts of present-day situations not only for changing industries such as fishing, forestry, agriculture and others, but they have also provided records of plant life, birds and other features of the environment. Industry, economy, demography and the broad spectrum of contemporary sociology are also described in detail.

In the subsequent chapters, the area corresponding approximately to the former counties of Kincardine, Aberdeen, Moray and Banff is presented as both a source of information and an explanatory guide. All the authors have lived and worked in the area, and therefore add personal experience and day-to-day involvement with the nature and development of the region — and, as such, bring a sense of realism and commitment that enhances the validity and value of these essays which present the reader with a comprehensive picture of this distinctive part of Scottish life and landscape.

Part one

THE ENVIRONMENT

Chapter one

MINERALS, ROCKS AND SOILS

Dr. Cornelius Gillen

INTRODUCTION

Over the last 15 years, the Grampian Region has attracted considerable attention owing to the presence in the North Sea of major oil and gas deposits. These fossil fuels occur in relatively young geological strata, but the history of the region stretches back more than 1000 million years, long before the North Sea ever existed. This chapter outlines the geological development of the region, from the formation of the Moine and Dalradian rocks, the Caledonian mountains and their great granite roots, through the Old Red Sandstone to the oil-bearing Mesozoic rocks and concludes with an account of the effects of the last Ice Age and the soils which formed after the glaciers finally melted.

MOINE ROCKS

The oldest rocks in the region are known as the Moine schists, a sequence of metamorphosed quartzites, schists and gneisses, 1000-800 million years old. These rocks occur in the north-west of the region, close to the boundary with Highland Region (Fig 1). Previously these rocks were referred to as the 'Central Highland Granulites' or the 'Younger Moines' to distinguish them from the 'Older Moines' NW of the Great Glen Fault. Piasecki (1980) has identified two subdivisions, an older Central Highland Division and, separated from it by a tectonic boundary known as the Grampian Slide, a younger Grampian Division.

Gneisses of the Central Highland Division occupy the ground between the Great Glen Fault and a line from Aviemore to Forres (Fig 1). They are coarse quartz-feldspar metamorphosed sediments with interleaved units of mica-rich schists and gneisses. One such schist band occurs at Branchill, 8 km (5 miles) SE of Forres, and in the crags near Pluscarden Abbey. Piasecki (1980) quotes an age of 1000 million years

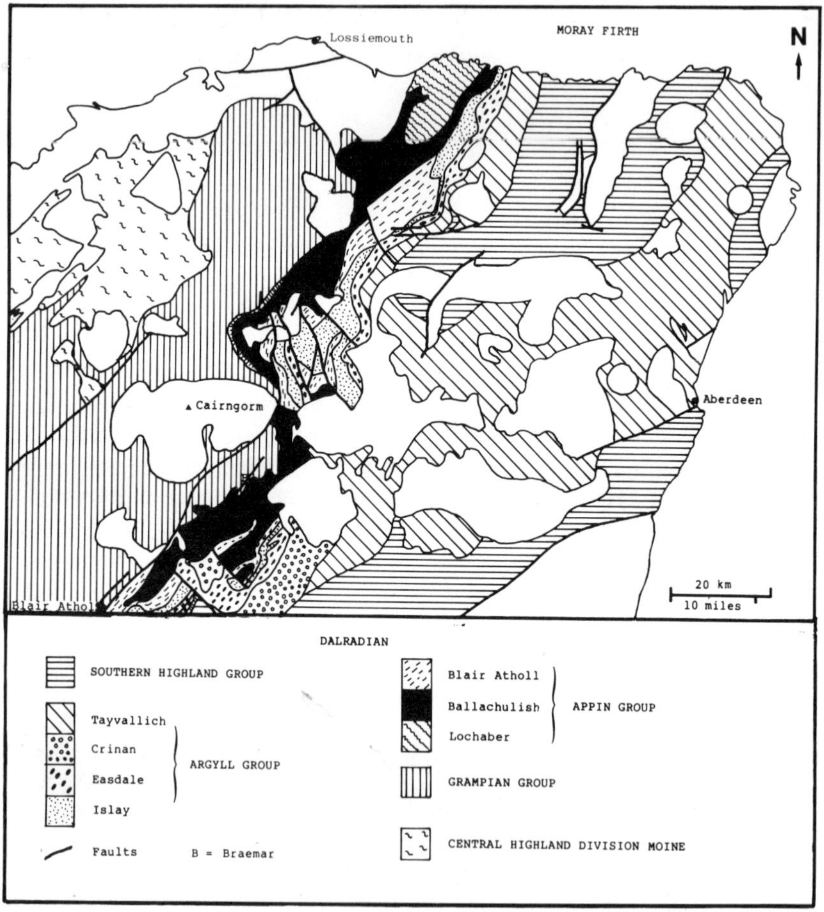

Figure 1 — Distribution of Moinian and Dalradian Rocks.

for the Central Highland Division and concludes that the rocks were deformed and metamorphosed during the Grenville mountain-building event.

Rocks of the Grampian Division sedimentary cover are younger, less metamorphosed, finer grained and less deformed than the basement Central Highland Division gneisses. The two divisions are in tectonic contact along the Grampian Slide. A tectonic slide is a class of fault that formed at deep levels within a mountain chain during folding and high pressure and temperature metamorphic conditions. Major breaks occur along lithological boundaries (i.e. different rock types respond differently to stress) and the rocks are thinned and stretched, often parallel to original bedding planes and sedimentary boundaries. The resulting rocks are thinly banded, platy mica schists, known as 'tectonic schists' (Hutton 1979). The Grampian Slide stretches from south of Forres to Lochindorb, Grantown and Aviemore. It has been investigated in detail at Ord Ban, 5 km (3 miles) SW of Aviemore by Piasecki (1980). The tectonic slide here replaces a sedimentary unconformity (Piasecki and van Breemen 1979). Grampian Division rocks are mostly quartz-rich metamorphosed sediments, originally sandstones with subordinate shales and limey mudstones, laid down in shallow-water marine conditions. The Ben Rinnes and Cairngorm granites were intruded into these rocks after they had been deformed in the Grampian mountain-building event. The schists at the base of the Grampian Division are known as the Monadhliath Schists. Some controversy surrounds the Grampian Division. Harris *et al* (1978) called these the Grampian Group and put them into the Dalradian succession. This has not been widely accepted on account of pronounced geochemical, geophysical and lithological differences between Moine and Dalradian rocks (Lambert *et al* 1982; Plant *et al* 1984; Hall 1985; Anderton 1986). Recently, Harris (1983) reverted to the three-fold division of the Dalradian, though Johnson (1983) points out that some of the Grampian Group quartzites are in stratigraphic continuity with the overlying Appin Group (Lower Dalradian) rocks.

DALRADIAN ROCKS

Dalradian rocks account for the most extensive outcrops in the region. They are referred to as the Dalradian Supergroup, which is divided into three Groups and a number of smaller subdivisions or Formations (Table 1). The rocks form part of the Caledonian fold belt which stretches from Connemara in west Ireland through Shetland north to Greenland, Norway and Spitsbergen (Fig 2). The Dalradian is an enormously thick pile (at least 10-15 km or 30-45,000 feet thick) of sediments ranging in age from 700 to 550 million years. They were folded and

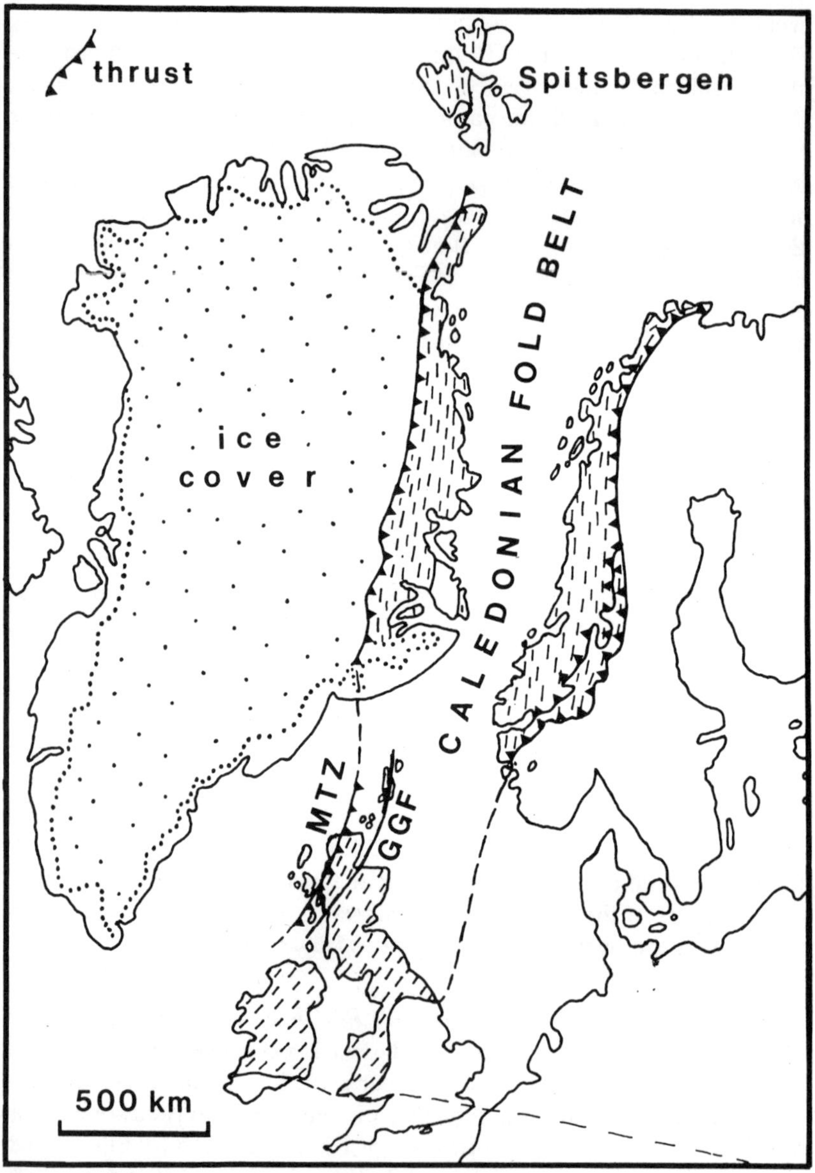

Figure 2 — Extent of Caledonian mountain chain.

metamorphosed during the Grampian Orogeny (an early phase of the Caledonian mountain-building event), 550-450 million years ago.

Broadly, Dalradian sediments evolved as a progression from shallow water marine sands, deposited on a stable, slowly subsiding shelf, to deep water turbidites, deposited by turbulent, submarine mud flows, reflecting rapid subsidence and tectonic instability of the area. Earthquake shocks sent loose muddy sediments down slope into the basin. Faulting during deposition resulted in deep basins with thick sediments, sequences of which varied from one fault-bounded basin to another (Anderton 1982, 1986). Towards the top of the Argyll Group the sediments are quite mixed and include limestones (as at Boyne Bay and Ballater). Pillow lavas and volcanic tuffs also occur, as at Ardwell Bridge, Cabrach. Volcanic activity is another sign of instability in the area.

The increase in tectonic instability, marked by faulting, earthquakes, slumping of sediments and volcanic activity, can be viewed in terms of thinning, stretching and eventual rupture of the continental crust, leading to the opening of the Iapetus Ocean during the early Cambrian or at the end of the Precambrian, around 600 million years ago. The rifting apart of the continent and the birth of this ocean are marked in the SW Highlands by the eruption of the Tayvallich lavas (Table 1).

Prior to the opening of Iapetus, Scotland was situated on a crustal plate that included Greenland, NW Newfoundland and possibly Scandinavia (McKerrow 1982), although Soper and Hutton (1984) have argued that the Baltic region was quite separate from Scotland. Southern Britain and SE Newfoundland had a very different history during later Precambrian times. They were probably situated on a small continental plate far from northern Britain and did not come into contact with the rest of the Caledonian fold belt until the Iapetus Ocean closed. It was at this time that the three continental plates collided and the ocean disappeared by being subducted (forced down) beneath the continents (Fig 3).

In terms of depositional environments, Dalradian rocks can be divided into two parts, below and above the Port Askaig Tillite, which is also present in Banffshire (Table 1). The lower part — Grampian and Appin Groups — consists of thin formations of sands, muds and carbonates, deposited on a stable tidal shelf or marginal marine environment. The shelf subsided slowly during sedimentation. The upper part of the Dalradian — Argyll and Southern Highland Groups — starts with the tillite, a glacial deposit from a widespread Precambrian (650 million years ago) glaciation. The overlying shelf sediments gradually give way to deep water turbidites, related to fault movements during sedimenta-

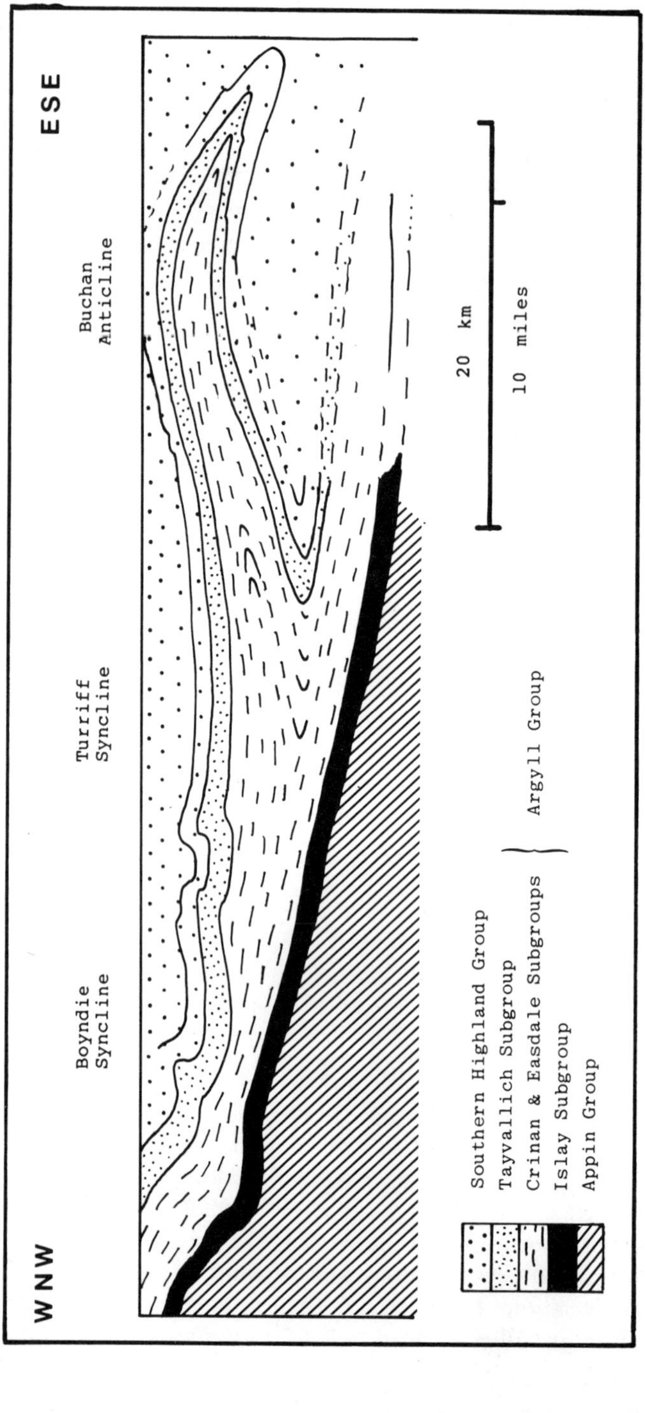

Figure 3 — Cross-section showing the structure of the Grampian Region (modified from Kneller 1986).

tion, so that fault-bounded basins subsided rapidly as sediments poured in.

Fossils in the Dalradian of NE Scotland are extremely rare and equivocal. The MacDuff slates in the Southern Highland Group (Upper Dalradian, Table 1) may contain Lower Ordovician fossils (Downie *et al* 1971) near the top, and the MacDuff boulder bed is thought to be a glacial deposit of Ordovician age. Dalradian rocks are well exposed on the Banffshire coast and full details are given in a new excursion guide to the area (Trewin *et al* 1986).

HIGHLAND BORDER ROCKS

Along the Highland Boundary Fault there is a narrow belt consisting of strips of altered serpentinites, gabbros, pillow lavas, cherts and jaspers, black phyllites, quartzose sandstones, conglomerates, limestones and amphibolites. Individual rock types are often separated from one another by faults and thrusts in this Highland Border Complex and it is possible that individual fragments may originally have been quite unrelated.

The Complex consists of two sequences, an earlier one of pillow lavas, black shales, cherts, turbidites and serpentinites, representing a

TABLE 1

DALRADIAN STRATIGRAPHY OF NORTH-EAST SCOTLAND

GROUPS	SUBGROUPS	BANFFSHIRE	ABERDEENSHIRE	AGES
SOUTHERN HIGHLAND		Macduff Slates Boyndie Bay 'Group' U. Whitehills 'Group'	Collieston Formation	Cambrian 600 m.y.
ARGYLL	TAYVALLICH	L. Whitehills 'Group' Boyne Limestone	Ellon and	
	CRINAN	Cowhythe Gneiss	Aberdeen	625 m.y.
	EASDALE	Portsoy 'Group'	Formations	
	ISLAY	Durnhill Quartzite Tillite		Vendian 650 m.y.
APPIN	BLAIR ATHOLL	Sandend 'Group'		
	BALLACHULISH	Garron Point 'Group' Findlater Flags		Riphean
	LOCHABER	West Sands 'Group' Cullen Quartzite		> 700 m.y.
GRAMPIAN	(Probably correlates with the Moine Schists)			? 1000 m.y.

slice of ocean floor crust. Unconformable on this sequence is a younger succession of limestones, conglomerates and cross-bedded sandstones, representing marine sediments in an ocean basin that was becoming progressively shallower. Dalradian rocks were folded before this younger succession was deposited. The entire Complex was probably forced into place, over a long period of time, as a number of small thrust and fold fragments (See Curry 1986; Henderson and Robertson 1982; Harte *et al* 1984, 1986; Curry *et al* 1982, 1984). Good exposures of the complex are to be seen just north of Stonehaven (Gillen and Trewin 1986).

THE GRAMPIAN OROGENY

The Grampian Orogeny is a sequence of events — folding, metamorphism, igneous intrusion, thrusting, faulting and uplift — which affected Dalradian and Highland Border rocks during late Cambrian to early Ordovician times (550-475 million years ago).

Increasing temperature and pressure, combined with variations in the chemistry and pressure of water and other fluids, due to burial, folding and compression caused original sediments to be altered. The resulting metamorphic rocks have different minerals and textures from their parent rocks. North-east Scotland is world famous for its two distinct types of metamorphic sequence. Barrow (1893) described his 'Barrovian zones' in Glen Esk, while Read (1952) first described the contrasting 'Buchan zones' in Banff and Buchan. Barrow's sequence is based on minerals in original shaly rocks and is divided into chlorite, biotite, garnet, staurolite, kyanite and sillimanite zones in order of increasing metamorphic grade (mainly increasing temperature). Harte (1986) describes an excursion to this classic area. The Buchan zones are characterised by chlorite, biotite, cordierite, andalusite and sillimanite or staurolite in schists (Hudson 1986).

High-grade metamorphic rocks (those with high temperature sillimanite) have been interpreted as being related to the intrusion of gabbros at Insch, Huntly, Portsoy, Haddo, etc. If these bodies were forced into the country rocks at the peak of metamorphism, they would have carried a considerable amount of additional heat that may have been responsible for the sillimanite gneisses (Ashworth 1975; Fettes 1970; Kneller and Leslie 1984). Partial melting of some of the schists and gneisses has produced mixed rocks called 'migmatites' near Fraserburgh and Cairnbulg (Kneller 1986).

FOLD STRUCTURES

The dominant feature of the structure of Dalradian rocks is the presence of large-scale overfolds termed nappes. These structures affected enormous thicknesses of sediments and resulted in the rocks of much of NE Scotland being turned upside down. Four main episodes of folding affected the rocks, the nappes being the first (Kneller 1986). Intense compression and flattening produced a cleavage in the folded rocks, mainly by the growth of platy mica crystals. The peak of metamorphism in the region is associated with the third set of folds and is around 500 million years in age, this being the time of intrusion of various granites and gabbros. The fourth and last episode of folding was responsible for producing the 2-3km (1-1½miles) wide zone of steeply dipping rocks parallel and adjacent to the Highland Boundary Fault and known as the 'Highland Border steep belt' or 'down-bend' (Harte *et al* 1986; Fig 3).

In the Buchan District, the metamorphosed sediments of the Southern Highland Group lie the right way up in a synclinal fold. The district is cut by a system of steep, narrow shear belts in which the rocks were intensely flattened, sheared and recrystallised at temperatures around 600°C. The shear belts have experienced a long history of igneous intrusion, including the 'Younger Basic' gabbro masses. The gabbros are frequently sliced up and disrupted and many of their thermal metamorphic aureoles (heat-affected zones) have been removed by shearing. Shearing probably began around 480 million years ago, shortly after the intrusion of the gabbros (at 490 m.y.) and during the third phase of regional deformation (Ashcroft *et al* 1984; Kneller 1986; Kneller and Leslie 1984).

The overall structure of the Dalradian rocks of Buchan is largely controlled by the Boyndie syncline, a first-phase fold, and the third-phase Turriff syncline (Read 1923). To the east and south, Argyll Group rocks are exposed in the core of the Buchan anticline, a broad arch-like structure of the third phase. Details of the folding and metamorphism on the Banffshire coast are to be found in Roberts and Treagus (1981), Gillen (1986) and Hudson (1986).

IGNEOUS INTRUSIONS: GABBRO AND GRANITE

The two main types of igneous activity in the region are the Younger Basic plutons (also called the Newer Gabbros), 490 million years old, and the Newer Granites, 410 million years old (Figs 4, 5).

The Younger Basic rocks consist of peridotites, gabbros and norites, some of which display rhythmic layering possibly due to crystal settling during cooling. In many cases the surrounding country rocks have been affected by thermal metamorphism, and the deep-seated intrusions are surrounded by a heat affected zone or contact aureole. The main masses are at Belhelvie, Insch, Huntly-Portsoy, Morven-Cabrach, Haddo House and Arnage. They were intruded at the peak of metamorphism,

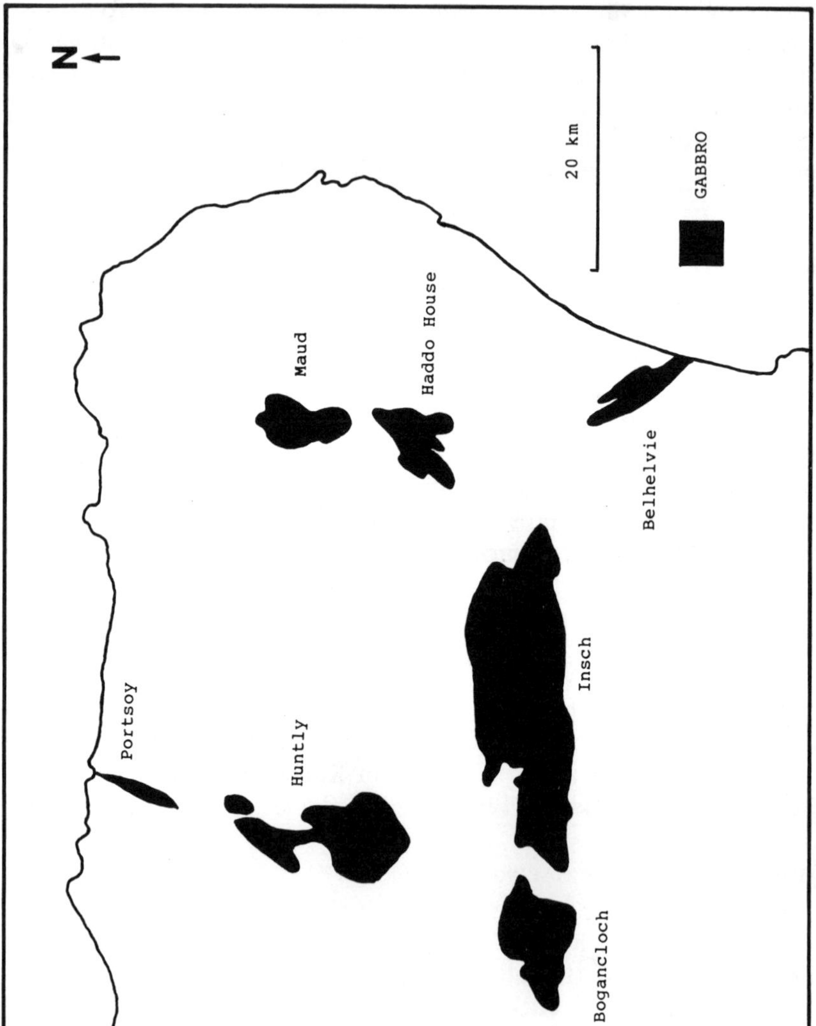

Figure 4 — Distribution map of basic igneous intrusions.

between the second and third phases of regional folding. The intrusions were fragmented and disrupted by shear zones or thrusts after they had crystallised (Kneller and Leslie 1984; Leslie 1986; Ashcroft *et al* 1984; Munro 1985; Munro and Gallagher 1985).

The region is known for its abundant granites — Ben Rinnes, Cairngorm, Glen Gairn, Lochnagar, Ballater, Kincardine, Bennachie, Torphins, Crathes, Hill of Fare, Alford, Peterhead, Strichen and Aberchirder to name a few. These granites are Silurian to Devonian in age, and were intruded into the Caledonian mountain belt after the Dalradian rocks had been folded, metamorphosed, cooled and uplifted.

Pankhurst and others (1982) have divided the intrusions into two groups, an earlier one of variable composition and a later suite of pink biotite granite. Members of the first group range in composition from diorite to granite, with granodiorite being the most abundant type. These bodies, which were forcibly intruded, include the Lochnagar granitic complex, consisting of nine phases of intrusion arranged in concentric zones with diorites in the periphery and granodiorites and adamellites towards the centre (Oldershaw 1974). The Aberdeenshire granite complex shows a rather similar style of sequential intrusions.

Granites of the second group are 400-410 million years old and include Bennachie, Peterhead, Ballater and Cairngorm. The Cairngorm granite is a discordant stock-like intrusion, consisting of the main feldspar-biotite granite and a porphyritic feldspar granite. Contacts between these two units are steep, as are the external boundaries of the entire mass with the surrounding Moine rocks (Harry 1965). An extensive discussion of Caledonian igneous rocks is to be found in Brown (1983).

The granite industry has been important in Aberdeenshire since at least the 18th century. Drum Castle, Crathes Castle and St. Machar's Cathedral are older buildings of granite. Rubislaw Quarry in Aberdeen was opened in 1741 and it became the largest man-made excavation in Europe (170m, 500 ft deep). Aberdeen and Kemnay quarries produced 'silver' granite, while red granite was extracted from the Peterhead quarries at Stirling Hill. Hamilton (1963) presents an interesting historical survey of the granite industry.

OLD RED SANDSTONE

Old Red Sandstone rocks were deposited as thick continental sediments, at the end of the Caledonian mountain building episode. The sediments, derived from the erosion of the young high mountains in the north, were spread out by rivers across the Midland Valley in the south, and merged into lake deposits in the Orcadian Basin of North-east Scotland, the Moray Firth, Orkney and Shetland. At the time the Old

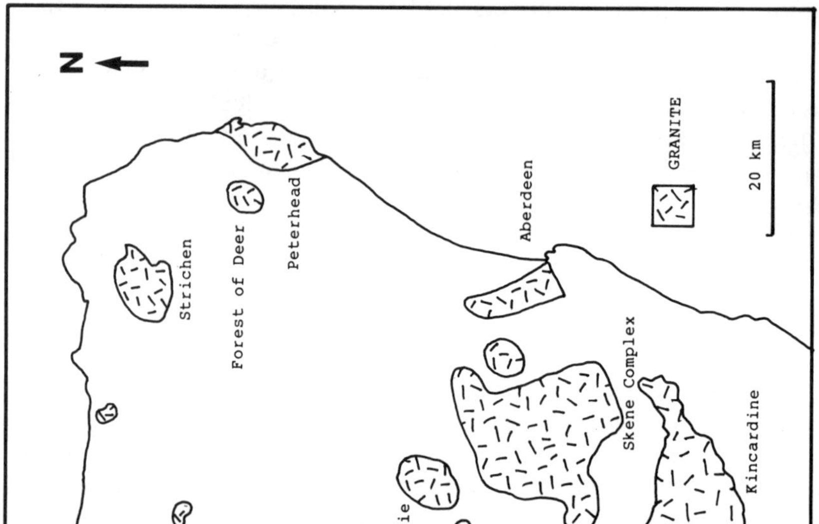

Figure 5 — Distribution map of major Caledonian granites.

Red Sandstone was being deposited during the Devonian Period 360-400 million years ago, Scotland lay in the interior of an enormous continent consisting of Britain, Scandinavia and much of North America. Our latitude then was 20°-30° south of the equator and a semi-arid climate prevailed in the lee of the Caledonian mountains. The sediments were deposited in alluvial fans, rivers and lakes, unconformably on top of the eroded landscape of Moine and Dalradian rocks.

Lower Old Red Sandstone sediments and lavas occur in the Midland Valley in the Strathmore Syncline, a fold running parallel to the Highland Boundary Fault (Fig 6). The fault marks the edge of the Midland Valley graben or down-faulted trough. The succession is represented by 9 km (30,000 ft) of sandstones, calcareous mudstones, conglomerates, siltones, shales and volcanic lavas (Table 2).

Alluvial fans built out from high uplands to the NW and SE, producing thick, coarse conglomerate sequences. Cross-bedded sandstones were the product of braided rivers that flowed across alluvial plains. Volcanic hills temporarily restricted the drainage and caused local shallow lakes to form (Mykura 1983). These rocks are well exposed on the coast south from Stonehaven (Gillen and Trewin 1986). At Crawton there is a 30 m (100 ft) volcanic formation, consisting of andesites and basalts with large tabular crystals of feldspar and gas cavities filled with quartz, chalcedony, amethyst and calcite (MacGregor 1968; Trewin 1986).

North of the Dee, Lower Old Red Sandstone (ORS) sediments occur in a number of isolated outliers at Aberdeen, Tomintoul, Rhynie, Cabrach and Turriff (Fig 6). The Rhynie outcrop is famous for its fossil chert, a silicified peat deposit containing perfectly preserved primitive land plants and the earliest known insects. Deposition in this northern area was mainly in alluvial fans or temporary lakes. Coarse breccias and conglomerates occur at the base of the Lower ORS, containing pebbles and boulders of Dalradian rocks, followed upwards by igneous rock fragments.

The Middle Old Red Sandstone forms the bulk of the Turriff outlier and also crops out extensively between Rothes and Buckie, and as small outliers SW of Elgin. The Middle ORS of the Orcadian Basin varies from being mainly cyclic lake deposits in the north, in Caithness, to mainly river sediments south of the Moray Firth. Fossil fish beds occur at Gamrie and Fochabers (the Tynet Burn), which probably represent an interruption of river sedimentation by an unusually large extension of the Orcadian lake (Trewin 1984, 1986; Gillen 1986).

A considerable thickness of Upper ORS overlies the Middle ORS around Elgin and Rothes. The sequence consists of grey to red cross-

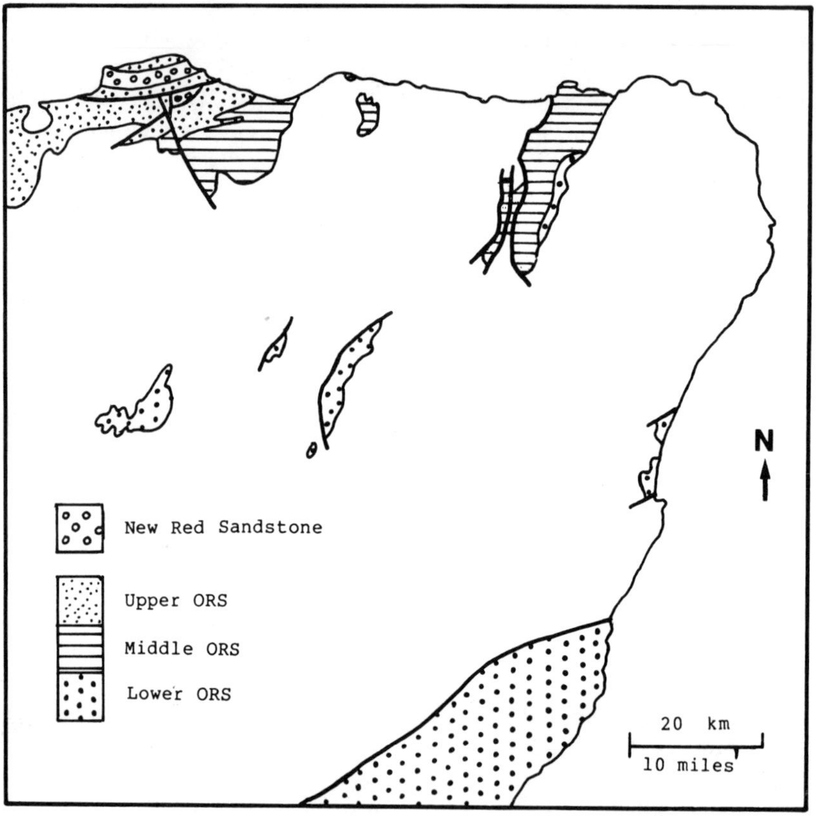

Figure 6 — Old Red Sandstone and New Red Sandstone outcrops.

TABLE 2

OLD RED SANDSTONE (DEVONIAN) SUBDIVISIONS IN NORTH-EAST SCOTLAND

EPOCH	STAGES (age in m.y.)	GROUPS (thickness)	STRATHMORE — MIDLAND VALLEY	MORAY FIRTH — ORCADIAN BASIN
LATE DEVONIAN	(360) FAMENNIAN (367)		St Cyrus Sandstone	Rosebrae Beds
	FRASNIAN (374)			Alves Beds
				Scaat Craig Beds
				Whitemire Beds
				Nairn Sandstones
MIDDLE DEVONIAN	GIVETIAN (380)		(Middle ORS absent here)	
				Hillhead Group
				Inches Group
				Leanach and Dores Sandstone
	EIFELIAN (387)			Nairn and Clava Beds
EARLY DEVONIAN	EMSIAN (394)	STRATHMORE (1700m)		Buckie Beds and Crovie Gp (Turriff)
	SIEGENIAN (401)	GARVOCK (1300m)		
	GEDINNIAN (408)	ARBUTHNOTT (2200m)		(Lower ORS in Aberdeen, Cabrach, Turriff, Rhynie and Tomintoul outliers)
		CRAWTON (700m)	Crawton Volcanic Fm. Tremuda Bay Volc. Fm.	
		DUNNOTTAR (1700m)	Dunnottar Castle Cgl. Downie Point Cgl.	
PRIDOLI (Silurian)	(414)	STONEHAVEN (1500m)	Carron Formation Cowie Formation	

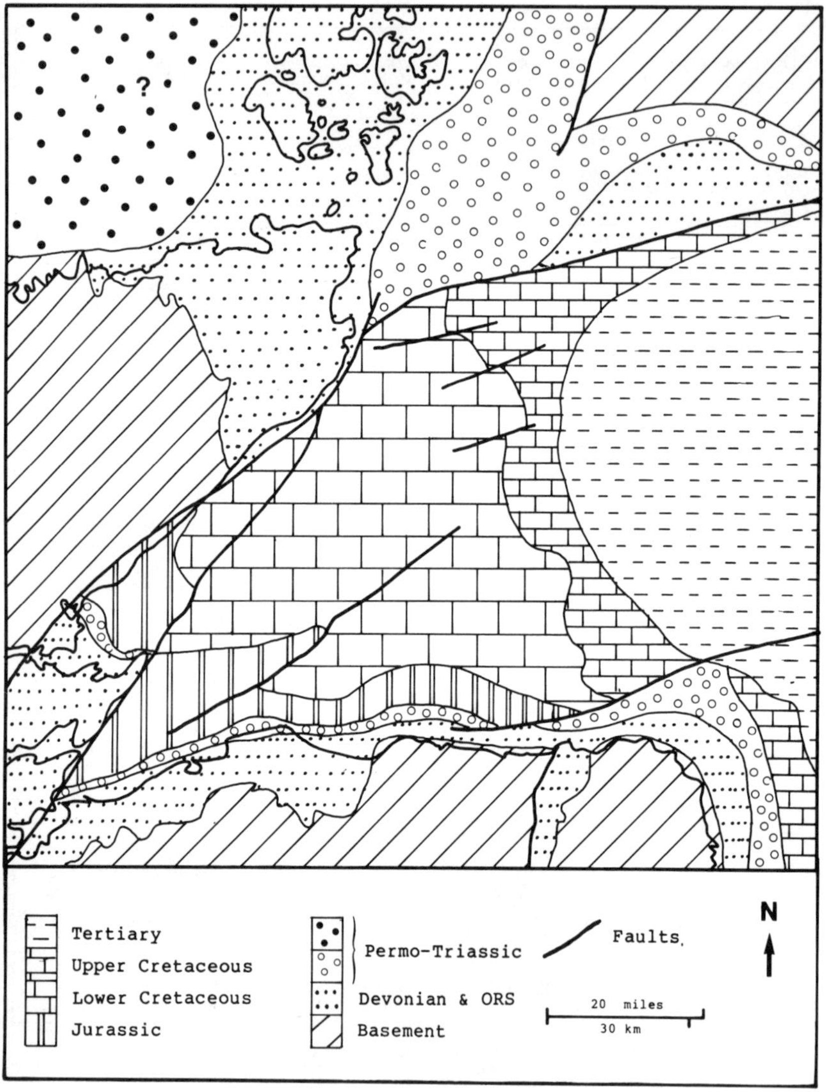

Figure 7 — Geology and structure of the Moray Firth.

bedded sandstones with thin conglomerates, subordinate mudstones and several fish beds. These sediments are the deposits of northward flowing braided streams and meandering rivers which drained into a basin to the north of the Moray Firth. In the west of the region, the highest unit, the Rosebrae Beds, oversteps older formations and rests directly on Grampian Group Moine rocks.

HIGHLAND BOUNDARY FAULT

The Highland Boundary Fault is a complex zone of faults, the main one being a plane that dips steeply to the north-west. Parallel to the fault is the major Highland Border Downbend, a fourth generation fold structure in Dalradian rocks to the north of the fault, with relative movement upwards on the NW side. The downbend may lie structurally above a major step in the basement and is associated with uplift of the flat belt of Dalradian rocks in the late Ordovician, 450 million years ago (Harte *et al* 1984). Within the complicated fault zone, thin strips of Highland Border Complex rocks occur in thrust or unconformable contact with Dalradian rocks and both are in turn overlain unconformably by Old Red Sandstone. The steep attitude of rocks along the fault zone is probably due to vertical movements, but thrust or strike-slip (sideways) movements are also indicated (Harte *et al* 1984). The Highland Border Complex was probably thrust into place at a depth of 10-20 km (6-12 miles), before the formation of the downbend and uplift.

The development of the Strathmore Syncline in ORS rocks (Fig 6) is related to Devonian movements on the Highland Boundary Fault. The syncline runs parallel to the fault, but disappears in the south-west Highlands where the Lower ORS is unfaulted (Kneller 1986; Mykura 1983).

A number of other steep faults trending NE and ENE parallel to the Highland Boundary Fault also occur. These acted as sites for the later intrusion of dolerite dykes in the Upper Carboniferous, 300 million years ago. Faults of this generation were later reactivated and controlled the development of the Moray Firth basin during Permian to Mesozoic times.

PERMIAN AND MESOZOIC ROCKS

Narrow outcrops of Permian, Triassic and Jurassic rocks occur along the Moray Firth shores, from Burghead and Hopeman to Elgin and Lossiemouth (Figs 7,9). Much greater thicknesses are found in the Moray Firth Basin and northern North Sea (Figs 7,8) and are the source of the rich oil and gas deposits.

The Permo-Triassic ('New Red Sandstone') sediments are unconformable on or faulted against Old Red Sandstone, and like the latter they

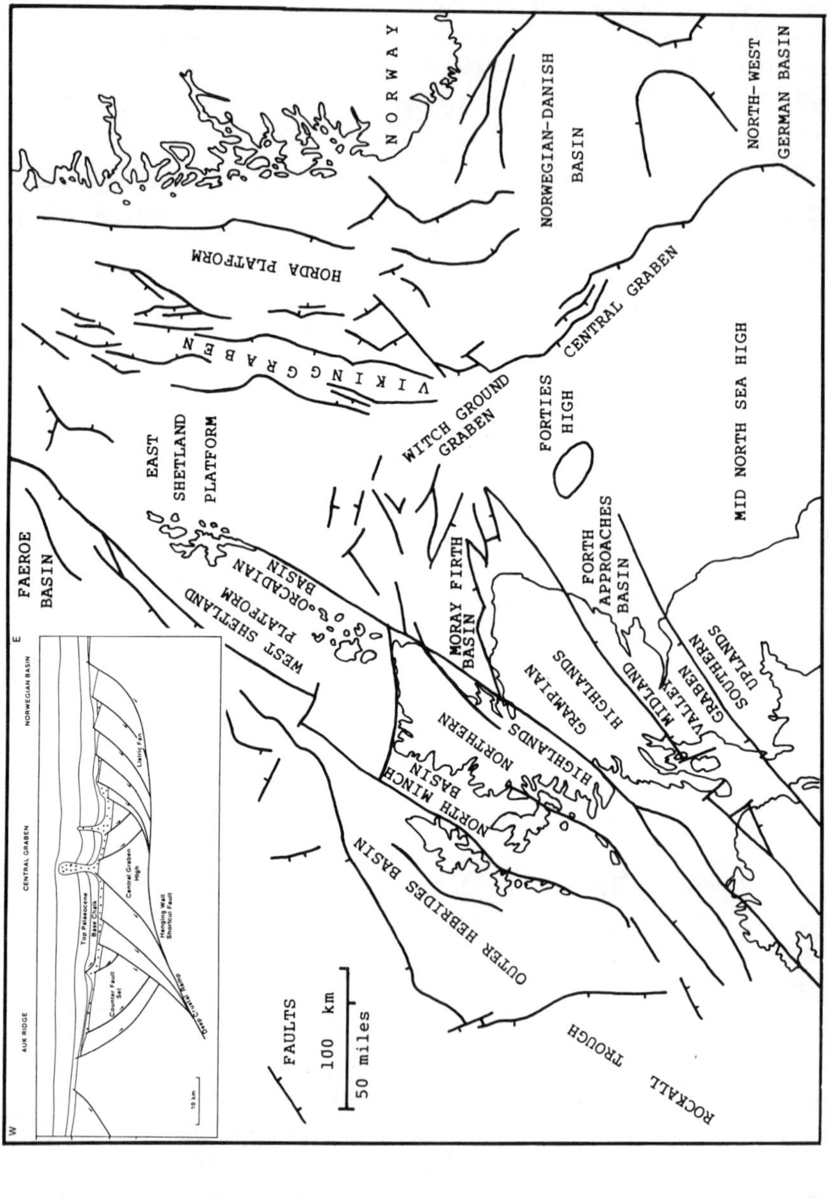

Figure 8 — Structure of the North Sea; inset shows details of graben structures (after Gibbs 1984).

consist of red beds where the colouration is due mainly to iron oxide (haematite) in the cement around quartz sand grains. The red beds are mainly continental in origin and contain few fossils, apart from the reptile skeletons and footprints near Elgin and Hopeman. The oldest formation on shore is the Hopeman Sandstone, consisting of dune-bedded desert sandstones containing wind-faceted pebbles. It is unconformable on the ORS, but the two rocks look so similar that they were mistaken at first. Reptile finds prove a late Permian or early Triassic age. The overlying Burghead Beds are unfossiliferous Middle Triassic yellow, cross-bedded river deposits. Above lies the third unit of the New Red Sandstone, the Late Triassic Lossiemouth Sandstone, Sago Pudding Stone and Cherty Rock. The aeolian Lossiemouth Sandstone contains a reptilian fauna (Peacock *et al* 1968; Lovell 1983; Gillen 1986). King's College chapel, Old Aberdeen, is constructed from yellow Hopeman Sandstone.

Older rocks are found offshore: the Early Permian Rotliegendes, consisting of 500 m (1800 ft) of fluvial and aeolian sandstones, mudstones and evaporites, and the overlying Late Permian Zechstein Group — 1500 m (4900 ft) of marine carbonates and evaporites. Oil has been found in these Permian rocks, principally in the Zechstein carbonates, e.g. the Argyll and Auk fields (Lovell 1983; Duff 1983). The Permo-Triassic sandstones offshore are 300-500 m (1000-1800 ft) thick SE of the Great Glen Fault. They are unconformable on the ORS and are themselves overlain unconformably by Jurassic rocks (Lovell 1983). A very narrow outcrop of Lower Jurassic is found at Lossiemouth (Peacock *et al* 1968; Gillen 1986). Much thicker Triassic deposits are found farther out into the North Sea in the northern Viking Graben and Central North Sea (Fig 8), where the sequence is over 1000 m (3300 ft) thick (Woodland 1975; Glennie 1984).

In the North Sea a thick Middle Jurassic sequence of non-marine sandstones, shales, thin coals and marine sands contains some of the principal oil reservoirs so far discovered. Interbedded basaltic lavas and tuff (ash) are present in the Piper Field in the east Moray Firth basin, comparable with much more substantial Middle Jurassic volcanic deposits in the Forties Field of the Central Graben.

Upper Jurassic Kimmeridgian black bituminous (organic) shales and mudstones are widely distributed in the North Sea and are generally thought to be the source rock of the oil (Hallam 1983; Duff 1983). Similar rocks occur onshore in Sutherland, between Brora and Helmsdale. Most of the oil and gas deposits have been found in fault-bounded basin structures called grabens (German *Grabe* = 'grave'). Traps are mainly tilted fault-blocks, others include salt domes and reser-

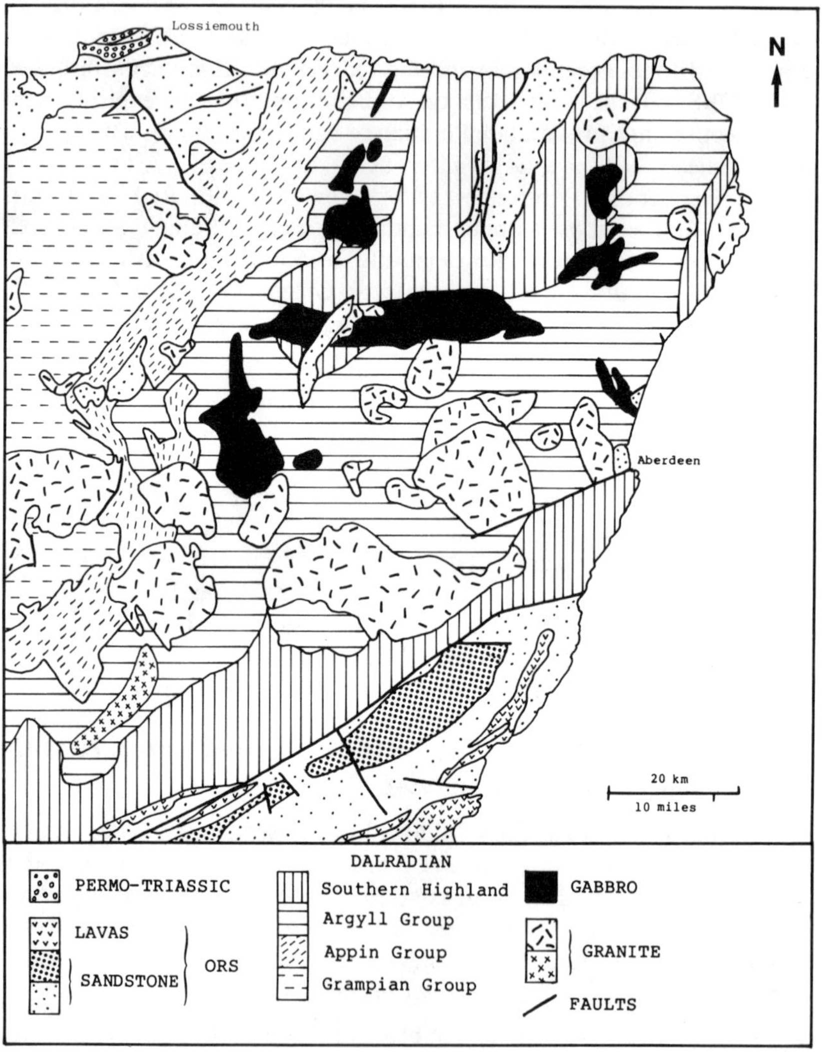

Figure 9 — Geological map of the Grampian Region (after survey maps and Kneller 1986).

voir rocks draped over basement highs. Reservoir rocks are sandstones of Jurassic to Tertiary age, or Zechstein (Upper Permian) carbonates.

Solid outcrops of Cretaceous rocks are absent from North-east Scotland, but fairly large ice-carried erratics brought inland from the North Sea floor are found near Fraserburgh. Upper Cretaceous rocks occur everywhere in the North Sea (Fig 7), including 1400 m (4600 ft) of chalk in the Central Graben, gradually giving way to shales in the northern Viking Graben (Woodland 1975).

GEOGRAPHY OF PERMIAN TO JURASSIC TIMES

During the Early Permian (about 275 million years ago), the Grampian Region was at around 15° north of the equator at a time of widespread desert conditions throughout Europe. The area around the

TABLE 3

1000 MILLION YEARS OF EARTH HISTORY IN GRAMPIAN REGION

ERA	PERIOD	AGE OF BASE IN M.Y.	MAJOR ROCK-FORMING EVENTS
CENOZOIC	RECENT	0.01	Uplift; raised beaches; modern rivers and coastal landforms.
	QUATERNARY	2	Ice Age: erosion in uplands, drift and fluvioglacial deposition in lowlands.
	TERTIARY	65	Widespread erosion by rivers; North Sea deposition.
MESOZOIC	CRETACEOUS	144	Warm tropical sea in area of North Sea, little relief on land.
	JURASSIC	213	Shallow tropical sea, fine sediments laid down in North Sea grabens; oil source.
	TRIASSIC	248	Deposition of New Red Sandstone, desert floor and river sediments, salt evaporites; reptiles.
PALAEOZOIC	PERMIAN	286	
	CARBONIFEROUS	360	Quartz-dolerite dyke swarm. No sediments.
	DEVONIAN	408	Old Red Sandstone deposition in lakes and alluvial fans on slopes of Caledonian mountains. Great Glen Fault, Highland Boundary Fault, granites.
	SILURIAN	438	Folding, metamorphism, Grampian Orogeny, intrusion of gabbros, thrusting, uplift.
	ORDOVICIAN	505	
	CAMBRIAN	590	Dalradian sedimentation in fault basins; opening of Iapetus Ocean.
PRECAMBRIAN	VENDIAN	670	
	RIPHEAN		Deposition of Moinian rocks (Grampian Group).
		1000	

Moray Firth was a low-lying basin containing sand dune fields and wadi deposits of intermittent torrential rivers, surrounded by the arid uplands of the Grampian mountains. In the Late Permian, the edge of the Zechstein Sea was close to the present shoreline of the Moray Firth. East of Aberdeen, great thicknesses of halite (salt from evaporating sea water) accumulated.

In the Early Triassic the lowlands around the Moray Firth were being filled with evaporites and sands from the uplands, while the North Sea was occupied by shallow lakes. In Late Triassic to Early Jurassic times a shallow tropical sea transgressed into the Moray Firth area (Lovell 1983). By the end of the Triassic, relief was greatly subdued and erosion and deposition had almost ceased. Rejuvenation in the Jurassic led to the deposition of deltaic and estuarine sediments in the Moray Firth. Major transgressions of the sea took place in the Upper Jurassic and again in the Upper Cretaceous, the latter representing an important world-wide rise of sea level (Hallam 1983).

STRUCTURE OF THE MORAY FIRTH AND NORTHERN NORTH SEA

The northern North Sea is dominated by graben structures, indicating stretching of the basin, with subsiding fault blocks rotating along curved faults, steep at the surface and shallowing at depth (Fig 8). Slip on these faults occurred in distinct episodes, during the Triassic, Late Jurassic and Early Cretaceous, with sedimentation continuing to fill up the basins. As stretching of the basin continues, second and third order fault sets become established and the result is a complex-looking pattern of rotated wedges (Fig 8b); [fuller details of the mechanism are given in Gibbs (1984), while Beach (1984) discusses the structure of the Witch Ground Graben]. Barr (1985) concluded that the Inner Moray Firth basin was produced by curved faulting above a flat-lying zone of slip near the base of the crust, related to large-scale thinning and stretching of the lithosphere (crust + upper mantle) that produced the North Sea grabens. Complications arise because the brittle crust behaves differently from the underlying ductile material during stretching. The Inner Moray Firth basin contains over 3000 m (10,000 ft) of Jurassic and Lower Cretaceous sediments in the vicinity of the Great Glen Fault (Chesher and Lawson 1983).

TERTIARY AND QUATERNARY

During Tertiary times, 65-2 million years ago, the North Sea was again a major sedimentary basin which received over 3000 m (10,000 ft) of sands, shales, mudstones and volcanic ash in the most rapidly subsiding part. At the same time (65-50 million years ago), the Inner

Hebrides volcanic province was being formed, with the intrusion of central complexes in Skye, Rhum, Ardnamurchan, Mull and Arran. The west coast was uplifted by over 1500 m (4900 ft) and an easterly-dipping slope was established over northern Scotland (Vann 1978). It was probably at this time that the main river pattern became established and huge volumes of rock were stripped off the Highlands by easterly-flowing streams and deposited in the North Sea basin. Isolated hilltop gravel deposits occur in Buchan — the Windyhills and Buchan Ridge Formations. These consist of flint and quartzite pebbles in a sandy-clayey matrix and are considered to be late Tertiary in age (Hall 1982, 1985). During the Tertiary, the climate was warm and humid, with weathering effects penetrating deep beneath the land surface. Glacial and recent erosion have failed to strip off this veneer of weathered rock completely (Kneller 1986).

Climatic conditions in northern Europe deteriorated rapidly at the end of the Tertiary, plunging Scotland into a glacial epoch some two million years ago, at the start of the Pleistocene. The great ice age (see Chapter 2) was characterised by numerous fluctuations from glacial to mild climatic episodes, with the last ice disappearing 12-10,000 years ago. The Grampian Region was covered by ice during the glacial episodes, but it has been argued that parts of 'moraineless' lowland Buchan were not glaciated for much of the time. Erosion features are absent from the Buchan Plateau, while deeply weathered rock and late Tertiary gravels are preserved.

The Cairngorms and the Mounth were areas of extensive upland glacial erosion, as witnessed by the great corries, U-shaped valleys, smooth, rounded granite tops and glacial troughs (Loch Einich, Loch Avon. Glacial deposits in the highland areas are represented by moraines and in lowland areas by water-laid deposits such as river terraces and sands and gravels of eskers and kames deposited from streams flowing beneath the ice sheet. Tills predominate around the east, deposited by ice moving SE from the Moray Firth. Greyish-blue tills in the north include fragments of Mesozoic rocks, while the red tills of Strathmore and northwards contain much Old Red Sandstone, which is responsible for the colouration. Meltwater features abound in Strathmore, mainly as broad fans of glacial outwash from rivers that flowed down from the melting edge of the ice sheet as it retreated into the Grampian hills.

In the Moray Firth, glacial drift up to 70 m (230 ft) occurs in five elongate E-W basins, parallel to the coast between Lossiemouth and Fraserburgh.

SOILS

The soil types which have developed in the Grampian Region since the end of the Ice Age are due to the interplay of a number of factors, principally parent rock type, climate and topography. Parent rocks are mostly Dalradian and Moine schists and Caledonian granites, with gabbros and Old Red Sandstone making up the remainder (Fig 9). Topographic areas consist of the Moray Firth lowlands, the Buchan Platform, the Grampian Highlands and the Strathmore lowlands. Climatic regions vary from the warm and moderately dry sheltered Moray Firth shores through the fairly warm and moderately dry Buchan and Strathmore areas to the wet and progressively cool, cold and very cold hilly and exposed mountainous parts (Birse and Dry 1970).

Thus the region's soils are predominantly derived from acid parent materials. Around three-quarters of the land area is occupied by nine soil associations out of 56 associations covering the Eastern Scotland Soil Survey Map (1:250 000 scale, sheet 5, Walker *et al* 1982).

In the Moray Firth lowlands, the red and yellow Old Red Sandstone sediments have an associated drift of reddish brown sandy loam. The dominant soils are podzols derived from acid parents, with a characteristic rather coarse texture and free drainage (Walker *et al* 1982). The fluvioglacial, raised beach and alluvial soils contain a very high percentage of quartz sand. Soil instability is a common feature and wind erosion has been responsible for much damage — witness the Culbin Sands of Moray (Ross 1976).

The lowlands of Buchan and Aberdeenshire are mainly dominated by gentle, rolling topography, the land being underlain by Dalradian schists and quartzites (e.g. Mormond Hill), with granite around Peterhead and the Skene Lowlands, and the Old Red Sandstone in the Turriff syncline. Acid and podzolic soils predominate, with restricted occurrences of brown forest soils, as in the Insch valley, where there is good arable land. Soils of the Inch Association (Walker *et al* 1972) are developed on drift derived from gabbro and hornblende schist, a metamorphosed igneous rock. It is noteworthy that the Insch gabbro (Fig 9) has weathered out to produce low ground; the higher hills in the Glens of Foudland are made of hornfels, heat-altered slates surrounding the intrusion. The slates of this area were once extensively worked.

In the Strathmore part of the Midland Valley, Old Red Sandstone forms the parent material and brown forest soils are widespread on till deposits. Humus-iron podzols are not extensive and are thought to be recent degradation products from brown forest soils. Parent materials are rather coarse fluvioglacial sediments in Strathmore and Howe o' the Mearns.

The Grampian Highlands include the highest plateau in Britain, at 1300 m (4250 ft). The main rock type is granite, which has been moulded by ice to form broad, smooth, rounded, convex hill tops rising steeply from wide U-shaped valleys. The Dee is the main river, which flows eastwards, like the Don, while tributaries of the Spey and Deveron drain to the north. Glacial drift is widespread and thick in valleys, with hillsides covered in a thin stoney veneer of local drift. Fluvioglacial terraces are common in the low ground. Alpine and subalpine soils are common on the Cairngorm plateau and on lower north-facing steep slopes. They are coarse, free draining and podzolic, reflecting the coarse acid nature of the parent material and the cool climate. Peaty podzols occupy the ground below 600 m (1970 ft) in the wetter west of the region. Heather moorland is indicative of the dominating podzolic soils. The main zone of blanket peat formation lies between 550-750 m (1800-2450 ft). In the west, blanket peat is associated with peaty podzols, while at high levels hagged peat occurs in sheltered hollows and is found with alpine and subalpine soils (Walker *et al* 1982).

Chapter two

THE LANDSCAPE

Prof. David Sugden

INTRODUCTION

In the last few years work on land and offshore in the North Sea has revealed exciting and surprising new insights into our understanding of the land surface of Grampian Region. One realisation is that parts of the land surface are extremely old. For example, if you stand on the summit plateau of the Cairngorms or on the Hill of Dudwick in central Buchan you will be on a land surface which has remained essentially unchanged for over 10 million years or longer. This great antiquity is remarkable when we realise that in the western Highlands of Scotland the land surface has been lowered by many hundred metres and completely transformed in the same time span. A second striking realisation is that the old land surface has survived repeated inundation by ice sheets during the Ice Age. These ice sheets were up to 1700 m (5575 ft) thick over Buchan and yet, unlike in the western Highlands, or indeed the eastern Grampians, there is little sign of their presence except in thin surface deposits. It is the purpose of this chapter to try and explain these and other distinctive characteristics of the Grampian landscape.

The main factors affecting the landforms of an area are firstly, the geological base and secondly the surface processes attacking the geological base. These latter processes change over time and the present landscape is a palimpsest of distinctive landforms created by the sequence of processes. The earliest landforms in Grampian Region date from conditions before the Ice Age and reflect sub-tropical/warm-temperate conditions. Another distinctive set of landforms relates to glacier expansion during the Ice Age when polar conditions affected the landscape. Finally, there are those landforms characteristic of the present-day cool-temperate processes which have existed since the last glaciation and during earlier interglacial periods. The sequence of processes and its duration is shown in Fig 10. Tropical conditions affected Scotland in the early Tertiary period from 66 - c.38 million years ago. Sub-tropical conditions occurred from c.38 - 10 million years ago with warm temperate conditions lasting until after three million years ago. Alternating polar and cool temperate processes have affected Scotland for the last 2.4 million years. The last glacial episode ended about 10,000 years ago, since when cool-temperate conditions have lasted until the present day.

This chapter first describes the main landforms of Grampian. It then tries to explain the landforms, first in terms of the role of the geological base and then in terms of the sequence of (a) sub-tropical/warm-temperate, (b) Ice Age and (c) cool-temperate processes. Finally the conclusion highlights the wider significance of Grampian landforms.

THE LANDFORMS

The topography of Grampian Region consists of stepped plateaux which rise from the coast to the Cairngorm Mountains (Fleet 1938; Fig 11). Although there are many irregularities, three main plateaux can be recognised. The highest comprises the summit plateau of the Cairngorms and Lochnagar and its gently undulating nature is well seen in the exhilarating high level walk between Cairngorm and the highest summit, Ben Macdui, at an altitude of 1309 m (4295 ft) (Plate 2). The Cairngorm massif rises abruptly above a second Grampian plateau which surrounds it at an altitude of 750-900 m (2460-2955 ft) and slopes gently north-eastwards, eastwards and south-eastwards to altitudes of 400-600 m (1310-1970 ft). This latter surface consists of broad summits whose concordant heights over distances of up to 80 km (50 miles) are well seen on a clear day. For example, it is possible to stand on the slopes of Ben Avon and look eastwards across several skylines to the craggy summit of Bennachie (528 m; 1732 ft) just west of Inverurie. Alternatively, one can stand on the summit of Bennachie and see the uprising massifs of Cairngorm and Lochnagar. Another impressive example of this plateau extends as the Mounth Plateau between Lochnagar and the sea. It is 700-800 m (2295-2625 ft) high near Lochnagar but declines in altitude eastwards where it is more dissected. In several places isolated hills rise abruptly above the overall plateau level, for example Morvern (871 m; 2858 ft) and Mount Keen (939 m; 3082 ft).

River valleys have cut into these high plateaux giving smooth yet often steep valley sides with angles up to 30°. Often the valleys meander sharply, for example in upper Strathdon. Generally the plateau is more broken up near its eastern and northern margin, especially where the valleys have broadened out to form basins, such as at Alford, Tarland,

Time before present (m = million years)		Epoch	land-forming processes
Present			
		Holocene	cool temperate
10,000			
		Pleistocene	glacial/periglacial (with brief cool temperate interglacials)
c. 2.4 m			
		Pliocene	warm temperate
5 m			
10 m	Late	Miocene	
14 m	Middle		sub-tropical
22 m	Early		
		Oligocene	
38 m			
		Eocene	tropical
55 m			
		Palaeocene	
65 m			

Figure 10 — The sequence of land-forming processes affecting Grampian and their approximate ages.

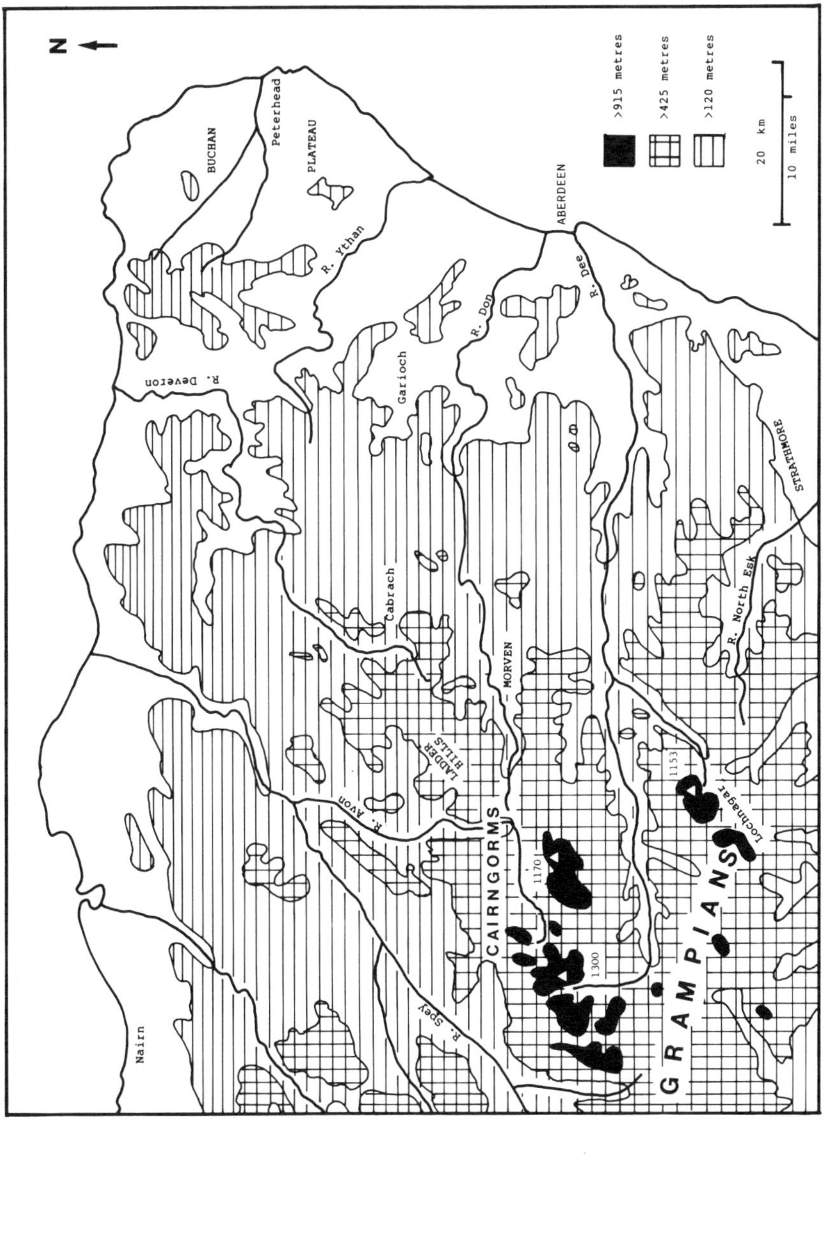

Figure 11 — The topography of North-east Scotland (after Clapperton and Sugden 1977).

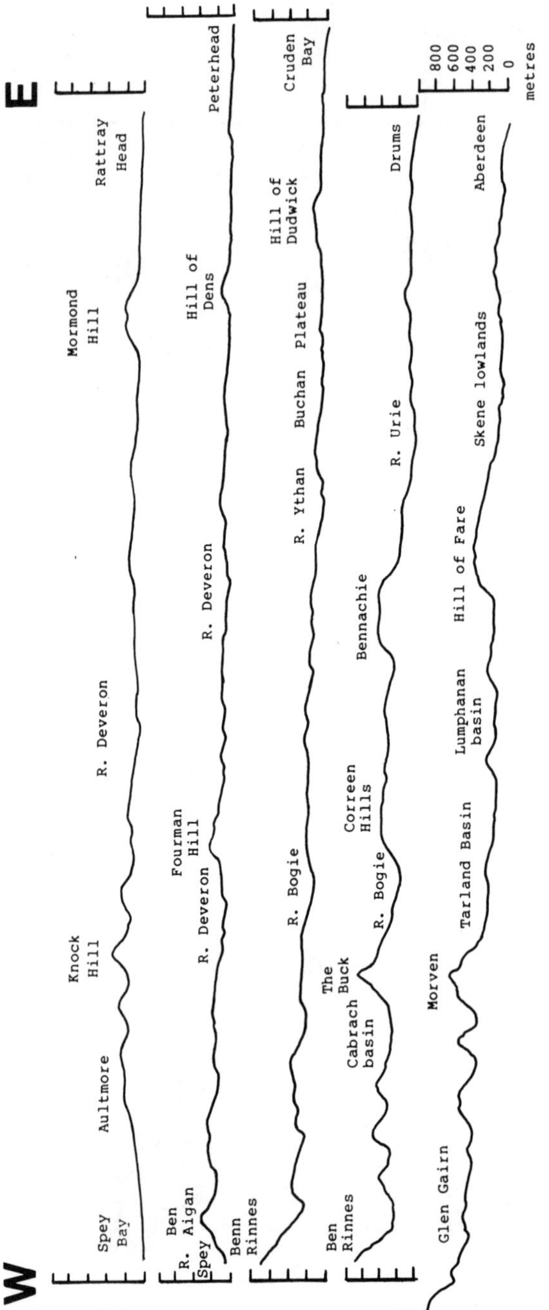

Figure 12 — Topographic profile across North-east Scotland (after Hall 1983).

Knock, Aberchirder and the Braes of Glenlivet. Of these the Howe of Alford is the most striking with the River Don entering and leaving a 10 km (6 mile) long basin via narrow valley sections. The two master river valleys in the region are those of the Spey and the Dee and both cut across the lie of the underlying geology. The Spey is typical of many rivers in the north-west of the region in that it flows from south-west to north-east. The Dee is typical of many eastern rivers such as the Don and South Ugie which flow from west to east. A major watershed between the two groups of rivers runs eastwards from the Cairngorms towards the vicinity of Troup Head between Banff and Fraserburgh.

The third level known as the Buchan lowland, is separated from the upland Grampian plateau by an abrupt slope which is well displayed on the eastern flanks of Bennachie and the Hill of Fare, west of Aberdeen (Fig 12). The Buchan lowland and its continuation in the Moray lowlands extends between the uplands and the straight coastlines of North-east Scotland. It extends inland for a distance of up to 40 km (25 miles) at an altitude of 60-150 m (195-490 ft). although there is considerable relief in detail, the main feature is gently undulating topography with few sharp breaks of slope. Shallow basins occur, such as at Maud and New Pitsligo. The most conspicuous features are upstanding isolated hills, for example Brimmond and Tyrebagger near Aberdeen and Mormond Hill near Strichen (Fig 12). The lowland plain is cut across rocks of different type and over most of its area bedrock is near the surface. Near the coast, however, in the vicinity of Elgin, between Rosehearty and Peterhead and between Cruden Bay and Aberdeen the bedrock is obscured beneath thick glacial deposits. On the coast itself there are extensive sand beaches associated with these zones of deposits.

THE GEOLOGICAL BASE: ROCKS, STRUCTURE AND TECTONICS

The rocks of Grampian have been described in Chapter 1 and they consist of metamorphics with localised intrusions of granite. The only important sedimentary rocks in the region are patches of Old Red Sandstone. However, there are thick sequences of sedimentary rocks offshore in the Moray Firth and North Sea basins. The region is the eastern part of a structural block bounded to the south by the Highland Boundary Fault, to the north-west by the Great Glen Fault and to the north and east by faults roughly coincident with the Moray and North Sea coastlines respectively (Hall 1963). The block, called the Grampian High, is itself broken into three main parts by fractures running along the Dee and Spey valleys.

Movements of the Grampian High block have been dominated by tilting associated with uplift of the western Highlands and subsidence in the North Sea basin. This tilting began some 70-80 million years ago in the Cretaceous period and has continued with breaks and reversals up to the present day. The original catalyst was the opening of the North Atlantic and the separation of North America from Scotland. This separation was accompanied by uplift in the western Highlands and by an early Tertiary phase of active volcanic and igneous activity which bequeathed the lavas of Mull and Skye. As the Atlantic spreading centre moved towards the mid-Atlantic, crustal cooling caused subsidence in western Scotland. However, subsequently in the late Tertiary, renewed uplift and tilting took place, possibly in response to the isostatic depression of the North Sea basin beneath the weight of accumulating sediment and the unloading of Scotland's land surface by erosion. This simple model of east-west tilting was complicated by local variations, for example, the Moray Firth basin comprising an additional focus of subsidence and doubtless contributing to the formation of secondary fractures within the main block.

The geological history of the Grampian High block has had an important effect on the region's present landforms. The courses of the two main rivers, the Dee and Spey (Plate 10) have exploited fracture lines. The position of the main watershed between those rivers flowing eastwards to the North Sea and those flowing north-eastwards to the Moray Firth lies between the basins of subsidence related to deposition off each coast Presumably the rivers which flow across varied underlying rocks owe their courses to the original tectonic tilting. The straight coastlines are related to old fracture lines and faults. Finally, the plateau surfaces are likely to owe their origin to episodic uplift of the block allowing rivers to incise and widen their valleys as they lowered the landscape to a new sea level. The decline in altitude of the main Grampian plateau from the Cairngorms towards the Moray and North Sea coasts is entirely consistent with the tilting of the Grampian High block.

THE EFFECT OF SUB-TROPICAL WARM-TEMPERATE PROCESSES BEFORE THE ICE AGE

Landforms of pre-glacial age are widespread in Grampian and they tell of conditions considerably warmer than those of today and akin to a warm wet maritime environment such as that of Louisiana in the southern United States. The most important relict from this period is the chemically-weathered rock which mantles the area. A typical section is shown in Plate 1 where below a thin layer of glacial till is *in situ* weathered bedrock, much of which can easily be excavated with a spade. In the lower part of the profile there are corestones of fresh rock surrounded by weathered rock which eventually gives way to hard bedrock with just a few patches of weathered rock. The weathered rock which is commonly over 5 m (16 ft) deep and exceeds 60 m (195 ft) depth in places, is widespread in Grampian. Over 500 occurrences are known (Fig 13). It occurs in Coire Raibeirt on the summit plateau of the Cairngorms (002037; Plate 2, as a widespread cover on the gentle slopes of the main Grampian plateau, where for example 10 m (33 ft) of weathered rock occurs on the Gaick Plateau (Barrow *et al* 1913) and over most of the lowlying Buchan lowland. It seems rare only in the Dee and Spey valleys and near the coasts.

In an important study Hall (1985) recognises two types of weathered rock. The most widespread is a granular sand and represents decomposed rock but without much alteration of the constituent minerals in the rock. The other type consists of a sticky, clayey, silty, reddish sand where advanced chemical action has produced high kaolinite contents. This latter type occurs extensively in central Buchan, especially on the Hill of Dudwick (Fig 14). On the basis of the depth and intensity of chemical weathering, the mineral characteristics and the presence of such weathering products in the earliest glacial deposits, Hall considers that the granular weathered rock is pre-glacial in age and developed during the Pliocene and early Pleistocene. The clayey weathering covers need a full sub-tropical climate and thus are likely to have formed earlier than 10 million years ago in the Middle Miocene.

Other pre-glacial deposits which have been discussed for 150 years are the Buchan gravels. They consist of rounded water-worn gravels which cap the hills of central Buchan, especially near Fyvie and Moss of Cruden (Fig 14). The gravels are mainly composed of quartzite, though flint is an important component of the eastern outcrops (Kesel and Gemmell 1981). The gravels are intensively weathered and contain fine kaolinitic material. Although there are still many uncertainties, the gravels are thought to be river deposits and the intensity of chemical weathering suggests that they too are Late Tertiary in age. They appear to have formed in a shallow valley. Since then there has been an inversion of relief. The resistant quartzite gravels have protected the underlying rocks from erosion and the rest of the landscape has been lowered to leave the gravels isolated on hill tops.

A third feature of pre-glacial age are the tors or curious wart-like masses of rock which are conspicuous on many gentle slopes in Grampian (Plate 6). The best examples are in the Cairngorms on Ben Avon and Beinn Mheadhoin but more accessible examples occur near the top of Cairn Gorm summit itself and near the top of the White Lady Chairlift. Other tors occur on the summit of Clach na Ben and Bennachie. They consist of solid granite bedrock with surfaces etched to

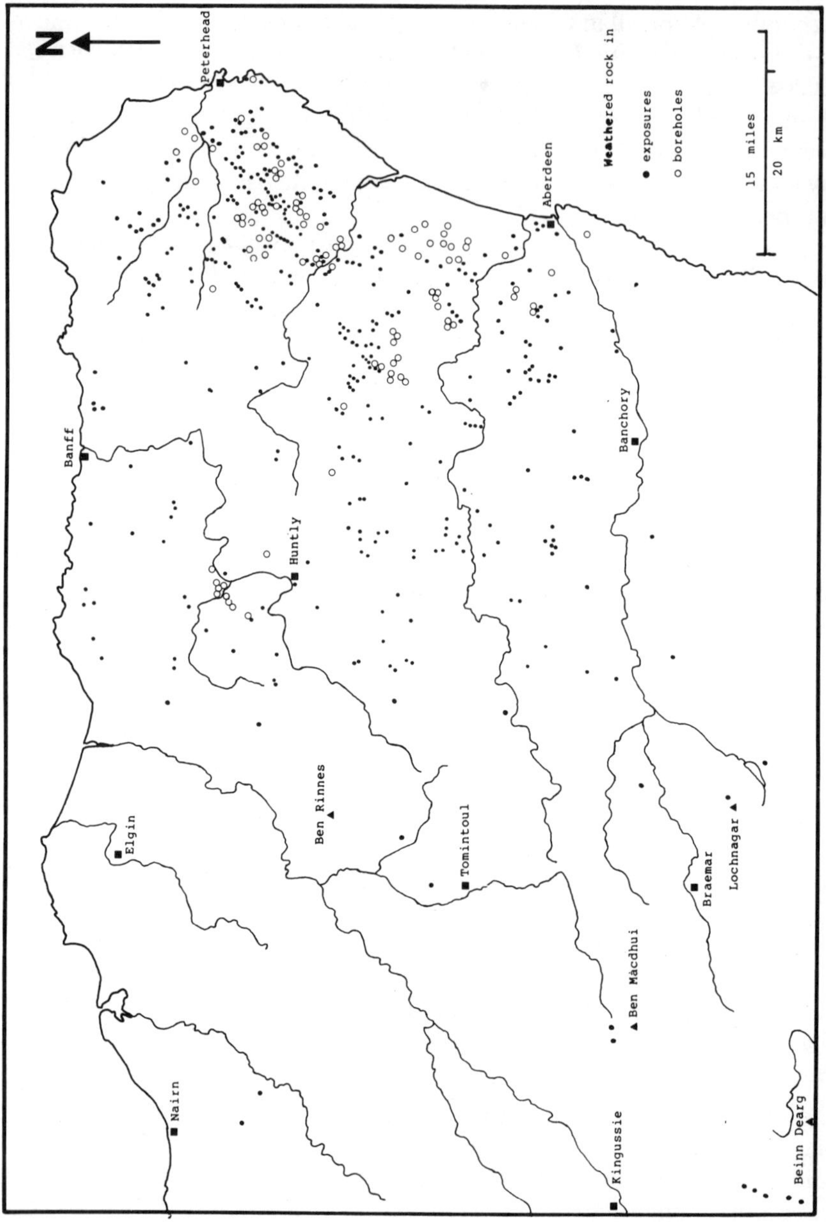

Figure 13 — Known occurrences of weathered rock in North-east Scotland (after Hall 1983, p. 96 and 131).

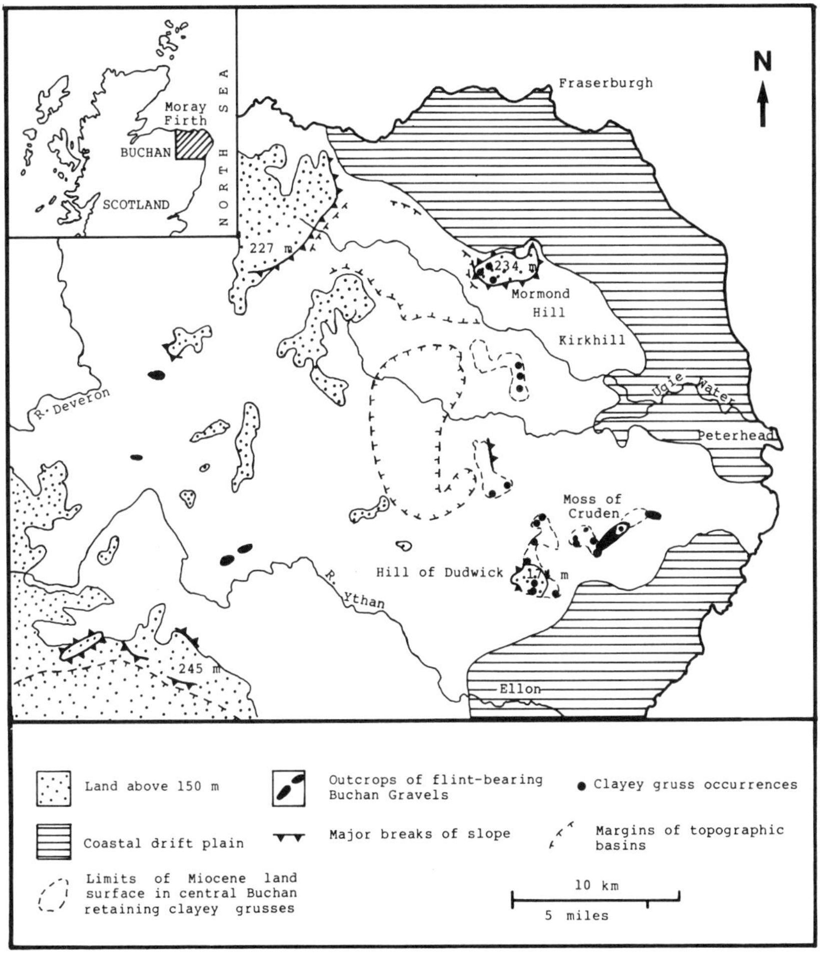

Figure 14 — Distribution of clayey, weathered rock with kaolinite, Buchan gravels and remnants of the Miocene land surface, central Buchan (after Hall 1985).

form horizontal and vertical cracks. Some tors such as Clach Bun Rudhtair on Ben Avon are over 20 m (66 ft) high, but a height of 10 m (33 ft) or less is more common. Tors are believed to form below ground in humid tropical and sub-tropical climates where chemical weathering attacks the underlying rock surface. The depth of weathering is irregular and depends on such factors as joint frequency. If the weathered rock is later removed then the underlying fresh rock surface is exposed with the bumps forming the tors. Incipient tors can be seen in some sections of deep weathering in Grampian, for example at Siverford, Cabrach. It seems likely that the Grampian tors are related to the same phase of deep weathering. They simply represent the exposed base of deep weathering where weathering products have subsequently been removed. If this interpretation is correct then the tor-studded gentle slopes of the Cairngorms represent a surface at least 10 million years old where the only subsequent modification has been the loss of a 10-20 m (33-66 ft) thick weathering cover.

Basins are a final category of landform which are typical of warm conditions where chemical weathering attacks the underlying rock (Thomas 1974). Certain rock types decompose more rapidly than others and are preferentially attacked. The process may result in the widening of a pre-existing valley or the excavation of a zone of deeply weathered rock. Although the relationship with rock type is not always obvious, there is a correspondence. Many basins have straight sides coinciding with a change in rock type. Basin floors are usually developed in granitic and gabbroic rocks which are highly susceptible to chemical decomposition (Hall 1983). Examples are the Tarland basin which is floored by biotite granite and the Maud basin whose floor corresponds with an outcrop of norite.

It is clear from the above that many major and minor features of the existing landscape were formed in warmer sub-tropical conditions. Presumably the oldest landscape, perhaps the longest surviving in the whole of Britain, is the summit plateau of the Cairngorms which may have formed in the mid to early Tertiary period. Subsequently, over a long time span the main Grampian plateau formed, probably as a plain of low relief close to the sea level of the time with rivers flowing eastwards to the North Sea and north-eastwards to the Moray Firth. Uplift of the uplands, probably in the late Tertiary, caused the rivers to cut down and form valleys and allowed the creation of the Buchan and Moray lowlands. Deep weathering attacked the land surface and exploited susceptible rocks to form basins. With a transition to cooler conditions at the end of the Tertiary and early in the Pleistocene, one would expect enhanced river and slope activity to remove the deep weathering cover from steeper slopes. It is interesting to discover that evidence of such enhanced erosion is recorded in late Tertiary North Sea sediments (Karllson *et al* 1974).

The upshot of this reconstruction is that the landscape of Grampian just before the Ice Age would have been remarkably familiar to any of its present inhabitants. The Tertiary vistas of gently rolling lowlands, the plateaux and valleys of the uplands and the basins would have been essentially the same as those of today.

LANDFORMS CREATED BY THE ICE AGE

About 2.4 million years ago the mid latitude areas of the Northern Hemisphere experienced the first of several glaciations. The early record of glaciation comes from analysis of deep sea sediments and these show a cyclic build-up and wastage of glaciers every 100,000 years or so separated by interglacial periods, such as that of the present, with an average length of 10,000 years. There is no information about early glaciation in Scotland, but glacial sediments in the North Sea show major ice sheets were in existence 700,000 years ago. Probably glaciers were present on the Scottish mainland on several earlier occasions. The glaciers modified the land surface over which they passed to varying extents and their impact is important if one is to understand the present landscape. Also characteristic of the Ice Age are cold periglacial conditions which apply in cold environments not covered by glaciers.

Two distinct types of glacier affected Grampian Region — ice sheets and corrie glaciers. Ice sheets form a dome of ice submerging the underlying topography. The ice flows outwards from the ice sheet centre. Corrie glaciers are small glaciers lying in basins carved into a mountain massif. They represent a marginal glaciation. In this section it is proposed to look first at the landforms of erosion and then at the landforms of deposition associated with these two types of glacier.

Landforms of Glacial Erosion

The main landforms of ice sheet erosion are U-shaped glacial valleys in the Cairngorms and Lochnagar massifs. These are marked by broad bottoms and steep, often cliffed sides. Sometimes they hold long lochs as in the cases of Lochs Avon, Einich, Muick and Callater. The troughs may be open at each end and form a through valley, as in the case of the Lairig Ghru; they may have a cliffed end as in the case of Loch Avon and Glen Einich, or they may be headed by corries as in the case of Glen Dee. There are two distinct sets of troughs in the uplands. First, there are those that radiate from the massifs, for example, Muick, Callater and Clova from the Lochnagar massif and Glens Dee and Derry from the Cairngorm massif. Second, there are troughs which cut across the main massifs, for example, Glens Geusachan and Einich and the Avon trough and Lairig Ghru in the Cairngorms.

Roches moutonnées are another landform which, if large, are related to ice sheet erosion. They form when ice passes over a bump, abrading the up-ice flank and quarrying rock from the lee side. A magnificent series of large roches moutonnées, significant on a world scale, exists in the Dee valley between Ballater and Braemar. Here hills and spurs several hundred metres high have classic asymmetric profiles. The western sides are smooth and the eastern sides are cliffed and rugged. The contrast is vividly experienced when driving along the valley; the drive from Ballater to Braemar reveals a rugged cliffed landscape while the reverse journey reveals smooth slopes. Other fine examples of roches moutonnées occur lower down the Dee Valley in the Dinnet area and in many parts of the Spey Valley. There are other zones of small roches moutonnées on the tops of upstanding hills in the lowlands and near the coast. Good examples are the top of Brimmond Hill and Cran Hill on either side of the Dee valley near Aberdeen.

Meltwater channels which breach watersheds are other landforms which relate to ice sheet erosion. They form V-shaped notches often with cliffed sides (Plate 8). Typically they cross a col in a watershed or are cut into the lee of it. In the past such channels have been regarded as lake overflow channels but it now seems likely that the majority of them, particularly those in the uplands, were cut by meltwater streams flowing beneath the ice, with most of the water coming from melting at the bottom of the ice sheet. They broadly reflect the direction of ice flow. There are many good examples, such as the col adjacent to Clach na Ben, the cliffed channel associated with the Burn o'Vat near Dinnet, the meandering channel used by the main road south of Kildrummy castle and the dramatic breach in the high watershed of the Ladder Hills on the road between Rhynie and Cabrach. In the lowlands meltwater channels create much of the relief on the Buchan lowland with a dense network of channels, big and small.

Corrie glaciation in Grampian affected the higher Cairngorm and Lochnagar massifs. Small glaciers carved armchair shaped hollows surrounded by cliffs (Plate 4). In places the corrie basin holds a lochan, as for example, Lochain Uaine (Ben Macdui) and Lochnagar corrie. The most impressive series of corries is in Upper Glen Dee and the view is especially striking from Ben Macdui summit. Most corries face between north and east because snow built up most quickly in the shady lee side of the mountains where snow blown from the plateau was best protected from the sun's rays.

The presence of both ice sheet and corrie landforms of erosion reflects the varied glacial history of the area. The corries are representative of cold periods which were either not cold enough or did not last long enough for ice sheets to build up over the mountains. Some may represent the early stages of a glaciation which eventually produced an ice sheet. Probably there were several distinct phases of corrie glaciation (Sugden 1969). The ice sheet landforms reflect different situations. The troughs which radiate from the main massifs may represent either an early stage of glaciation when the main ice sheet was beginning to build up or long periods when conditions were sufficiently cold to maintain local ice centres but not a full-bodied ice sheet. The relatively large size of the radial troughs favours the latter alternative. The remaining features of ice sheet erosion reflect erosion by a major Scottish ice sheet. Theoretical reconstructions of the maximum Scottish ice sheet show it was centred near Rannoch Moor and that it was 1800 m (5900 ft) high over the Cairngorms and only a little lower over Buchan. The reconstruction agrees with the landform evidence. The orientation of the troughs which cut across the Cairngorms shows that ice crossed the mountains from south-west to north-east (Sugden 1968). The erosional features along the valleys of the Dee and Spey reflect major ice streams taking ice to the North Sea and Moray Firth respectively. The general lack of erosional forms in the large area between the Spey and Dee valleys can be explained by this being an area of ice divergence between the main ice streams. Under such conditions the ice velocities would be low and, largely as a result, the temperatures at the base were so low that the ice was frozen to the underlying ground for much of the glaciation. Under such conditions there may have been little or no erosion. The same effect occurs at a smaller scale when hill massifs and plateaux cause the ice to diverge around them. Erosion can take place surrounding the upstanding hill mass in the presence of warm basal temperatures and water. At the same time the ice is frozen to the upland surface and in effect protects it.

This juxtaposition of glacial erosion forms, such as troughs, alongside relict pre-glacial landforms is evidence of the dramatic selectivity of ice sheet erosion. Grampian Region contains one of the world's best examples of a landscape of such selectivity. Nowhere else is there such an abundance of pre-glacial relicts in a glaciated area (Hall 1985), while the clear juxtaposition of pre-glacial tors on a hill mass breached by glacial troughs, as in the Cairngorms, can be duplicated only in parts of the eastern Canadian Arctic.

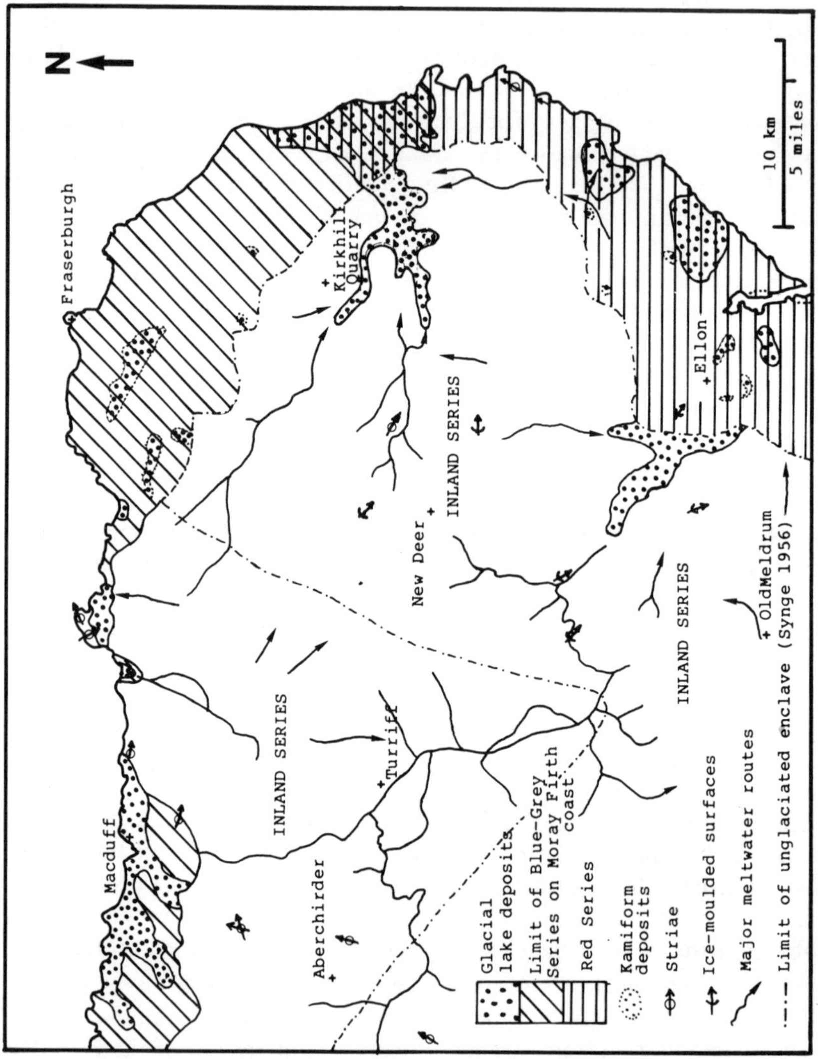

Figure 15 — The three series of drift deposits in North-east Scotland (after Hall 1984).

Landforms of Glacial Deposition

Ice Age glaciers covered all of Grampian with a cover of glacial drift. The drift consists of three main components:—

(a) glacial till which is the name given to debris laid down directly by glaciers; this encompasses isolated boulders, a mixture of boulders and sand or boulders and clay (formerly called boulder clay).

(b) meltwater deposits consisting of sand or gravel; these may mark the channels of sub-glacial rivers and form gravel ridges known as eskers or irregular mounds called kames; beyond the ice margin such rivers built up extensive outwash plains similar to the sandur plains of Iceland.

(c) lake deposits where fine silts and clays settled in the bottom of lakes impounded by glaciers.

Hall (1984), building on the fine work of Jamieson (1906) and Bremner (1943), found it helpful to distinguish three main series of glacial drift.

The **Inland Series** covers all but the coastal areas of Grampian and consists of material derived locally from ice moving across the area towards the North Sea and Moray Firth (Fig 15). In the uplands the till is thin but it may form a sheet several metres thick in valleys and basins. It usually consists of boulders in a sandy, gritty matrix. In lowland Buchan the till is usually 1-3 m (3.0-9.5 ft) thick and consists of boulders set in clay and fine silt. The meltwater deposits of this ice are concentrated in the larger valleys of the Spey and Dee where they add considerable detail to the landscape in areas such as Dinnet. Figure 16 shows the concentration of meltwater deposits in the Aberdeen area and demonstrates how the sub-glacial course of the River Don was different to the course used today.

The **Red Series** of drift deposits is thick and complex and lies in the coastal zone approximately between Aberdeen and Peterhead. The deposits, which may be over 20 m (65 ft) deep, owe their colour to the red Devonian rocks offshore and the deposit reflects onshore ice flow from the south. Individual landforms may consist of glacial till, meltwater and lake deposits, and it seems clear that the deposits originated in a complex ice edge position.

The **Blue-Grey Series** describes glacial drift along the Moray coast as far as Peterhead. The drift contains rocks derived from the bed of the Moray Firth and hence its distinctive colour. Again the drift contains glacial tills, meltwater and lake deposits. The meltwater kames and eskers are particularly impressive because of their size, for example, immediately east of Elgin, as also are the extensive spreads of deposits

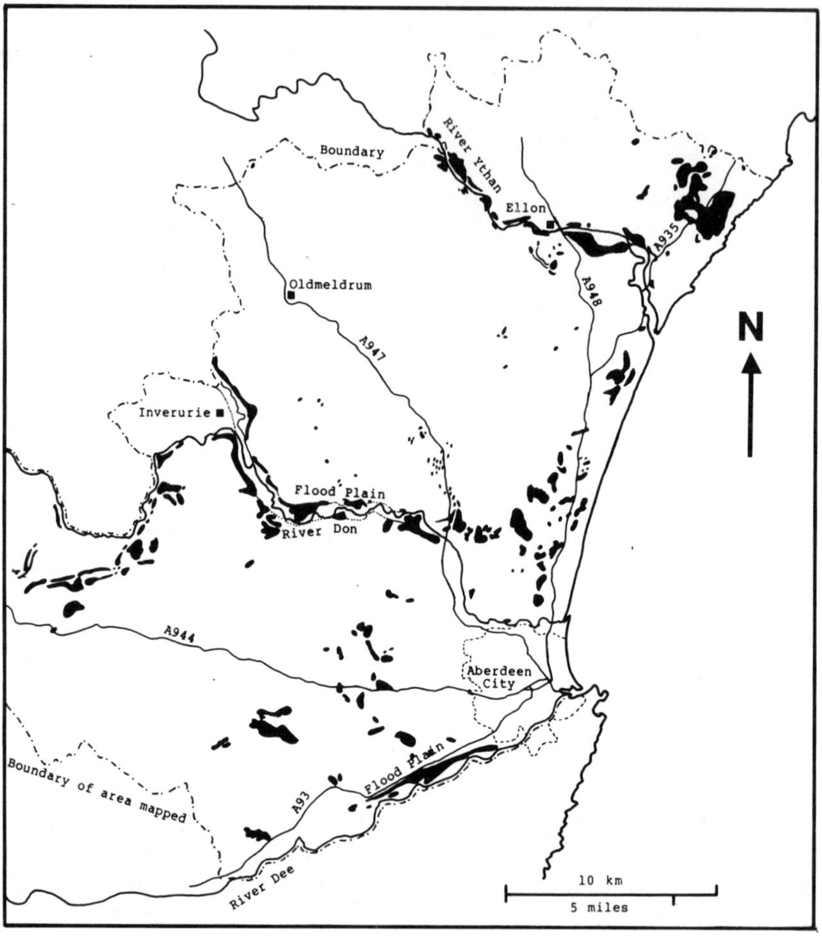

Figure 16 — Meltwater deposits in the Aberdeen area. The meltwater deposits of the Don demonstrate that the subglacial river took a different and more direct route to the coast. (Mapping by C. M. Clapperton, A. M. D. Gemmell and the author).

formed in lakes impounded by the coastal ice, for example, in the lower Spey valley (Bremner 1932) and coastal Banffshire (Fig 15).

Features which are conspicuous by their virtual absence in most of Grampian are terminal moraines which would have reflected an advance or a stillstand of the glaciers either during major glacial episodes or during retreat. The main exceptions are small arcuate boulder moraines in some of the corries in the higher massifs of the Cairngorms and Lochnagar.

Interpretation of the glacial deposits of Grampian is still very uncertain. The main problem is that the deposits are of different ages and dating is inadequate to reconstruct a clear sequence of events. Under these circumstances it is probably best to highlight the main discoveries.

(1). It is now known that major ice sheets extended across Buchan on several occasions. The evidence for this comes from a quarry at Kirkhill 13 km (8 miles) north-west of Peterhead (012529) which shows several glacial deposits, separated by old soils (palaeosols) representing interglacial conditions (Connell *et al* 1982). The sections reveal the existence of at least two and probably three ice sheets.

(2). The **Inland Series** of glacial drift reflects offshore movement of ice flowing from the Grampian Mountains. The **Red and Blue-Grey Series** reflect onshore movement from the North Sea and Moray Firth respectively. At present the relationships between the different series is difficult to unravel. Fig 17 shows an attempt to explain them in terms of two phases of one glaciation. In this scenario different flows might be dominant at different stages of the glaciation. For example, as the main Scottish ice sheet thinned the Grampian uplands and particularly the Cairngorms would divert more ice, thus enhancing flow in the Moray Firth and Strathmore icestreams at the expense of Grampian ice. This would allow ice to encroach upon Grampian's coasts at the end of the glaciation. Alternatively, the different stages of flow in Fig 17 may reflect different glaciations (Synge 1956; Sutherland 1984). If so, then a major problem is to find the limit of Grampian ice at the time of coastal glaciation.

(3). The lack of clear terminal moraines suggests a regular retreat of ice at the end of the last glaciation. Indeed, the main irregularities occur in certain topographic basins where patches of stagnant ice become isolated during decay. Such areas, for example the stagnant ice hollows occupied by Loch Kinord

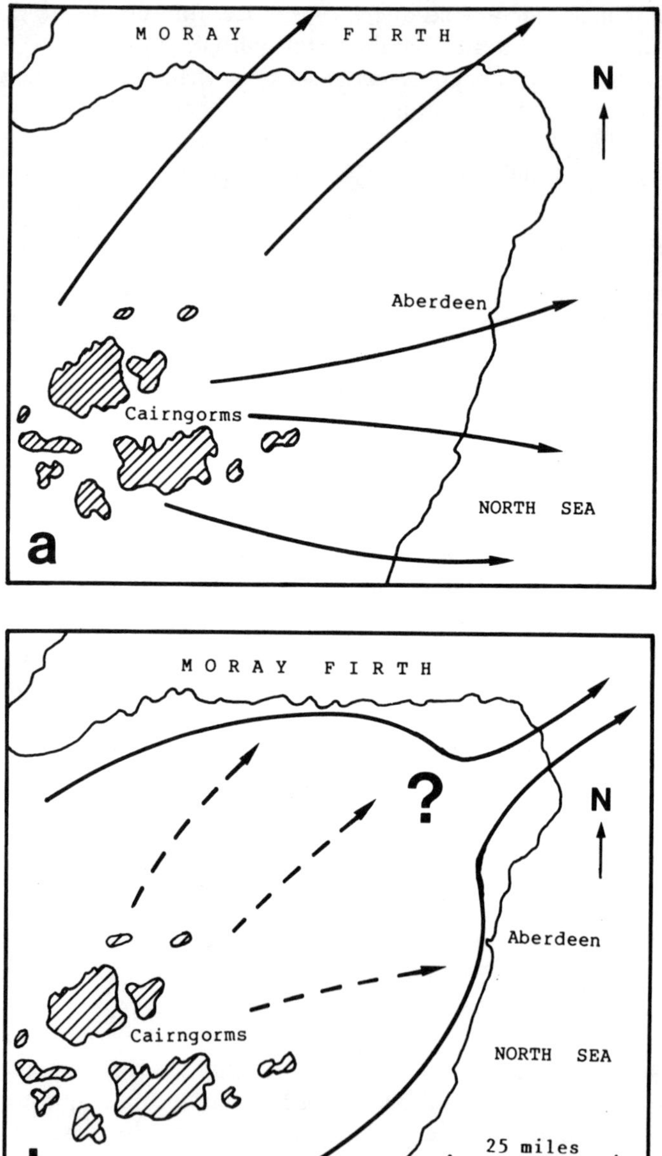

Figure 17 — Former glacier flow directions in North-east Scotland. (a) Flow indicated by major landforms of erosion and the Inland Series deposits. (b) The Flow indicated by the coastal Blue-Grey and Red Series. The different phases of flow may have occurred during one or separate glaciation(s).

near Dinnet, are the sites of complex meltwater deposits which plugged and buried the stagnant ice.

(4). A short sharp cold spell 10,000 years ago (Loch Lomond Advance) caused large glaciers to readvance in western Scotland. Sheila Rapson (1985) has shown that in Grampian the result of this cold snap was the creation of corrie glaciers which built the boulder moraines in a few favourable high corries.

Periglacial Landforms

At various stages in the Ice Age, Grampian and particularly the lowlands would have experienced Arctic temperatures during which permafrost occurred. At such a time the ground, apart from a thin surface layer which melts in summer, would have been permanently below freezing. If the ground temperature falls below $-19°C$ then it cracks into a polygonal pattern and ice wedges build up. Casts of former ice wedges are common in Grampian, especially in north-central Buchan (Gemmell and Ralston 1984). They are best seen in the form of crop marks in conditions of drought or from the air. Permafrost favours another process — gelifluction. In essence this is the downslope movement of the thawed ground in spring and autumn. It seems likely that much of the till deposits of Buchan have been displaced downslope by gelifluction. In the uplands such gelifluction caused lobes to form, often with loose stone boulders forming the downslope edge of the lobe. Excellent examples of such gelifluction lobes are seen on the upper slopes of the Cairngorms and Lochnagar. Probably many of these periglacial landforms were formed during the cold snap at the end of the Ice Age 10,000 years ago.

LANDFORMS CREATED BY COOL-TEMPERATE CONDITIONS

Cool-temperate conditions have existed in Grampian Region for some 10,000 years with a period of peak warmth some 5000 years ago. There has not been a sufficiently long time for such conditions to materially affect the landscape, but they do give an insight into conditions which may have occurred during many previous interglacial periods. There is not space to discuss the processes fully and so it must suffice to highlight a few main points.

First, there is a wide range of land-forming processes represented in an altitudinal transect from coast to upland. The Cairngorms represent an Arctic/Alpine environment where snow avalanches, permanent snowbeds and frequent frost produce characteristic landforms.

Elsewhere, temperate river and slope processes dominate, while at the coast there is an intricate set of wave and wind processes.

Second, it is likely that rates of land surface evolution are marked by brief periods of intense activity. One such period marked the transition from glacial to temperate conditions after 10,000 years ago. At this time slope processes were particularly important as the landscape adjusted to a new glacier-free regime. Glacially-steepened cliffs collapsed to form screes and the freshly exposed land surface was susceptible to erosion before it could be stablised by the growth of vegetation. Another such period of rapid erosion has occurred in the last 3000 years or so. As the climate has cooled and the vegetation cover been reduced, accelerated erosion has taken place. This effect is recorded in the high Cairngorm lochans by an influx of gravel which began 3000 years ago (Rapson 1983). Finally, the activities of Man have accelerated processes of erosion. Improved land drainage has increased the frequency and severity of floods and it is likely that this aggravated the floods of the Dee in 1829, 1901 and 1906. Deforestation, grazing and heather burning all reduce the vegetation cover and enhance erosion. It is notable that debris flows which scar many scenic slopes in the Cairngorms have been most active in the last 200 out of the 10,000 years of post-glacial time (Innes 1983). The ever increasing removal of trees and field boundaries is increasing the vulnerability of fields to loss of soil by wind action. Spring gales can reproduce dust clouds in Moray and elsewhere reminiscent of the dust bowl scenes of the United States in the 1930s. In terms of the long history of landform evolution we have unleashed the most destructive phase ever on Grampian's landscape.

CONCLUSION

The landscape of Grampian is a major national asset. It is one of the best preserved old landscapes in the temperate and northern latitudes of the Northern Hemisphere. It demonstrates better than anywhere else in the world the dramatic selectivity of erosion by major ice sheets. It provides within its boundaries a range of landforming processes as varied as anywhere in Britain including those of coastal, lowland, upland and Arctic/Alpine environments. Understanding the variety of present landforming processes, the varied glacial history and the long pre-glacial evolution of the landscape of Grampian Region will assuredly provide many challenges for years to come.

Chapter three

CLIMATE AND WEATHER

Dr. Jeffrey Stone

CLIMATE AND WEATHER

The climate of Britain has been presented as remarkable for its varied characteristics and the range of stresses and opportunities which it offers, both over area and through time (Manley 1970). The climate of Grampian is possibly even more remarkable in those same respects. On the one hand, the lowest temperature recorded under standard conditions in Britain was at Braemar; the highest recorded wind speed in Britain was on the high tops of the Cairngorms; the river systems of the Moray Firth lowlands have witnessed dramatic floods of historical renown deriving from storms in their high altitude catchments to the south; the region has the infamous Cockbridge-Tomintoul road which is so frequently made impassable by snow that it is a familiar phrase to radio listeners all over the country. On the other hand, with a south-west wind in autumn, the lowlands of the region occasionally enjoy the highest recorded daily temperatures in Britain; the north-west of the region has a justifiable reputation for sunshine incidence, and relative to much of Britain, the rainfall over the whole of the north-east lowlands is well below average. The contrasts in Grampian's climate are perhaps even more remarkable than those of Britain, bearing in mind the small proportion of Britain's surface area and latitudinal extent which is contained within the region.

It is not difficult to account in general terms for the wide variation of climatic experience in Grampian. The region has a long coastline to the east and north, and North Sea surface temperatures are high in winter, by comparison with European ground surface temperatures in similar latitudes. Nevertheless, the region stretches inland away from the sea for 70 km (43 miles) or more. By far the most influential factor is topography, however. In part, this is simply a factor of altitude, with

Ben Macdui, Britain's second highest mountain, giving the region a relief amplitude of over 1300 m (4265 ft). This largely explains climatic contrast within the region as a whole, but it is the varied relief which explains climatic diversity over the area of the region. The sub-arctic environments of the Cairngorm and Grampian summits are isolated by mountain passes which connect deep sheltered straths and basins such as Strathspey, the Alford Basin, Donside and the Dee Valley. The south-west of the region is characterised by substantial climatic differences over short linear distances in consequence of surface configuration, in contrast to relative climatic uniformity in the coastal lowlands of the north, or of the east including the Buchan plateau.

Relief is a prime factor in one other respect, however. Beyond the region, there is an effectively continuous chain of summits over 900 m (2950 ft) from the south-west to the north-west. A slight föhn effect in raising temperatures is thus not uncommon and is occasionally pronounced in the east of the region. It is commonly effective in dissipating cloud, so that the association of rainfall with the passage of fronts is not nearly so close as it is in the far west of Britain.

Grampian's weather in past centuries has yet to be adequately researched, although there is an indication of what might be revealed in the diary of Janet Dyce, compiled mostly in Kemnay from 1758 to 1795, when the hard winters which she records in the 1780's would have been a severe affliction (Pearson 1973). Systematic records were commenced at Strathdon as early as 1833. A meteorological observatory was founded in 1855 by the Prince Consort (Mossman 1896) and although no station on Deeside has recorded continuously since then, the establishment of several stations elsewhere on Deeside including Balmoral have resulted in an unusually detailed record (Manley 1978). Awareness of recent climatic events derives primarily from *The Meteorological Office Monthly Weather Report* which currently lists 21 stations widely distributed over the region from Forres to Stonehaven, although with a lowland predominance. In addition there are a small number of non-Meteorological Office stations (Harrison 1983), whilst Cairngorm summit is automatically monitored (Curren *et al* 1977). The records of a rather larger number of stations gauging only rainfall are accessible (Singleton 1985) and there is evidence in the literature of a number of environmental studies in Grampian Region which have generated weather data, but the latter rarely enter the national archive.

Average annual rainfall varies greatly within the region but very closely reflects altitude. The range is from over 2000 mm (80 in) on the Cairngorm summits to below 600 mm (24 in) on the east coast of Moray. However, that part of the region lying below 180 m (600 ft) generally receives less than 1000 mm (40 in), with coastal areas receiving less than 800 mm (32 in), as do several inland pockets on Deeside, Donside and Speyside (Fig 18). Annual cycles can be discerned from the mean monthly values of individual stations.

Table 4 Mean monthly rainfall (mm), 1949-1983.

	J	F	M	A	M	J	J	A	S	O	N	D
Craibstone (Aberdeen)	75	55	56	49	60	54	76	80	72	80	79	77
Fyvie	78	60	64	52	57	57	75	81	74	82	89	84
Forres	51	35	37	37	46	52	65	79	56	48	62	51
Braemar	92	61	61	51	66	51	57	80	80	92	88	98

In general, spring and early summer are dry seasons in comparison with late autumn and winter, but the wettest and driest months are not the same throughout the region. This is not surprising, considering the extent and topographical diversity of the region, but above all, bearing in mind the relatively low range between wettest and driest monthly means. In fact, monthly means obscure a significant feature of the rainfall regime and that is the considerable range of incidence for any one month at any given station. For example, during the 35 year period 1949-1983, the October monthly totals ranged from 28 mm (1.1 in) to 266 mm (10.5 in) at Braemar, from 20 mm (0.8 in) to 196 mm (7.7 in) at Fyvie and from 13 mm (0.5 in) to 237 mm (9.3 in) at Aberdeen.

Rainfall variability through time and over area is characteristic of the region. The major part of the region's rainfall originates, not in west or south-westerly air streams since these lose much of their moisture in the mountains to the west, but in air streams either from east to south or else from north-west to north-east (Plant 1969, 1970). These may occur in association with the depressions whose frontal systems induce more than 50% of the rainfall of the region (Smithson 1969), but it is noticeable that by comparison with stations farther west, the warm sectors add little rainfall and that maritime polar air is also a relatively insignificant source, having traversed the mountain barrier to the west. The non-frontal depression is a more significant source of rain bearing air streams in the east of Scotland than in the west. Atlantic depressions moving in a north-westerly direction across Scotland cause the winds over the region to veer from east to south, whilst depressions which have followed a more southerly track and become slow moving over the North Sea account for the high incidence of arctic air. A significant proportion of the region's rainfall derives from these non-frontal sources and is erratic in its incidence, being a product of showers of small extent and duration.

Rainfall variability is exemplified by the rainfall extremes which

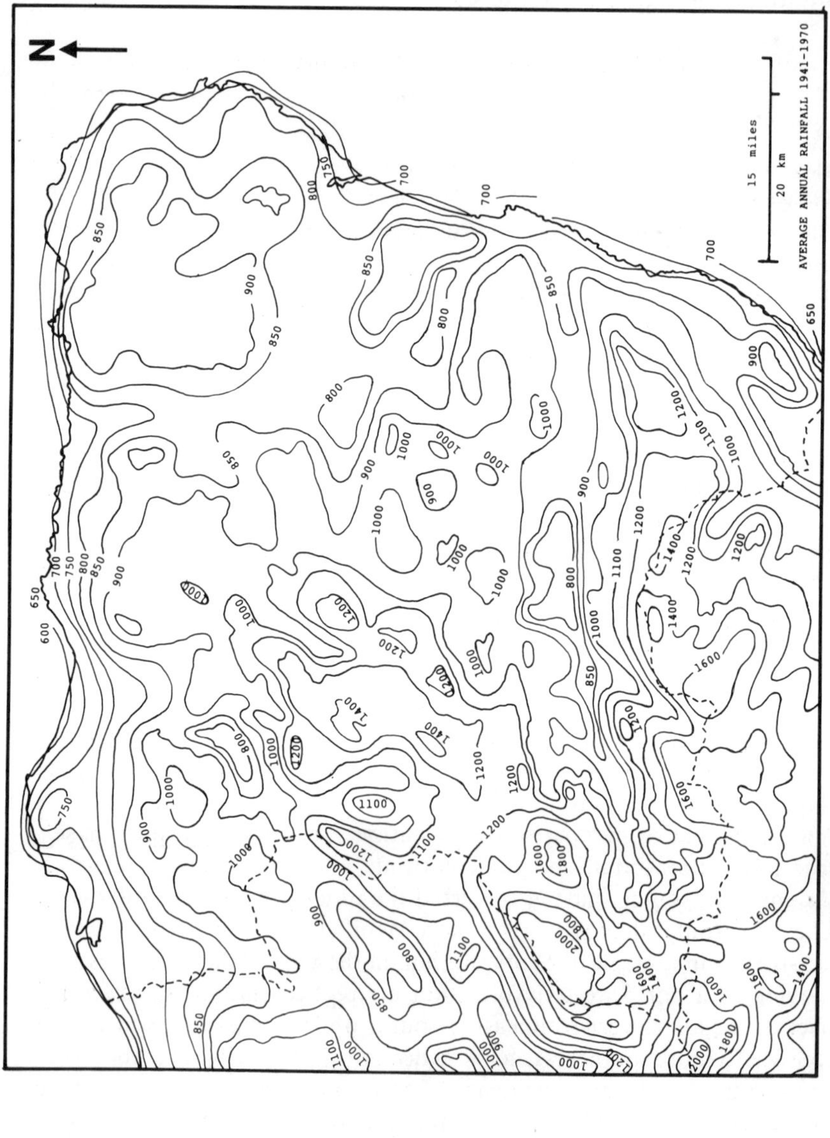

Figure 18 — Average annual rainfall, Grampian Region, 1941-1970.

have occurred in the region, although, ironically, one of the best known recurring extreme events is frontal in origin. The occasional intense summer storms of Moray are infamous and are usually related to occluded fronts, bent back and persisting over an area where orographic accentuation may occur. The flood of August 1829 was one of the greatest on record and has more recent counterparts in 1956 and again in 1970, with continuous rainfalls totalling over 250 mm (10 in) and 150 mm (6 in) respectively (Green 1971). In June of 1970, 93 mm (3.65 in) fell at Lossiemouth in 117 minutes. Another example of extreme rainfall incidence in the region was the 100 mm (4 in) recorded at Aberdeen on 3-4 October 1979, whilst the longer time period of November 1984 was remarkable for the occurrence over much of the east of the region of three times the monthly average, an event so unusual that it inspired a whimsical television weather forecaster on the national network to advise the citizens of Aberdeen to keep swimming!

Rainfall variability can also be emphasised by events at the low end of the spectrum. In the drought which affected much of Britain in 1975-76, Grampian Region suffered only moderately (Doornkamp 1980). It was only in the summer of 1976 that rainfall was seriously below average and indeed flow conditions in the River Dee had recovered to the level of the mean monthly discharge during the previous winter. Less well known is the Scottish drought of 1955, when lowland stations in the north-west of the region received less than 500 mm (20 in), much of that in December, or in the case of much of Grampian Region alone in Scotland, three successive dry years of 1971 to 1973. Throughout the period, some coastal locations where rainfall is normally low, received less than 70% of their annual average, a similar value to that recorded for the southern part of the region during the 16 months duration of the better known 1975-76 drought.

The use of the word "rainfall" has so far included all forms of precipitation, but snow deserves special mention since the region has the reputation as one of the snowiest in Britain (MacPherson 1960). The reality which is obscured by this generalisation is that the incidence of snow cover varies very greatly, not only within the region, but even more so, from year to year. During the severe winter of 1962-63, there were 43 days with snow lying at Elgin but in the following winter there was only one. For Balmoral and Dyce the corresponding figures were 89:35 and 63:12 (Met. Office 1983). These are of course all relatively low level observations and the figures would change rapidly with altitude. The rate of increase with altitude in the annual number of days with snow cover is reckoned to be about 11 per 100 m (328 ft) in North-east Scotland (Manley 1970). Hence, it is not unusual for snow banks to survive from one winter to another in the Cairngorms and occasionally on Lochnagar, although sufficient to attract skiers in late July as in 1973, is unusual (Spink 1973, 1980). Whilst highly generalised statements about duration of snow cover, or indeed depth, have little meaning for the region as a whole, it is the case that the Cairngorms experience the greatest depths and durations of snow cover in Britain (Ferguson 1985).

Two further atmospheric events related to rainfall are worthy of mention, if only because of exceptionally low incidences, and they are thunderstorms and damaging hail. Aberdeen has one of the lowest recorded thunderstorm incidences (about seven days per year) for any major centre of population in Britain (Plant 1970), whilst the north coast of the region has an even lower figure (Manley 1970). Inland records show a slightly greater frequency.

The factors determining the temperature regimes of Grampian are primarily latitude and altitude, and to a lesser extent, proximity to the sea as well as distance from the mainland of Europe. The effect of latitude is apparent not only in the low angle of the sun but notably in the lateness of spring followed by the long daylight hours of early summer. North Sea surface temperatures remain high in winter, relative to extensive landward surfaces in similar latitudes. Temperature graphs are therefore characteristically flat (Walton 1963), with the winter mean values of low altitude stations comparable with stations much farther south, but with winters longer in duration, with springs late and summers cooler.

Table 5 Average daily mean temperatures (°C)

	J	F	M	A	M	J	J	A	S	O	N	D
Braemar (339m)	0.4	0.5	2.7	5.2	8.2	11.5	12.7	12.3	10.3	7.5	3.4	1.7
Craibstone (91m)	2.4	2.6	4.4	6.5	8.7	11.9	13.3	13.1	11.7	9.1	5.3	3.5
Gordon Castle (32m)	2.9	3.2	5.2	7.4	9.7	12.9	14.1	13.9	12.3	9.5	5.7	4.0

Source: *Averages of temperature for the UK 1941-70, HMSO. 1976.*

The marked similarity between the above three stations which are widely distributed across the region reflects the fact that the differences in mean temperature between Scottish coastal and inland sites not much above sea level rarely amount to more than 1°C (Francis 1981). The small differences in part reflect the small altitudinal differences. A lapse rate of 0.64°C per 100 m (328 ft) has been observed for an altitudinal range of 275-585 m in the centre of the region (Jones *et al* 1979) and whilst Braemar is the highest station in Grampian with regularly published observations, some indication of the temperature regimes of the extensive areas of higher land can thus be extrapolated.

Average daily mean temperatures are somewhat abstruse statistical abstractions which mask significant real events. Variability is again characteristic, notably of winter regimes (Hamilton 1963) and stations within the region have held the British minimum recorded temperature for four out of the 12 months (February: Braemar -27.2°C; March: Logie Coldstone -22.8 °C; August: Balmoral -2.8°C; November: Braemar -23.3°C; Manley 1970). Air temperatures fall below 0°C at low altitude rural sites within the region on the order of 50 to 120 occasions per year, with more frequent occurrence of ground frost and considerable variation over quite short distances. A more pleasing feature is sunshine incidence which is comparable with sites in the south of England, with Grampian enjoying more winter sunshine and less summer sunshine. A small part of the early summer reduction for coastal stations is due to shallow fog or haar caused by the cooling of warm continental air by the surface of the North Sea. This occasional feature of the Grampian coasts can be frustrating since it is usually evident that warm sunshine is being enjoyed inland. The incidence of haar is greater on the east coast than the north and it should be stressed that the incidence of fog of all types is low by British standards and that good visibility is a feature of the region.

Although data are sparse, there is possibly more variation within the region in relation to wind than any other climatic element. If the north-east of Scotland is perceived as a windy part of the country, then its reputation is scarcely justified for much of lowland Grampian but it is fully justified in the case of the high summits. Average wind speeds throughout the year at Aberdeen are considerably lower than several more westerly and northerly stations (Manley 1970). Lowland sites in the region may be much influenced by the local topography, with Moray coastal stations relatively sheltered from the south and south-west but exposed to the north, the Buchan plateau more widely exposed and Deeside more sheltered from the north. There is no predominant wind direction which can be superimposed on this pattern, although north-west and south are relatively common. Low temperatures and high humidity may create a raw feeling to a wind whose speed is unexceptional by Scottish standards, while the mean incidence of gales at the region's two main airports of Dyce and Kinloss is less than 12 per year. However, Cairngorm summit offers an extreme contrast with a UK record gust of 246 k/h (153 mph) in 1986. Evidence from beyond the region suggests that the valleys of the uplands will give rise to pronounced distortions of surface wind speed, direction and gustiness, depending upon whether the air flow is cross-valley or along-valley (Gunn and Furmage 1986). Another local wind effect is the occurrence of on-shore summer sea breezes which have been recognised by participants in the weather-conscious sport of hang-gliding and occasionally induce cloud formation and rainstorms close to both the north and the east coasts (John 1980).

In order to amalgamate all of the various climatic elements into the composite climate circumstances of different parts of Grampian, a system of climatic classification is required. Two such systems have recently been devised specifically for Scottish circumstances and both emphasise the wide range of climates which are experienced within the region. The first is intended to depict the total climate for ecological research (Birse 1971). The climatic diversity of Grampian is made particularly explicit in the application of this classification, in that no less than 20 different sub-types are delimited within the region. The sub-types are identified under three major headings. The first of these is a thermal assessment and all seven of the thermal sub-divisions are represented in Grampian, from warm to extremely cold. Then there is an assessment of oceanicity measured by means of frost incidence and all three of the categories under this heading are to be found in Grampian. Lastly, there is a moisture assessment and four out of the five sub-divisions are represented, from fairly humid to extremely humid. A striking feature is the contrast between the extensive uniformity of much of the eastern and northern lowlands (humid, markedly oceanic and fairly warm to cool) with the diversity of the western and southern highlands, basins and valleys.

The second classification (Francis 1981) seeks to define agro-climatic divisions for areas with less than 1200 mm (47 in) of rainfall so that the mountainous south-west of the region is not covered. Average annual rainfall qualified by altitude provides the main classifying variable, with 11 other meteorological variables of particular significance to agriculture described for each type. The application of the classification to Grampian is interesting in that it points to climatic division of the relatively uniform lowland areas, incorporating a large number of atmospheric variables. For convenience, five areas of the Grampian lowlands are designated but three of the areas have a similar designation, so that effectively three lowland climatic types are differentiated. Firstly, there is the Moray Firth coastland, from Banff, east to include Elgin and Forres. This area has an annual rainfall of 720 mm (28 in), 1310 sunshine hours per year, 225 days per year during which access to the land is available to animals or can be worked by machinery, 1290 degree days above 0°C in the first six months of the year and an absence of frost from mid April. A second climatic type is found in lower Speyside and east through Keith, Huntly and Turriff, including all of Banff and Buchan District, the east of Gordon District, Aberdeen and Lower Kincardineshire and Deeside District. In this large area the higher annual rainfall is of the order of 850 - 900 mm (33-35 in), sunshine hours range from 1205 to 1320, access days to the land are much lower at 170-180, the corresponding degree day figures are also lower at 1090-1180 and frost may occur in late April or early May. The third climatic type completes the graduation in agricultural unfavourability and includes upper Deeside from Braemar to Ballater and west Gordon District between Huntly and Lumphanan except for the Alford Basin. Here the annual rainfall is 925 mm (36 in), mean monthly temperatures are 2°C lower than the Moray lowlands though sunshine hours (1200) are little less than the larger area to the east, days of access to the land are down to 160, degree days above 0°C in the first half of the year are much reduced to 990 and frosts are likely in mid May. The lowlands of Grampian Region clearly offer a range of climatic circumstances for agriculture.

Climatic variability in Grampian is further apparent from detailed studies which have been made in three contrasting environments, the mountain summits, the upper Don Basin and the city of Aberdeen. Not all have been examined in equal detail or over similar lengths of time but much information has recently come to light in these very different atmospheric circumstances.

Brief surveys of weather on Ben Macdui and elsewhere in the Cairngorms have been carried out (Dybeck and Green 1955; Baird 1957) but knowledge of mountain weather has recently been transformed by the establishment of an automatic recording station on the summit of Cairngorm (Curran *et al* 1977). Weather events are greatly intensified at very high altitude, so that even in summer there are conditions of considerable stress with intense precipitation, freeze-thaw cycling, great contrasts in humidity, much hill fog but also periods of strong sunshine (Barton and Bothwick 1982). Lightning discharge is more frequent than in the lowlands (Green 1974) but windspeeds are perhaps the most dramatic feature, since the massive rounded summit sometimes enhances windspeed by comparison with the free atmospheric air flow at similar altitudes. Gusts of 85 knots are common in winter and gales may be anticipated on more than 200 days per year (Barton 1984). Wind in association with snowfall is a main contributory factor in the several hundred avalanches which are now known to occur every year in the Cairngorm Mountains (Ward 1981).

A detailed mesoclimatic study of changes with altitude and aspect has been made in Upper Donside (Jones *et al* 1979), an area straddling the upper limits of the third of the three lowland agroclimatic types previously considered in the west of Gordon District. Some popular perceptions were refuted and others confirmed. In late summer, it seems that solar radiation exceeds receipt at lower coastal stations although air temperatures are lower throughout the year. Aspect on the relatively gentle slopes of the area is of little significance for temperature. Also surprising was the realisation that precipitation incidence was not much affected by altitude, with the mountain top of Scraulac receiving a similar amount to Glenbuchat Lodge, although some of the snowfall may not have registered at the summit stations. On the other hand, the use of tatter flags to assess wind speed showed that the form of the land was of little significance in affording shelter but that exposure increases markedly with altitude. Notable variations in agricultural potential were discerned within the small study area, particularly in relation to the length of the growing season.

A further locality in the region which has been the subject of several climatic studies is the city of Aberdeen. It has been known for some time that Aberdeen can generate its own heat island of the order of at least 3°C (Townsend 1948). More detailed work (McBoyle 1969) suggests that the nocturnally-pronounced heat island is located in the geographical centre of the city, rather than in the commercial, industrial and dense residential heart of the city. This is due to the coastal location, but topographic variation within the city is also an important determinant of the fine pattern of isotherms. The city's air is drier than in the surrounding countryside, despite the surface water of the docks. The city profile tends to reduce windspeed, although wind funnelling is notable not only in the wind tunnel which is a curious architectural feature of St. Nicholas House but also along the wide roads leading to the city centre from the outskirts. There is little evidence of additional precipitation as a direct responsibility of urban surfaces. There is, however, a distinct pattern to the incursions of haar over various parts of the city, with the centre of the city tending to be protected by its warm air, so that the haar occasionally forms a hood over the city centre.

Weather and climate in Grampian Region are sometimes causes of alarm or frustration but they are full of surprises and interest. For example, 1985 will long be recalled for its wet summer and indeed Aberdeen experienced rainfall 50% in excess of average in every month from March to September. Yet October in Aberdeen was extremely dry, with less than 8 mm (0.3 in) of rainfall, while sunshine for the year was above average at 1361 hours. Thunder was heard on only three occasions and gale force winds recorded only once in the entire year. On the other hand record minimum temperatures for November (-15.6°C) and December (-14.2°C) were recorded. The most remarkable feature of Aberdeen's climate is perhaps the variability of its weather, and in this respect, it typifies Grampian Region.

Chapter four

PLANT LIFE

Dr. Gordon Miller

INTRODUCTION

To those interested in wild plants, Grampian offers a remarkable variety of habitats for exploration, study and pleasure — perhaps unequalled elsewhere in Britain. More than 900 vascular species have been listed within the region from the coast, woodlands, farmlands, moorlands, mountains and open waters. These habitats span an altitudinal range of 1309 m (4296 ft), from sea level to the summit of Britain's second highest mountain, Ben Macdui. Each habitat has its own characteristic grouping of plants, suited to the local conditions of land form, rock type, soil and climate. Some species are large or bear attractive flowers, whereas others are inconspicuously small. However, all gain in fascination from the nature of their environment and from the particular place they occupy within it.

Grampian's plants have been catalogued and studied by a succession of botanists for a couple of centuries. Two classic accounts date from the mid 19th century (Macgillivray 1855; Dickie 1860) and there were several useful publications during the early part of this century (e.g. Trail 1902, 1923; Craig 1912; Burgess 1935). No comprehensive modern description of the Grampian flora exists, although Webster (1978) deals with the Moray district. Maps of the distribution of individual species within 10 km squares are given by Perring and Walters (1976).

A knowledge of how plants are influenced by their environment adds much to the understanding of vegetation. To the casual observer, the great complex of vegetation types in Grampian may appear to defy comprehension. However, close examination reveals patterns which relate to environmental variations and to the activities of man, both past and present. Climatic and soil conditions fix the land's basic potential for supporting vegetation. Within Grampian, there is a broad north-east to south-west gradient that reflects increasing altitude, exposure and rainfall: dry, lowland vegetation is widespread in the north and east, giving way to wet, upland communities in the south and west. Soils, their fertility and their drainage characteristics, superimpose local patterns. However, a proper appreciation of Grampian's plant life must take account of the historical impact of man.

INFLUENCE OF MAN

Long ago, most land below about 650 m (2130 ft) was clad with dense forest and scrub. McVean and Ratcliffe's (1962) reconstruction of this forest cover some 2000 years ago suggests a predominance of oak *(Quercus petraea* and *Q. robur)* on the old red sandstone soils of the Mearns and on the fertile soils of the Dee valley, mixtures of oak and Scots pine *(Pinus sylvestris)* in Moray and Buchan, and mainly pine on the higher, less fertile soils inland. Birches *(Betula pendula and B. pubescens)* were mixed through the pine and oak forests and formed a more or less pure fringe of scrub at the upper altitudinal tree limit. Thickets of alder *(Alnus glutinosa)* and willow *(Salix* spp*)* grew on seasonally swampy ground in valleys but, where waterlogging was permanent, trees gave way to open marsh and bog. Overall, perhaps 80% of the land surface of Grampian was wooded in one way or another.

Most of the forest has now gone, destroyed by man as his population density and his appetite for timber and farmland increased over centuries. At first, there was only a gradual attrition around the forest's edge. Buchan, the Mearns and other low lying land around the coast and in river valleys would have been cleared in medieval times. Meanwhile, the great forests of the Grampian hinterland probably survived more or less intact until the early 17th century, mainly because trees were difficult to extract. By the 18th century, however, access was easier, new extraction methods had been introduced, and large amounts of timber began to be exported from the region. Exploitation had almost ceased by the mid 19th century, when little of the primeval forest was left and natural regeneration was sparse owing to browsing by domestic livestock.

The deforested land on low ground was intensively farmed, especially where the soils were inherently fertile. Conversion to farmland involved drainage, removal of stones, enclosure, application of lime and manure, and cultivation. The Buchan area was thus transformed from poor land that supported only subsistence agriculture to today's fertile farmland in the course of 100 years. On high ground, the forest was generally succeeded by moorland which was used for free range grazing by farm animals or, from the mid 19th century onwards, for deer-stalking and grouse-shooting. Because of the generally poor soils and light grazing pressures, uncultivated semi-natural grassland never became widespread in the Grampian uplands.

By the beginning of the present century, undisturbed natural vegeta-

1. Weathered granite on the hill of Longhaven *(D. E. Sugden)*

2. Rolling upper slopes of the Cairngorms *(D. E. Sugden)*

3. Cairn Toul from the summit of Braeriach *(D. J. Bennet)*

4. Coire an Dubh lochan, Beinn a' Bhuird *(J. S. Smith)*

5. The Buchan plateau with Bennachie in the background *(J. Livingstone)*

6. Tors on Ben Avon in the Cairngorms *(J. S. Smith)*

7. The dramatic rock architecture of Mitre ridge on Beinn a' Bhuird *(D. J. Bennet)*

8. Meltwater notch of Clais Fhearnaig cut into the spur between Glens Luibeg and Quoich, Cairngorms *(D. E. Sugden)*

9. The Punchbowl, Linn of Quoich. Traditionally the 1715 Jacobite rising was concocted here by mixing a dram in the now ''bottomless'' pot-hole *(J. S. Smith)*

10. View of the River Spey *(Aerofilms Ltd.)*

11. A red deer calf, just 12 hours old *(L. MacNally)*

12. The pine marten is fond of eggs and can easily carry one away *(L. MacNally)*

13. A pair of wildcats. The male is much larger than the female *(L. MacNally)*

tion was confined almost entirely to inaccessible cliffs and to the high tops of the mountains. To the north and east, on the sandy soils of Moray and on the tills of Buchan and the Mearns, there lay urban areas, arable land, sown grassland and a scattering of tree plantations. Farther inland, on the less fertile podzols and peats, there was mainly semi-natural vegetation, composed of indigenous species but created by man's destruction of trees and maintained by continuous grazing coupled with repeated burning.

Although this picture remains broadly the same today, there are continuing changes of detail. The advent of modern herbicides has all but eliminated many of the weeds of arable land and road verges. Rivers and lochs are polluted with agricultural chemicals, sewage effluent and industrial discharges, so changing the water chemistry and disrupting the balance of plant and animal life. The semi-natural vegetation of the hinterland is equally vulnerable to man's growing influence. Alterations to the numbers and species of grazing animals can have profound local effects, in some cases allowing a reversion to woodland, in others causing a change from moorland to grassland. The upsurge in tree-planting that followed from the founding of the Forestry Commission in 1919 has wrought particularly obvious changes to both vegetation and landscape. Between 1921 and 1980, conifers were planted on some 12% of the land surface of Grampian (Forestry Commission 1984) and the pace of afforestation has accelerated noticeably in recent years (see chapter 14). Even the formerly undisturbed mountain tops are now threatened by the recently built network of bulldozed hill tracks, by the development of downhill skiing facilities, and by the general increase in the numbers of people seeking recreation in the hills.

Man, through his ability to pollute, cultivate, graze, fertilise, fell, burn, plant, bulldoze, trample, drain and poison at will, has become by far the most powerful agent causing rapid changes in vegetation. Such changes, measured on a time scale of decades rather than centuries, are operating continuously in all the varied plant habitats of the region.

THE COAST

The Grampian sea coast extends to over 260 km (160 miles) and includes cliffs, rocky shorelines, long stretches of sand, some shingle beaches and a few tidal river mouths. Because the coastline is relatively smooth and lacks the bays and long sea lochs so typical of the west coast, salt marshes are generally scarce and confined to river estuaries. The small salt marsh at the mouth of the North Esk at St Cyrus is well known but there is a more extensive marsh at Findhorn Bay containing good stands of eelgrass *(Zostera* spp*)* and glasswort *(Salicornia* spp*)*. Other salt marshes are fragmentary.

There is splendid cliff scenery near Stonehaven, between Cruden Bay and Peterhead, and around Pennan on the north coast. However, the most botanically interesting cliffs are at St Cyrus. Here, the fertile and easily weathered andesite lava is in a sheltered, sunny situation well back from the sea. The rich flora includes several species at or near their northern limit in Britain. Examples include clustered bellflower *(Campanula glomerata)*, wild liquorice *(Astragalus glycophyllus)*, Nottingham catchfly *(Silene nutans)* and the evil looking henbane *(Hyoscyamus niger)*, which is reputedly poisonous. By contrast, some colder, more shady sea cliffs on the north-facing Buchan coast hold small colonies of the arctic-alpine species purple saxifrage *(Saxifraga oppositofolia)*, mossy saxifrage *(Saxifraga hypnoides)* and roseroot *(Sedum rosea)* growing almost at sea level. Scots lovage *(Ligusticum scoticum)* is an especially characteristic cliff plant of these northern coasts and is unknown in England. The greatest rarity of Grampian's rocky coast, however, is undoubtedly Dickie's fern *(Cystopteris dickieana)*. This persists in sea caves near Aberdeen, where it was found in the mid 1800s.

The most extensive deposits of wind-blown sand are at Culbin (the biggest sand dune system in Scotland), Rattray Head, and Forvie. At Culbin, large stretches of the dunes and dune heath have been afforested and stabilised. At Forvie, however, the dunes are relatively undisturbed by man and are locally very mobile, with both sand erosion and accretion processes active. Forvie and Culbin have lime-poor sands and the successive stages of dune development culminate in acid dune heath with abundant heather *(Calluna vulgaris)*. At Forvie, crowberry *(Empetrum nigrum)* and lichens are also prominent components of the heath vegetation. By contrast, the sands at Rattray Head, and at the smaller dune systems of Cruden Bay and St Cyrus, are calcareous. At these sites there is dune grassland and the diverse floras include such uncommon species as purple milk-vetch *(Astragalus danicus)*, meadow saxifrage *(Saxifraga granulata)* and Baltic rush *(Juncus balticus)*.

Shingle communities are well developed at several places along the Moray Firth coast. Amongst the characteristic flora, the rare and decreasing oyster plant *(Mertensia maritima)* is prominent in a few places.

Lochs and Rivers

Grampian's lochs are concentrated mostly in the hills. The very highest is Lochan Buidhe at 1120 m (3670 ft), near to the summit of Ben Macdui, and several other tarns lie above the 900 m (2950 ft) contour. All contain acid, cold water and support little or no vegetation. At lower levels, down to about 300 m (980 ft), there are numerous other small lochs as well as a few larger ones, such as Lochs Avon, Builg and Muick. These have more vegetation than the higher lochs but the acid, nutrient poor waters limit the range of plant species. In shallow marginal water with fine inorganic sediment, shoreweed *(Littorella uniflora)*, bulbous rush *(Juncus bulbosus)* and lesser spearwort *(Ranunculus flammula)* are common. Peaty sediments tend to support a different set of species, including bottle sedge *(Carex rostrata)* and water horsetail *(Equisetum fluviatile)*. Sheltered situations favour white water-lily *(Nymphaea alba)* and pondweeds *(Potamogeton* spp*)*.

Many of the lowland lochs have been diminished or even eliminated by drainage and others enriched by drainage of nitrate and phosphate fertilisers from adjacent farmland. Loch of Skene, for example, has been contaminated in this way to such an extent that its submerged flora is seriously depleted as a result of algal blooms during summer. However, the marginal vegetation of common reed *(Phragmites australis)* and willow *(Salix* spp*)* scrub remains intact. Lochs Davan and Kinord are good examples of lowland lochs that are not seriously affected by pollution.

Loch of Strathbeg, at sea level between Fraserburgh and Peterhead, is the largest of Grampian's lochs. It is shallow, situated amongst calcareous sand dunes some 1 km (0.6 miles) from the sea and is fed by streams draining from farmland. Not surprisingly, the water is very rich in nutrients and the vegetation is correspondingly luxuriant, with extensive reed beds. Loch Spynie, near Elgin, is also nutrient rich and is botanically interesting because it holds several southern species rare in northern Scotland. These include water-violet *(Hottonia palustris)*, bulrush *(Typha latifolia)* and hemlock water-dropwort *(Oenanthe crocata)*, one of Scotland's most poisonous plants.

The region is well drained by rivers running north and east. Gradients from source to mouth are generally steep, so rivers are usually fast flowing and liable to spates. The largest are the Findhorn, Spey, Deveron, Ugie, Ythan, Don, Dee and North Esk. Their waters are generally cold and fairly acid. All are polluted to some extent along their lower sections by sewage effluent, industrial discharges and chemical seepage from agricultural land.

The Dee, relatively unpolluted and flowing rapidly through scenically beautiful countryside, is perhaps the region's most famous river. It rises at 1220 m (4000 ft) on the Braeriach plateau and, presumably because the water is cold, acid and turbulent, truly aquatic plants are scarce throughout its length. Only water star-worts *(Callitriche* spp*)* and alternate water-milfoil *(Myriophyllum alternifolium)* are at all common. Most botanical interest centres on the banks. To a great extent, the plants growing there come from habitats close to the river or are typical wetland species such as marsh-marigold *(Caltha palustris)* or lesser spearwort. However, some sections of the river between Braemar and Banchory are of exceptional interest. There are scattered remnants of the mixed deciduous woodland that once clothed the bottom of the Dee valley. On grassy banks used by fishermen, the annual mowing of the vegetation has created attractive meadows containing melancholy thistle *(Cirsium heterophyllum)*, spignel *(Meum athamanticum)*, globeflower *(Trollius europaeus)* and several other showy tall herbs. Elsewhere, stretches of shingle support a fascinating mixture of arctic-alpine plants, their seeds presumably washed down from higher ground, as well as azure patches of the Nootka lupin *(Lupinus nootkatensis)*. This beautiful plant is an alien but was introduced to the Dee and to the Spey in the 19th century.

Woodland

Conifer plantations are by far the most common type of woodland. Some blocks of Scots pine, established many decades ago, have long been thinned and the ground vegetation has come to resemble that of the native pinewood, including some of the scarce species. For example, the Forestry Commission's coastal plantations at Culbin and Roseisle, dating back to the 1920s, contain well established colonies of creeping lady's tresses *(Goodyera repens)*, lesser twayblade *(Listera cordata)* and the spectacular one-flowered wintergreen *(Moneses uniflora)*. It is not known whether these have been introduced or are natural colonists.

The chief remnants of the truly native pinewoods are to be found in Deeside on coarse textured acidic podzols derived from granite. The two largest forests are Glen Tanar, near Aboyne and Ballochbuie, on Balmoral Estate. The forest of Mar is much smaller and is fragmented amongst Glens Quoich, Lui and Derry. It does, however, contain some especially fine 'granny' trees up to 350 years old. The ground vegetation in these woods is generally dominated by heather or by blaeberry *(Vaccinium myrtillus)*, depending on the amount of shade cast by the trees. Amongst the typical pinewood herbs, creeping lady's tresses and chickweed wintergreen *(Trientalis europaeus)* are widespread, whereas the delicate pink blooms of twinflower *(Linnaea borealis)* are very localised.

Although they may appear to be natural, these pinewoods have been managed for timber production in times past. Indeed, Glen Tanar is still a commercial forest. Some felled areas were left to regenerate naturally but there has been a good deal of planting also. The successful natural regeneration of the pines is problematic. It depends on the coincidence of a good seed year with the availability of a suitable litter and moss-free seed bed and on the absence of heavy grazing. Regeneration is sparse or lacking at Mar and Ballochbuie but is prolific in some parts of Glen Tanar, protected by a deer fence.

Oak and birch woodland is generally found on brown forest soils or humus iron podzols in valleys and on lower hill slopes. Oakwoods are few and mostly planted, although long enough ago for the vegetation to have assumed a natural appearance. There are three important semi-natural planted oakwoods in Deeside — at Craigendarroch by Ballater, at Dinnet Bridge, and at Drum Castle — and one at Darnaway in Moray. Generally the soils are acidic brown earths which do not support a particularly rich flora. Bracken *(Pteridium aquilinum)*, wood anemone *(Anemone nemorosa)* and creeping soft-grass *(Holcus mollis)* comprise much of the ground vegetation but Dinnet is notable for having wild strawberry *(Fragaria vesca)*, stone bramble *(Rubus saxatilis)* and common wintergreen *(Pyrola minor)*. Other noteworthy oakwoods are the Paradise wood near Monymusk on Donside and the Gight Woods near Fyvie. These relatively undisturbed woods include significant numbers of other trees such as ash *(Fraxinus excelsior)*, wych elm *(Ulmus glabra)* and hazel *(Corylus avellana)*, and there is a rich ground flora. Elsewhere, ravines, such as Den of Finella in Kincardineshire and Den of Pitlurg in Banffshire, house fragments of the mixed deciduous woodlands which were formerly widespread on what is now good farming land.

Birchwoods are by far the most common type of semi-natural woodland in the region, although few are to be seen on the windswept farmlands of Buchan. On land below about 350 m (1150 ft), these woods tend to be composed primarily of the tall, elegant silver birch *(Betula pendula)*. On higher ground, it is the stocky downy birch *(B. pubescens)* which is more often predominant. Because of their light, winged seeds, birches are eager and rapid colonists of open ground. Woods can originate from the felling of a primary pinewood or oakwood, from the abandonment of farmland, or from the infrequent burning and light grazing of moorland. The ground flora of birchwoods is therefore very variable in composition, ranging from species characteristic of the acid soils of pinewoods to those typical of species-rich grassland.

One of the finest examples of a primary birchwood is at Morrone, near Braemar. Local pollen records suggest that here the vegetation has changed little for thousands of years. The soil is a fertile brown loam, in places flushed by calcareous springs, and so the ground flora contains an outstandingly rich and colourful variety of species. There is also a locally dense understorey of juniper *(Juniperus communis)* which helps to protect the ground vegetation from the many grazing red deer *(Cervus elaphus).* All in all, it is an extraordinary birchwood, probably unique in Britain.

Woods of alder *(Alnus glutinosa)* grow on swampy ground around lochs and along the margins of rivers. These often contain various species of willow and marsh plants, particularly sedges *(Carex* spp*)* and rushes *(Juncus spp).* Coralroot *(Corallorhiza trifida)* is an uncommon and easily overlooked component of this vegetation. Good examples of mixed wood of alder and willow may be seen at Loch of Park in Deeside, Loch of Skene near Aberdeen, Loch of Strathbeg on the Buchan coast, and Loch Spynie in Moray.

MOORLAND

Heather-clad hills are an essential feature of the traditional Grampian landscape. These treeless, uncultivated, seasonally purple moorland tracts are a justly famous attraction for tourists, naturalists, hillwalkers and those who pursue game. This type of vegetation was formerly widespread in north-west Europe, from Scandinavia to Spain, but has now been largely converted into agricultural land or forestry plantations. The world's last great stretches of heather moorland are part of Scotland's heritage.

Much of this moorland is well below the altitudinal limit of tree growth, yet trees are usually notable by their absence. The reason for this is that tree seedlings are killed by repeated burning and by the continual grazing by sheep, red deer and mountain hares *(Lepus timidus).* Periodic burning is, of course, deliberate management to maintain large stocks of red grouse *(Lagopus 1. scoticus)* for shooting and to provide ample young heather for sheep to eat. Wherever burning and grazing pressures are relaxed, trees can and do colonise. Several examples can be seen in Deeside, notably the invasion of the Muir of Dinnet by birch and the rapid extension of young pines above 600 m (1970 ft) on hills near Ballater. Most heather moorland is thus an artefact which, given the right conditions, will revert to woodland. Only above the tree-line, on exposed coastal cliff tops, on dunes, and on waterlogged soils can it be considered as natural.

Moorland vegetation varies with altitude, exposure, drainage, grazing and the time elapsed since burning. On well drained iron humus and peaty podzols, heather often grows alone or in association with bell heather *(Erica cinerea),* blaeberry, or cowberry *(Vaccinium vitis-idaea).* Mosses are abundant under the canopy formed by these low-growing shrubs. With increasing altitude or exposure, lichens gain prominence and the heather becomes sprawling and wind-clipped. With increasing soil wetness, on peat, peaty podzols and peaty gleys, heather gives way to cross-leaved heath *(Erica tetralix),* deersedge *(Trichophorum cespitosum),* hare's tail cottongrass *(Eriophorum vaginatum)* or purple moor-grass *(Molinia caerulea)* and the vegetation grades into bog with pools and abundant *Sphagnum* moss. At high altitude on peat, crowberry *(Empetrum nigrum)* appears and the spectacularly white flowers of cloudberry *(Rubus chamaemorus)* are prominent in June.

At least two moorland sites call for particular comment. Muir of Dinnet on Deeside has some outstandingly attractive stretches of heather moor on brown podzolic soils. These relatively fertile soils support a distinctive community containing an unusually wide range of species. Heather shares dominance with bearberry *(Arctostaphylos uva-ursi)* and is associated with petty whin *(Genista anglica)* together with an unusual mixture of herbaceous species, bryophytes and lichens. Of particular note is the large stock of intermediate wintergreen *(Pyrola media),* possibly more abundant here than it is anywhere else in Britain.

The other notable site is near Rhynie. Here there is a variety of vegetation types — heather moor, bog, juniper scrub and base rich flushes, some of which contain the very rare and elusive marsh saxifrage *(Saxifraga hirculus).* However, the most interesting feature of this area is the outcropping of a magnesium-rich rock, serpentine. This carries a very restricted but distinctive flora, including thrift *(Armeria maritima)* and common scurvygrass *(Cochlearia officinalis),* which are normally confined to the coast, spring sandwort *(Minuartia verna),* and the very rare moss *(Grimmia alpestris).*

MOUNTAINS

To the south and west of the region there lies a peripheral rim of high hills, running from the Mounth in the south-east, through the Cairngorms, to the Hills of Cromdale in the north-west. These mountains include several of the highest summits and the most extensive area of mountain plateau in Britain. Here, the terrain and climate combine to reproduce conditions similar to those of the remote arctic tundra.

The vegetation reflects the hostility of a harsh and demanding environment — cold summers, irregular winter snow cover, frost heave, severe wind exposure, and acid, stony, infertile soils. Above about 650 m (2130 ft), trees and tall shrubs cannot grow except in very sheltered locations. The low-growing vegetation forms patterns related to the duration of snow cover, which in turn depends upon local topography and shelter: snow is blown from exposed ridges and summits and deposited in sheltered hollows, gullies and corries.

On exposed areas with only light snow cover, heather is predominant up to about 900 m (2950 ft), where it grows as a dense prostrate mat in which individual stems are aligned in the direction of the prevailing wind. Other dwarf shrubs grow amongst the heather, notably bearberry and trailing azalea *(Loiseleuria procumbens)*, which is speckled with small pink flowers in June. Above the heather zone, mountain crowberry *(Empetrum hermaphroditum)* becomes one of the most common shrubby species, often growing intermixed with blaeberry, cowberry, stiff sedge *(Carex bigelowii)*, woolly fringe moss *(Rhacomitrium lanuginosum)* and sometimes a mass of reindeer moss lichens *(Cladonia* spp*)*. On the very highest and most wind-blasted summits or ridges, tussocks of the wiry little three-leaved rush *(Juncus trifidus)* form mosaics with patches of lichen, moss and loose gravel. This so called 'wind desert' is found only in the Cairngorms above about 1050 m (3440 ft) and is particularly extensive on the summit plateau of Ben Avon (Plate 6).

In sheltered places, where snow accumulates in winter and lingers late in spring, the vegetation is very different. At lower levels, within the heather zone, such snow patches are outlined in summer by the fresh green leaves of blaeberry and sometimes have a few plants of stiff sedge and of dwarf cornel *(Chamaepericlymenum suecicum)* as well as a variety of mosses. With increasing altitude and duration of snow-lie, snow-bed vegetation comes to be dominated by mat-grass *(Nardus stricta)*, often in association with deersedge. On the great plateaux of Ben Macdui, Braeriach, Beinn a' Bhuird, Ben Avon and White Mounth, there are patchworks of three-leaved rush and mat-grass which faithfully reflect the pattern of snow deposition in winter. In especially sheltered and sunless pockets lie the very late snow-beds, which do not melt before late summer. These carry few or no vascular species but are carpeted with mosses and liverworts.

The mountain rocks of Grampian are mostly hard, acidic granites and granulites which weather slowly to form shallow, stony, infertile soils containing little lime. Such soils do not support a particularly rich plant life but nevertheless harbour several interesting rarities. Perhaps the most outstanding of these is the alpine sow-thistle *(Cicerbita alpina)*, a tall blue-flowered plant of shady cliff ledges. This grows at only four known locations in Scotland, one being on Lochnagar and another at the head of Glen Callater. Two other rarities of the acid rocks and soils at Lochnagar are worth mentioning. Highland saxifrage *(Saxifraga rivularis)* is a small arctic plant on wet mossy rocks close to long-lived snow patches. The second rarity is dwarf birch *(Betula nana)*, a knee-high shrub which probably grew much more extensively on the upper slopes of our hills long ago.

It is well known that mountain vegetation is much more varied where there are outcrops of limestone or calcareous schists. Such rocks are rare in Grampian but exposures do occur at high altitude in Glen Callater, at Craig an Dail Bheag and at Cairnwell. Also, amongst the massive granite formations of the Cairngorms, little pockets of calcite and epidote locally enrich a few crevices and ledges. The flora of these places includes many species from diverse habitats, both lowland and upland, but it is the special group of scarce montane plants that is of particular concern. It includes small shrubs such as whortle-leaved willow *(Salix myrsinites)* and mountain avens *(Dryas octopetala),* which have handsome white flowers up to 4 cm (1.5 in) across. A kaleidoscope of colour — shades of yellow, purple, blue, pink and white — is provided by the herbaceous species yellow saxifrage *(Saxifraga aizoides)*, purple saxifrage *(S. oppositofolia)*, alpine speedwell *(Veronica alpina)*, moss campion *(Silene acaulis)*, alpine mouse-ear *(Cerastium alpinum)* and others.

It is, however, the rare and the elusive that excite most attention. Mountain sandwort *(Minuartia rubella)*, alpine milk-vetch *(Astragalus alpinus)*, tufted saxifrage *(Saxifraga cespitosa)*, alpine fleabane *(Erigeron borealis)* and alpine woodsia *(Woodsia alpina)* all number amongst the most rare and exquisite species in the British flora and all can be found on calcareous crags on Grampian's mountains. Their pursuit, observation and capture on colour film can be a compelling hobby but it demands rock-climbing skills, patience, endurance and, not least, a good head for heights.

Chapter five

BIRD LIFE

Mr Nick Picozzi

Grampian encompasses dramatic cliffs, sand dunes, estuaries, rivers, lochs, quiet glens, farmland, forests ancient and new, broad moorlands and finally sweeps majestically up to the high arctic plateaux and corries of the Cairngorm mountains. Add to this the vibrant colours of autumn, the icy rivers and snow clad hills of winter, the summer nights of perpetual twilight and you have one of the most beautiful and exciting parts of Britain for any lover of fine country. The bird life is as rich and varied as the landscape itself.

Many birdwatchers are content to spend most of their time at the coast, so that is where this tour of Grampian's birds begins. One of the largest seabird colonies on the east coast of Scotland lies 6 km (4 miles) south of Stonehaven, on the strange compacted boulder cliffs of the RSPB reserve at Fowlsheugh. It is most easily approached from the small car park at Crawton, not far from the busy main road. Although the full extent of the colony is best appreciated from the sea, the surprise of looking over the cliff edge for the first time to be greeted by the upwelling sound and smell and sheer spectacle of so many birds is quite unforgettable. Counts in 1982 of 39,000 Guillemots and 8000 Razorbills do not seem exaggerated. There are about 300 Puffins, which are conspicuous at rest, but can also be picked out in flight by their dumpy appearance, all-black wings and whirring flight. Up to 29,000 pairs of Kittiwakes and numerous Fulmars and Herring Gulls complete the sea birds of the cliffs, but Cormorants, Shags and Eider Ducks are present on the sea and the little island of Craiglethy just off the shore. The doves that nest on the cliffs are no longer pure Rock Doves, although many still closely resemble that ancestor of all domestic pigeons with its white rump and black-barred wings. The Peregrine Falcon used to breed here too, and following its current revival of fortunes, may do so again. It has certainly been present recently as the plucked keel and wings and the fluttering pile of pigeon feathers in the grass attest. There are other good, though smaller, seabird colonies to the north at Whinnyfold, the Bullers o'Buchan and Troup Head.

The lighthouse at Girdleness at the entrance to Aberdeen harbour, and the nearby allotments attract migrant birds and on occasion almost as many birdwatchers. Binocular and camera-laden visitors from all over Britain came in October, 1979 to see an Isabelline Wheatear; only two had previously been recorded in Britain. The sewage outfall here is a great attraction for scavenging gulls, and among hundreds of the commoner species, Iceland, Glaucous, Mediterranean and Little Gull can sometimes be found. Purple Sandpipers and Turnstones skulk among the rocks at the tide's edge from autumn to spring, and are barely visible until they move. Red-throated Divers moult and winter just off-shore all along the east coast from Aberdeen northwards. They can be seen from Girdleness, as can other seabirds on passage such as Gannets, skuas and shearwaters from June to September. The allotments may seem an unlikely place for birds, but on east winds in dull weather in spring and autumn, they provide the first shelter and food for tired migrants arriving here from across the North Sea.

The beautifully cultivated parks of Aberdeen are rather barren areas for birds. However, the big trees along the River Don in Seaton Park have breeding Tree Sparrows, which are generally scarce in Grampian. The private gardens of Rubislaw Den may still have the elusive Hawfinch breeding in this, the bird's most northerly known location. Aberdeen city itself has birds which have adapted to an urban environment. Herring Gulls nest on roof tops, even near the centre of the city, and Oystercatchers nest on the gravel of the flat-topped roof at Foresterhill hospital and elsewhere, where they feed their young by carrying food up to them. Several pairs of Kestrels nest on the grey granite towers and spires that serve as urban cliffs. They hunt for birds and mice in the open green areas nearby and along the links between the Dee and the Don. Some nest in the vast quarry at Rubislaw from which the grey granite of Aberdeen was won.

The main coastal areas for breeding or wintering wildfowl in Grampian are the Ythan estuary, Spey Bay and Findhorn Bay. The most important lochs are those of Skene, Davan, Kinord, Strathbeg and Spynie. The Ythan estuary lies 20 km (12 miles) north of Aberdeen at Newburgh. The river flanks the long spit of the Sands of Forvie NNR which is famous for its large population of Eider Ducks and its tern colony. In August and September, a walk from the Ythan mouth inland up the Tarty burn can produce a wide variety of waders, some still in breeding plumage. Greenshank and Spotted Redshank are often here along with the numerous Common Redshank. In the quieter stretches and muddy drains, Green and Wood Sandpipers may be found while along the sea shore, Sanderling run back and forth at each wave edge. The large Curlew flocks are joined by small numbers of Bar-tailed Godwits from Siberia and there are Dunlin, Knot, Turnstone, Golden and Grey Plover and many more on the mud banks, islands and mussel beds near the river mouth. All four species of skua may be seen here in September, although the Long-tailed and Pomarine are scarce. They chase the terns and gulls, forcing them to disgorge their last meal, but are well able to find food for themselves.

In summer, visitors to the sands of Forvie are required to keep to the paths as the dunes are full of nesting birds. If undisturbed, Eiders in the heathland of the stable part of the dunes do not leave their nests to feed until the young hatch. When dry, the young are led to the sea or the river where family parties join into crèches. There are a few pairs of Red Grouse on the heath, and Shelduck, Oystercatcher and Ringed Plover nest in the sand dunes and the slacks between them. In the summer, there is a large colony of Sandwich and Arctic Terns and Black-headed Gulls among the marram grass clumps at the southern tip of the dunes. A few pairs of the now rare Little Tern also nest here. Visitors are not allowed into this part of the reserve to avoid disturbance.

In spring and autumn, small patches of willow scrub tucked in the dune slacks are a haven for migrant birds. Rarities such as a Red-breasted Flycatcher, Icterine, Yellow-browed and Barred Warbler, can sometimes be found among the commoner warblers and Goldcrests or the less common, but regular Redstarts and Pied Flycatchers. Very large falls of migrants are unusual, but there is always the thrill of the unexpected, like the flick of a Merlin as it flies low and fast through the dunes to surprise a pipit.

In October, great numbers of Redwing and Fieldfare arrive from Scandinavia. When they move inland up the valleys they soon strip the rowan trees of their berries. In some years, small flocks of Waxwings come too, usually stopping first in the coastal towns and villages to feed in gardens on Cotoneaster and Berberis berries. They are always very tame and the first indication of their presence is often a bell-like trill as they call to each other.

Pinkfooted and Greylag geese arrive at the end of September and spend their first few weeks feeding in the fields of the Buchan plain and farther inland. There are few sights to compare with thousands of geese flighting into a roosting loch at sunset, skein after skein for half-an-hour and more. At the Loch of Strathbeg, an RSPB reserve behind the coastal dunes between Fraserburgh and Peterhead, peaks of 20,000 Pinkfeet were counted on 12th October, 1984 and 4150 Greylags were counted on 10th

April, 1984. In Deeside, Greylag numbers have built up dramatically in recent years, from 800 in November, 1974 to 15,000 in November, 1985. They roost on Lochs Davan and Kinord, but are surprisingly elusive in the fields by day. Other species are seldom found except for Barnacle Geese which are regular visitors in small numbers. Wintering ducks add to the number and variety of resident species. Long-tailed Ducks on the Ythan fly upriver close to the water, dropping in with a splash to be swept back to the coastal sand bar. With this duck on the river and Snow Bunting feeding along the tide-line a truly arctic flavour is brought to this corner of Grampian in winter. More unexpected are the Ruddy Ducks which have recently started to breed at Strathbeg and Cotehill loch near Collieston. Strathbeg is of international importance for the large numbers of Whooper Swans (up to 500) which are present in October and November. Many also winter in the area, leaving only if the loch freezes.

On the rivers, the main birds are Goosander, Dipper, Grey Wagtail, Common Sandpiper and Oystercatcher. A few pairs of Common Terns nest on shingle islands. Most Dippers nest in the small tributaries of the big rivers from sea level to as high as 920 m (3000 ft) in the Cairngorms. They are seen more often on the big rivers in winter and may feed then by jumping into the water from the ice flows which jostle down stream. Their song is a perfect match for water tumbling over rocks. They build their nests in the banks of hill burns and under bridges which offer suitable support for the domed nest, always built above moving water.

The agricultural plain of Buchan is not much visited by bird-watchers, yet some of the most important changes to our bird fauna are taking place there. Agricultural practices such as subsidised drainage of wetlands are affecting Redshank and Snipe in particular, as they need wet areas for feeding. The Oystercatcher, which is a relatively recent colonist of the farmland away from rivers, seems undeterred by these activities and is increasing. The status of other farmland birds such as Linnet and Corn Bunting may be changing and needs to be studied. An atlas of the birds of North-east Scotland which is being prepared by local birdwatchers will be a great help in showing where the main changes in bird distribution and numbers are taking place.

There is a great variety and abundance of woodlands in Grampian. Conifer plantations of all ages, particularly post-war plantings, are widespread. Before the land, usually heather moorland, is afforested it is often burned and deep ploughed. Grass and herbs, not previously common, grow among the regenerating heather and young trees and this attracts mice and voles. These in turn bring in predators such as Short-eared Owl and Hen Harrier. Blackgame are also attracted by the more varied vegetation. Curlew continue to nest at low density for a time but Golden Plover are lost immediately, as eventually are all the birds mentioned when the tree canopy closes. They are replaced by other species such as Goldcrest, Cole Tit, Chaffinch and Woodpigeon. Crows nest in the taller trees, and their old nests are sometimes used by Kestrels and Tawny and Long-eared Owls. Sparrowhawks colonise woods at the pole stage and in some mature woods Goshawks are now nesting. Unfortunately, the older woods that suit them best are usually felled within a few years of Goshawks arriving. Ospreys are increasing, and one or more can be seen fishing in Findhorn Bay during the summer. In the last 20 years, Jays and especially Magpies have become quite common and their spread may be due as much to the increase in afforestation as to a reduced number of gamekeepers which has eased the persecution of these species. Ravens are now very scarce breeders in the region. Both the Carrion and Hooded races of the Crow breed and hybridise freely. For reasons which are not understood, the Carrion Crow is slowly replacing the Hooded Crow. Green Woodpecker, near the northern limit of its range, is also increasing.

All too often, birchwoods die out, mainly because the regeneration is so heavily grazed. The Muir of Dinnet NNR in Deeside, is exceptional, and birch has become widespread across this former grouse moor since the last war. The woods hold a good variety of birds, including Redpoll and summer migrants such as Tree Pipit and Willow Warbler. Two oakwoods, one south of the river at Dinnet and one on Craigendarroch at Ballater are of special interest. Although they were planted, there appears to have been oak on both sites since the last Ice Age. Migrant Wood Warblers and Redstarts add their songs to those of the commoner resident birds like Great and Blue Tit, Song Thrush and Robin.

Deeside also has some fine remnants of the native pine forest that once covered much of the Highlands. The best examples are at Glen Tanar, Ballochbuie and Mar; fine old forests these with some trees 200 years old and more. The largest member of the grouse family, the Capercaillie breeds here. The cock is a huge bird, the size of a Turkey, and yet its display calls deep in the forest in late April are barely audible to the human ear at more than 100 m (328 ft). The cocks strut across the lek (display ground) with head thrown back, neck stretched, tail upright and fanned and wings arched low by their sides. They fight viciously and have extra strong skulls to withstand the often severe blows from an opponent's beak. Even so, fatalities do sometimes occur. The display period is restricted to just two or three weeks in April. At its peak, the smaller, brown hens visit the lek and are mated by the most dominant male. Nests are very hard to find in the deep tussocky heather and blaeberry that form the dense ground layer of this ancient forest. Other interesting birds here are Siskin and Scottish and Common Crossbills. The Scottish Crossbill is Britain's only endemic full species. It has a huge beak for tackling pine cones, whereas the finer beak of the Common Crossbill is more adept at prising seeds from spruce and larch cones. Crossbills are among the earliest birds to nest. Some do so in January and have young on the wing by March. Both species may nest in the same wood and repeated searches have shown no evidence of hybridising, which helps confirm the full specific status of the Scottish Crossbill.

Golden Eagles sometimes nest in pine trees on the edge of deer forest, but most pairs have other nest sites on crags and rock faces. A pack of Red Grouse flying across a hillside is often a sign that an Eagle is close. Many visitors to the Highlands mistake Buzzards for the much scarcer Eagles. This is not surprising, as hunting ranges of Buzzard and Eagle overlap to some extent on the lower moorlands. Against the sky with nothing for scale, the best way to distinguish soaring birds is to look at the set of the wings: those of the Eagle are normally held flat and slightly forward of the body with the flight feathers stiffly separated. The Buzzard glides with wings held slightly above the body, and it does not fly with the same deliberation as the Eagle which usually takes just a few, deep wing beats between long glides.

The bird which most typically spans the transition from forest to moorland is the Black Grouse. In winter it is found in birch scrub and open pine woods; at other times of the year on nearby moorland. The Black Grouse is one of the most handsome of our game birds, but it has declined greatly in numbers this century, as game bag figures show. In Grampian, although still widespread, it is not sufficiently common now to be considered worthwhile shooting. Like the Capercaillie, Blackcocks display on a lek. It is usually on the moor on a bog or short heather, or in a field. The main display period is from mid-March until May when cocks may visit the lek in the evening as well as at first light. Their bubbling call and whiplash hiss as they "flutter-jump" up to 2 m (6 ft) into the air carries for up to 2 km (about 1 mile) on a still morning. There is great excitement when the Greyhens arrive in late April and early May and the cocks' displays then become intense as they spar with their neighbours. The most dominant cock, usually at the centre of the lek, mates most of the hens. Cocks take no part in parental duties, unlike Red Grouse whose mating system is quite different.

Out on the moors, Red Grouse take up territories in August and September in a flurry of activity at dawn. Territories are visited daily except when completely snow-covered; the grouse then form packs, feeding wherever snow has been blown clear of their main food (heather) and roosting in snow holes. As the snow clears, territories are reclaimed. Ideally, each territory has short heather for feeding and long heather for nesting. For this reason, moors are burned to form the patchwork of heather of different ages which is the sign of a well-managed moor. Red Grouse chicks are escorted by both parents often to a damp area to feed on insects. Greyhens take their young to similar areas and it is clear that these are of great importance for young gamebirds which feed largely on insects until 2-3 weeks old.

The most common song bird of the moorlands is the Meadow Pipit, which is an important prey for Hen Harriers and Merlins. It is much favoured by Cuckoos as a host for their eggs in May. Of all birds of prey on the moors, the least tolerated by gamekeepers is the Hen Harrier, because it kills grouse chicks in summer. Furthermore, if a harrier flies across a grouse drive in autumn it can temporarily scare the grouse away and spoil that part of the shoot. Many harrier nests are destroyed, even though birds of prey are specially protected by law. Despite this the harrier is widespread again in Grampian after being lost as a breeding species from most of the Scottish mainland through intense persecution earlier this century. Ringing recoveries suggest that some of the birds which recolonised Grampian came from the population in Orkney where harriers continued to breed almost undisturbed. Harriers have a particularly interesting mating system as males often pair with more than one female. A study in the early 1970's showed that most males on a moor in Deeside were monogamous. Observations over recent years suggest that polygyny has become widespread on the same moor and elsewhere in the region. The reason for this change is unknown.

Merlins breed all through the moorlands, but are often fairly silent and inconspicuous until the young fledge, so can be overlooked. Their numbers, although low, have been stable over the last 10-15 years except in newly afforested areas where sites have been lost as the trees have grown. The Peregrine, that most majestic of falcons, has made a remarkable recovery since the 1960's when its numbers generally were greatly reduced by pesticides. These came from prey species such as Pigeons which had eaten treated grain. This seriously affected breeding behaviour in most parts of Britain and few young were reared. Grampian Peregrines were not so badly affected, as Red Grouse formed the bulk of their diet. Following bans on the most harmful pesticides, Peregrines have recolonised areas from which they were lost, with Highland and Grampian birds acting as the nucleus. Not only are most of the former sites now occupied, but they are breeding in new eyries, and even on the ground in some parts of the region where suitable cliffs are already occupied. In time they should return to more of our sea cliffs. There are few more evocative sounds than that of a Peregrine's rasping call at a nest cliff on a high lonely corrie.

No birdwatcher should miss the chance to visit the mountains but should be warned that the weather can change for the worse in a very short time, no matter how perfect the dawn. For those less able, Snow Bunting and Ptarmigan may be seen in winter from the roadside at the Cairnwell at the head of Glen Shee. In summer, visitors can take a chair lift here to the Ptarmigan country at the top. Hill birds are often at low density and can be very secretive especially when nesting in June and July, but May is a good month to visit as the birds are displaying then. On one Grampian hill, the song of the Skylark and the trill of the Dotterel can be heard together. Ptarmigan run silently ahead, tails flicking, across the rocks and wind-clipped dwarf heath, then explode into flight. They are most conspicuous when still in their white winter plumage if "caught out" by a rapid thaw. In summer, they are the colour of rocks and lichens, blending perfectly with them. It is striking how tame many of these birds are. If you stand still, Dotterel may run towards you to sit on the nest they left at your approach. Dunlin are also tame, but do not so readily betray the nest. Only the Golden Plover is really wary.

For some people, these hills have an appeal which far outweighs the effort of reaching the top. Part of the magic is woven by the birds, like the unseen Ring Ouzel whose wild song echoes round the corries against the sound of running water or the sudden gust of wind on an otherwise calm day. An Eagle sweeps round a cliff, a Ptarmigan croaks in alarm, a Snow Bunting song-flights like a black-and-white moth across a boulder-strewn plateau. Where better to complete this brief tour of the bird life of Grampian?

Chapter six

OTHER WILD LIFE

Dr. Mark Young, Dr. Brian Staines
Professor Paul Racey, Dr. Peter Maitland

MAMMALS

Grampian Region, with its great variety of habitats, has the full complement of terrestrial mammals found in Scotland. Nearly all species have very wide habitat tolerances and can be found throughout the region in a variety of locations from coast to mountain top.

INSECTIVORES

Both common and pygmy shrews are found from low ground to high moors. Watson (Nethersole-Thompson and Watson 1981) has found both species at 1128 m (3700 ft) on Cairngorm. The common shrew, like the wood mouse will occasionally enter houses in winter; we once readily tamed one which fed from a saucer on a diet of bread, milk and raw mince in our cottage at Durris.

The distribution of the water shrew is uncertain, but it is probably more widespread than is generally believed. The clean and quiet waters of Grampian seem ideal for its existence.

It is always surprising how one finds moles even in the most remote places. Although commonest on fertile, permanent pastures, where there is an abundance of earthworms, they can be found wherever there are good natural grasslands or there has been human settlement or reclaimed land. So, moles still persist around abandoned hill farms, high up the glens, isolated by tracts of moorland, and it is fascinating to speculate how these creatures colonised these areas in the first place.

Hedgehogs are most frequent in the richer oak, beech and birch woods, and in large parks and gardens. They are scarcer on the more acid moors and in dense or old conifer plantations. Watson (Nethersole-Thompson and Watson 1981) has, however, found them above 457 m (1500 ft) in Glen Gairn and on Invercauld.

LAGOMORPHS

The mountain hare, with its white winter coat, is a characteristic animal of the North-east moors and mountains. It is more numerous here than in any other part of Britain, reaching densities of 50/km^2 (19/mile^2) in good areas (Watson and Hewson 1973). Many thousands are shot in annual hare "drives", and there is a good market for their meat in Germany. Mountain hares are primarily associated with moorland, not necessarily the mountains, and they can be found at sea level in parts of Moray where the moors reach the coast. Heather, blaeberry and the draw-shoots of cotton-grass are their major foods. Good moorland management with controlled burning for red grouse benefits these hares greatly. The brown hare, on the other hand, is primarily a grass feeder and is associated with the lower and more fertile grasslands. In recent years their numbers have apparently dwindled and there is much concern for their future in some areas. Although no one knows for certain the reasons for the decline of brown hares throughout Britain, changes in agriculture seem a likely cause for their current scarcity.

It may be surprising that the rabbit, probably the most commonly seen wild mammal, is a relatively recent addition to the fauna of North-east Scotland. According to Nethersole-Thompson and Watson (1981), rabbits first appeared in upper Aberdeenshire in 1833 at Alford but by 1843 they were "numerous and destructive". During the first half of this century rabbits were a major agricultural pest. However, in 1954 a Kincardineshire farmer introduced myxomatosis into the area which devastated the local rabbit populations. In the North-east this disease greatly reduces the stocks in the autumn, but some individuals survive over-winter to restart the population cycle the following spring. There is some evidence that myxomatosis is having less impact that before, either due to more animals becoming immune or the strain of virus becoming weaker. Certainly over-wintering populations appear to have been larger in recent years. Mainly associated with farmland, rabbits can be found high up the glens on pastures or natural grassland and around old crofts and shielings; they have been recorded above 457 m (1500 ft) in Glen Eye and Glen Derry and above 488 m (1600 ft) in Strathdon (Nethersole-Thompson and Watson 1981).

In at least one isolated population around 366 m (1200 ft) in Glen Dye, I found many black individuals. Although they were obvious to any predator when they were feeding on open grassland, they blended perfectly with their background when they ran into the cover of peat banks or heather.

RODENTS

Wood mice and bank voles are commonest in broad-leafed woodlands and on farmland, especially where dry-stane dykes and scrub around the edges of fields give them plenty of cover. Both live also in conifer plantations, especially when these have reasonable areas of larch, and are found in lower numbers on the moors. Wood mice have been recorded in some of the remote mountain bothies and occasionally on the Cairngorm plateau above 1219 m (4000 ft; Nethersole-Thompson and Watson 1981). They will frequently "invade" houses during the winter months, but unlike the ubiquitous house mouse usually leave again by the spring.

The field vole is probably the most widespead and abundant small mammal in Grampian Region. In young forestry plantations it can reach densities as high as 50-100/ha (20-40/acre). Populations of field voles have cycles of abundance with peaks at roughly four-year intervals when they can reach pest proportions and cause considerable damage to young trees. These voles are important food items for predatory mammals and birds such as foxes, pine martens, tawny owls and kestrels.

The black form of the water vole predominates in the Grampian area. Colonies are found in or around the clean burns, pools and lochans in the lowlands, and as high as 1006 m (3300 ft) on Lochnagar and in some parts of the Cairngorms.

The common or brown rat was introduced into Britain during the 18th century, and 100 years ago it was still rare in many country districts in Grampian, where the black or ship rat predominated. Since that time, the brown rat has spread into the cities, farms and abandoned hill crofts. The black rat, renowned as the carrier of bubonic plague, is now rare in Britain. It is still found in the harbour area of Aberdeen; at least two "infestations" have been reported there within the last decade.

A popular rodent of the pine woods of North-east Scotland is the red squirrel. It was almost extinct in the Grampian area by the beginning of Victorian times, but subsequently recovered, reaching a peak in numbers earlier this century. Red squirrels are still common but not as numerous as 100 years ago. Populations can fluctuate widely, possibly related to the varying abundance of conifer seed, their major food in winter, or to a pox virus disease which is found in squirrels throughout the country. Being largely diurnal, red squirrels are more frequently seen than other rodents. The British variety has a creamy-white tail in summer. However, some individuals seen in Grampian retain a dark tail throughout the year. The dark tail is a characteristic of some continental varieties, and its occurrence in the North-east is probably a result of introductions of red squirrels from the continent from the middle of the 19th century (Ritchie 1920).

The American grey squirrel was introduced into Scotland between 1892 and 1919. Its northward spread was checked from Dundee in the east to Comrie in the west until the late 1960s but by 1970 grey squirrels had spread over the hills into the Dee valley. A few are regularly seen in lower and middle Deeside, especially in the western suburbs of Aberdeen and in Banchory, and even as far west as Dinnet. Grey squirrels occur around Lhanbryde, near Elgin, but this population is apparently isolated from the Deeside one; its origins are a mystery.

CARNIVORES

The stoat is commoner than its smaller cousin the weasel. They are both more plentiful on the lower fertile ground and around broad-leaved woods and scrubland, although they will extend on to the moors. They use dry-stane dykes for cover and nest sites, and the writer knew of one family of stoats living and breeding under an old sheet of corrugated iron by the Char Cottage in Glen Dye. Stoats will frequent suburban gardens, living off the food placed on bird tables, and even on some unsuspecting birds themselves!

The otter is found in all the major rivers in the region, in many of the tributaries and in the lochs and lochans. It also can be seen on the higher bog pools, especially when frogs are spawning and providing a good source of food. Otters are less common in the Dee valley than, for example, in the Spey, and they are less frequently seen along the Grampian coasts than around the western and northern shores of Scotland.

Mink were introduced into fur farms in Britain from 1929 onwards. Escaped animals first bred in the wild in England in 1956, and in Grampian Region probably around 1962. They are now more widespread and more numerous than otters. Mink occupy nearly all the major rivers and tributaries and are frequently seen around Loch Muick. Unlike the otter, whose main food is eels and other fish, mink have a more catholic diet taking many different birds and mammals as well as insects.

Badgers are likewise found throughout Grampian, especially in the lower valleys, but they are less common in the hills. Compared to the south of England, they are usually in fairly low numbers, except in the hillier areas of Buchan where the soils seem ideally suited for their setts and the rich pastures provide plenty of earthworms, their favourite food.

Two species of carnivore that have shown a welcome revival in recent years are the wildcat (Plate 13) and the pine marten (Plate 12). They were rare throughout Scotland by the end of the 19th century, but since then both species have increased their range. More forests, coupled with the decrease in persecution from gamekeepers, are likely to be the main factors responsible for their recovery.

The red fox, also, has shown a dramatic rise in numbers and range. According to Nethersole-Thompson and Watson (1981) "in the 1930s and 40s they were unknown in Buchan, lower Deveron and lower Donside." They have now, however, colonised all of Grampian Region right to the coast and have even spread into suburban Aberdeen.

Deer

The two indigenous species of deer, red and roe, are also extending their range in Grampian Region. Roe deer are essentially woodland dwellers, although some live on the high moors. The writer has seen them at 548 m (1800 ft) in Glen Dye and at 685 m (2250 ft) at Glen Shee, several kilometres from the nearest woodland. There has been a big increase in numbers in recent years, and they are now regularly reported in suburban Aberdeen!

Red deer (Plate 11) may be generally thought of as animals of the open hill but they originally lived in woodlands. In recent years they have colonised the extensive forests planted since the 1950s. Numbers of red deer in the eastern Grampians have more than doubled from 1965 to around 25,500 in 1986. Woodland red deer are generally bigger, produce more young and live in much smaller groups than those living continually on open moorland. Both red and roe deer cause considerable damage to forestry plantations and to agricultural crops.

Reindeer, extinct in Scotland by the 12th century, were reintroduced into Rothiemurcus Forest in 1952 and now range over a wide part of the higher Cairngorms. Their numbers are kept to around 80 head.

Two other introduced species of deer are also found in Grampian. Small numbers of fallow deer have been known for many years in the woods around Fochabers and sika deer have been seen around Loch na Bo, near Elgin (Richter 1976). Sika deer are spreading rapidly throughout northern and western Scotland and are common around Culloden and Glen Mazeran; it is only a matter of time before these deer colonise the extensive spruce and pine plantations of Grampian. Apart from the damage they cause to forestry through browsing shoots of young trees and eating the bark of older ones, they also hybridise with the native red deer thus causing concern for the genetic integrity of the native red deer stock.

Small numbers of feral goats occur south-east of Lochindorb and are occasionally seen across the Grampian border on the Hills of Cromdale.

SEALS

Grey and common seals are frequently seen around the Grampian coasts. Breeding colonies of common seals do not occur here, but there are many instances of individual common seals breeding along the Morayshire and Aberdeenshire coasts. Grey seals do not breed here.

The terrestial mammals of Grampian are widespread and many are increasing. With more afforestation giving them protection and security and a greater source of food, we can only expect a further expansion of range of some of the more interesting species, which a few decades ago were regarded as rare or endangered.

APPENDIX

	Common name	Scientific Name
INSECTIVORES	Common shrew	*Sorex araneus*
	Pygmy shrew	*Sorex minutus*
	Water shrew	*Neomys fodiens*
	Mole	*Talpa europaea*
	Hedgehog	*Erinaceous europaeus*
LAGOMORPHS	Rabbit*	*Oryctolagus cuniculus*
	Mountain hare	*Lepus timidus*
	Brown hare	*Lepus capensis*
RODENTS	Bank vole	*Clethrionomys glareolus*
	Field vole	*Microtus agrestis*
	Water vole	*Arvicola terrestris*
	Wood mouse	*Apodemus sylvaticus*
	House mouse*	*Mus musculus*
	Brown rat*	*Rattus norvegicus*
	Black rat*	*Rattus rattus*
	Red squirrel	*Sciurus vulgaris*
	Grey squirrel*	*Sciurus carolinensis*
CARNIVORES	Stoat	*Mustela erminea*
	Weasel	*Mustela nivalis*
	Mink*	*Mustela vison*
	Otter	*Lutra lutra*
	Badger	*Meles meles*
	Wild cat	*Felis silvestris*
	Pine marten	*Martes martes*
	Fox	*Vulpes vulpes*
SEALS	Grey seal	*Halichoerus grypus*
	Common seal	*Phoca vitulina*
UNGULATES	Red deer	*Cervus elaphus*
	Roe deer	*Capreolus capreolus*
	Fallow deer*	*Dama dama*
	Sika deer*	*Cervus nippon*
	Reindeer*	*Rangifer tarandus*
	Feral goat*	*Capra* (domestic)

*Introduced species into Britain

BATS

The number of bat species resident in Britain declines with latitude. Only three are found in Grampian, close to the northern border of their European distribution, compared with 15 in the south of England. The Scottish species are the ubiquitous pipistrelle *(Pipistrellus pipistrellus)*, the commonest British bat and at 5-6g (1/5 oz) one of the smallest; the long-eared bat *(Plecotus auritus)* (9g) and Daubenton's bat *(Myotis daubentonii)* (10g; 2/5 oz). There are an increasing number of records of Natterer's bat *(M. nattereri)* in Grampian, including a recent summer record of a pregnant female on the Moray coast, which suggests that this species is breeding in the region (P. A. Neville, personal communication). In addition, vagrant bats such as the particoloured bat *(Vespertilio murinus)* with white tips to its fur and a resulting frosted appearance, are occasionally blown from Europe during autumn gales to land on North Sea oil rigs and the Scottish mainland.

Bats first appear in numbers in Grampian each year in early May when they take up residence in the roof spaces of dwelling houses. They are thought to have evolved in deciduous forests, living in rot holes in trees or behind bark. Now that such forests have been felled to build houses and ships, bats rely on man-made roosts in the roof spaces of dwelling houses. Long-eared and Daubenton's bats roost in the apex of the roof in contact with the timber and colonies may number a few dozen to 200 respectively. Pipistrelles on the other hand are crevice seekers, squeezing between timber and stonework, and sometimes forming colonies of over 1000 breeding females.

Summer maternity colonies consist of pregnant females, occasionally accompanied by males born the previous summer and not yet sexually mature. Each female gives birth to a single young, occasionally twins, at the end of June or beginning of July, suckles her young for about a month and then departs the roost. The young remain for a few more weeks before they too depart during September. Although adult male bats are excluded from these maternity colonies they can be caught by mist netting in feeding areas. They probably lead a solitary existence, roosting under eaves and in crevices, until the time of mating in September and October. After mating, spermatozoa are stored by females throughout hibernation, to avoid having to find a mate when they are in the poorest body condition on arousal from hibernation in spring.

During summer, bats emerge from their roost each evening at dusk. The first pipistrelles and long-eared bats generally emerge about half an hour after sunset and Daubenton's bat a little later, about an hour after sunset. Pipistrelles prefer to forage in well-wooded river valleys, over water or around deciduous trees at the height of the thickest foliage where insect densities are greatest. Recent surveys along Deeside have shown that there are over 50 bat roosts in a 30 km (18 miles) stretch of the river valley. Such a high density of bat roosts has not previously been recorded and suggests that the river valleys of Grampian may be sites of national importance for bats during summer.

During pregnancy, pipistrelles generally have a single foraging flight each night, and feed mainly on the dusk peak of flying insects. They feed rapidly, capturing up to 10 insects a minute, by means of their sophisticated sonar system using high frequency sounds. They also drink from the surface of ponds and rivers while in flight. After parturition, they return to the roost in the middle of the night to suckle their young and then leave again for a second foraging flight as dawn approaches, to take advantage of the second nightly peak of flying insects. When foraging, pipistrelles establish beats, by flying up and down the same path for 15-20 minutes, before flying in a straight line to another area where they set up another beat. The same bat frequently forages at the same time and place each night in a routine known as traplining (Racey & Swift, 1985).

Pipistrelles feed mainly on caddis flies and long-horned flies, together with mayflies and lacewings when these are available (Swift, Racey and Avery 1985). The fact that most of these insect groups are associated with water explains the bats' preference for foraging in riparian situations. Daubenton's bats have a similar diet to pipistrelles and also feed over water (Swift and Racey 1983). Long-eared bats specialise on a diet of moths and beetles. As well as catching insects in free flight, they can hover in and out of the foliage, and are thought to glean insects from the leaves and bark (Swift and Racey 1983). In addition to their distinctive ears, they also have large eyes, so that sight may be as important as hearing in finding their food.

In contrast to their abundance during summer, bats are seldom found in Grampian in winter and it seems likely that they migrate south to latitudes where the winters are less severe and where they can feed during mild nights (Avery 1985).

The numbers of bats in western Europe have declined dramatically in recent decades (Stebbings and Griffith 1984) due mainly to loss of roost sites, increased use of remedial timber treatments in roof spaces (Racey and Swift 1986) and the widespread use of agricultural pesticides. The traditional barley and beef agriculture of Grampian involves few insecticides and may contribute to the region being such an attractive place for bats during summer.

AMPHIBIANS AND REPTILES

Grampian is too cool an area to be favourable for amphibians and reptiles, which are "cold-blooded" and so need sunny conditions to allow them to warm up sufficiently to conduct their lives; however, in spite of this, the region is home to at least three species of each group. The term "cold-blooded" is misleading. Certainly these animals do not use an internal regulatory system to maintain a constant high body temperature but they do have a range of behavioural techniques which help to keep them warm. These are best developed in the reptiles and are exemplified by the common lizard, which is a fairly widespread animal in Grampian Region. Lizards sunbathe when they wish to warm up, choosing a sheltered place and aligning themselves so as to receive maximum warmth and this is when they are most often seen. Only when sufficiently warm do they then move off to hunt. Lizards are found mainly in sheltered places and especially like old walls, path edges, clearings and rocky areas, where open sunning spots are adjacent to shelter. They feed on a variety of insects, spiders and other small invertebrates and, although they may "stalk" these, they may also wait until the prey comes near enough for a sudden dart forward to catch it. When warm they can move extremely quickly and can even catch active insects like flies. They have a well-known defence, in that they can shed their tails when alarmed or captured and this is most disconcerting to their attacker, especially because the tail may continue to twitch for a while. The lizards' tails then regrow slowly and you often see them with a shortened version, telling of past alarms.

Slow-worms are related to lizards, but have no legs and are not so agile. They feed on slower moving prey, including slugs and worms and, although quite widespread, are more restricted than lizards to warm, sheltered places. Whereas lizards may be found quite far up the valley sides and out on moorland up to 600 m (2000 ft), slow-worms are more often seen in the valley bottoms near streams and rivers. By day they are generally hidden under flat stones and are usually discovered when these are lifted up, but they can sometimes also be found foraging or sunning themselves. Young slow-worms are a creamy-yellow colour on the back, in two broad longitudinal stripes, but there is no obvious explanation why this is advantageous to them.

Adders are Grampian's only snake and are quite common in the river valleys and moors, up to about 500 m (1650 ft), on dry, sunny slopes but are absent from more exposed places. Like the other reptiles they hibernate in crevices and holes, where the temperature remains fairly constant and only emerge to warm up when the spring sunshine returns. Often they hibernate in groups, before spreading out during the summer, and in the spring they are commonly seen whilst sunning themselves. Then they are cool and sluggish and so cannot avoid humans very easily; some care is needed to avoid disturbing them. Of course they have a poisonous bite but this generally has only fairly mild effects and far fewer people die from snake bites in Britain than die from allergic reaction to bee stings. In any case adders are shy of man and generally slip quietly away when danger approaches. Their venom is used to kill lizards, small rodents and other prey and is very effective on these small animals.

Like the other two species of reptile the adder bears live young, although inside the female the young begin within an egg, and this is presumably because our climate is not sufficiently warm to allow the eggs to be incubated successfully outside the parent. Farther south in Britain the grass snake lays eggs and sometimes chooses a warm compost heap as an incubation site!

Only one type of newt is reliably reported from our area and that is the palmate newt. Both other British species, the crested and common or smooth newt, have been recorded in the past but are generally more southern in their distribution. The palmate newt male has a fine filament projecting from the end of his tail, especially in the breeding season, and the female also has a blunt point there; however, in other respects, and particularly outside the breeding season, they have few distinguishing features and generally resemble small specimens of female smooth newts. The "palm" referred to in their name is an inconspicuous webbing of the feet. Palmate newts are widespread in small ponds, sheltered areas of lochs and lochans and in some backwaters of our rivers, but need still water and an absence of fish predators. They are often very common in artificial fire dams and are quite tolerant of acid water in moorland lochans. They are found from sea level up into the upper valleys and lower moors at about 500 m (1650 ft) but, although the adults do leave water to forage in damp lochside vegetation, they are rarely seen away from the water and the best way to find them is to approach pools slowly on warm days and to look especially at the areas where sun shines down through to the bottom near the edge. Even then their olive brown colour makes them hard to see.

Frogs and toads venture farther from water, especially the latter, which only use it as a breeding site. A traditional spawning pool may be visited by thousands of toads at mating time in spring and the croaking males are a dramatic sight and sound. These arrive first and then compete vigorously for the females as they approach. The spawn is laid in long strings, draped around water plants, unlike the familiar masses laid by the frog. For most of the year toads forage singly well away from the favoured breeding sites and, although they are active mostly at night to avoid the warmer, drier conditions by day, they are dry skinned and are fairly independent of water. They feed on a great variety of invertebrates, ranging from slugs and worms to beetles and flies and they catch all these using a sticky tongue, which they flip out rapidly at prey which comes incautiously close. As with most reptiles and amphibians they only respond to moving prey and appear very foolishly indifferent to possible delicacies which have the sense to sit still.

Frogs have a moist, smooth skin, by contrast to toads and, although they also hunt on land, they have to remain in humid areas, close to open water and with plenty of damp shelters where they hide by day. They are quite tolerant of cold, however, and can be found well up to 800 m (2625 ft) in the hills, wherever suitable breeding ponds occur. In spring the masses of spawn are conspicuous in small pools and ditches but often opaque, cloudy patches of dead spawn are present, showing the effects of frost. Sometimes spawn or small tadpoles are found in mere trickles on paths; some of these survive by wriggling down into more substantial streams or pools but others die as the water runs out in the summer. Of all Grampian's reptiles and amphibians the common frog is the most abundant and obvious and this is in pleasant contrast to much of lowland Britain, where pond drainage and the use of insecticides have reduced frog populations dramatically.

INVERTEBRATES

The full story of the invertebrate animals of Grampian will never be told. How could it be when you consider that the number of different species which are present will certainly run into many **thousand** and that many of these are such unconsidered and unstudied animals as threadworms, mites and plant bugs. Nevertheless we are slowly unravelling the fascinating life stories of some of these animals and this section describes the history of a selected few of the more obvious types. Interestingly, everyone who has begun to study a previously neglected group of Grampian's invertebrates has found rare and unexpected creatures, often emphasising the unusual environment offered by the region and especially the extreme conditions found in the Cairngorm range.

"Invertebrates" are not a naturally homogenous group but include all animals without a backbone, ranging from the tiniest protozoan to the complex and more familiar insects, molluscs and worms. Everyone encounters some of these every day and their variety of form and way of life are an inexhaustible source of fascination and intrigue. The most obvious and best loved are probably the butterflies and moths, of which

Grampian has about 900 different species so far recorded, and included in these are many that are rare and dramatic.

Butterflies, like all flying insects, need warmth to enable them to fly. They also need a nectar source to provide the fuel for flight, and their caterpillar juvenile stages (larvae) are usually specialised to feed on only one type of wild tree or plant. The consequence of this is that to find butterflies you must visit relatively sunny and sheltered areas, where there is still a range of natural plants, and in Grampian two types of place are favoured. The sheltered and flowery coastal areas, such as Stonehaven, Muchalls, Cullen or Speymouth are one, and the sheltered, grassy glens, such as Glen Slugain, Inchrory and Glen Buchat are another. We have no nationally rare butterflies in Grampian but attractive species, such as the Dark-green Fritillary, the Common Blue and the Scotch Brown Argus are found in both these contrasting areas. The Small Blue, which is sadly very local in Scotland, may also be such an example. It is best known from the Moray coastal fringe but there is a recent tantalising record from Glen Ey where its larval foodplant, the Kidney Vetch, certainly occurs.

In complete contrast the mountain tops are the homes of only a few specialised moths. One is an enigma. The Mountain Burnet moth occurs in Britain only in one or two small colonies on the hills near Braemar and yet its foodplant, Crowberry, is almost universal. Others are more widespread and often show extreme specialisations. The Black Mountain moth, for example, is matt black, to help it to absorb what little heat is available on the Cairngorm plateau, and the fat-bodied females usually find it too energetic to fly and so scuttle about the rocks instead.

The moorlands, which characterise so much of Grampian, are where several exotic insects are found. In early summer it is common to see the brilliantly green Tiger Beetle scuttling along sandy paths amongst the heather and then flying busily off when approached too closely. Its larvae reside in tunnels at the bottom of small pits and live by preying on smaller creatures which tumble into these traps. Also, in the early season the male Emperor moths fly erratically across the moors searching for the females, which attract them by a scent which is active over several kilometres. Both sexes are ornamented by large "frightening" eyespots to deter predators, whereas their huge larvae are beautifully camouflaged, being apple green with black bands and with pink spots which mimic heather flowers.

Two other large moths also occur on the same moors and are rather similar. Both are warm brown as adults and use scent to attract the males to the females, just as the Emperor moths do. The males smell this with their antennae, which are feathery, so as to be extra effective. The two are the Northern Eggar, a northern race of the Oak Eggar which frequents lanes and commons in southern Britain and whose very large furry larvae take two seasons to grow to full size, and the Fox moth, which also has a hairy brown larva. Their thick hair coat protects them from most would-be predators but even so some specialists (perhaps cuckoos included) relish them. The Fox moth larva hibernates fully grown and is a familiar and conspicuous sunbather in autumn and especially again in early spring.

There are welcome signs that undefined climatic changes are allowing the spread eastwards of some species. The Scotch Argus butterfly has spread along the Moray coastal zone right round into Deveronvale and Donside; the Speckled Wood is moving along behind and is now east of the Spey; and the Orange-Tip and Ringlet have recently greatly expanded their range throughout inland Grampian. Such changes occur constantly but these days the scarcity of suitable natural habitats is rather restricting and our marshland species, such as the Small Pearl-bordered Fritillary are contracting as their homes are progressively drained.

Small lochs and even peat pools are the usual habitat of the aquatic larvae of Dragon and Damselflies. On Deeside there is a nationally rare species, the Northern Damselfly, (easily confused with the much commoner Common Blue Damselfly), and this species is a true Highlander being found otherwise only in a restricted number of places in the central highlands. It is a delicate insect with a blue body, a common colour for Damselflies, whereas our most widespread species, the Large Red Damselfly, is a bright red colour. A visit to a moorland area, where there are lochs and streams and also some birch trees to provide cover, will often allow several species to be seen, including the robust and beautiful Gold-ringed Dragonfly, whose larvae live in streams and which is fortunately still common in Scotland, but is becoming rare in the rest of Europe. Another widespread species, the Four-spotted Chaser has a flat brown body and rests conspicuously with its wings held out flat, often on heather, in its moorland habitat.

The unpolluted rivers and burns are fairly cold and well oxygenated throughout the year and are known internationally for their aquatic life. In particular they are the habitats for the larvae of Stoneflies and Mayflies, both of which are characteristic of such types of river. The Dee is especially rich in them with a preponderance of Stoneflies in the upper reaches and of Mayflies lower down. If you turn over a fist-sized rock from the middle reaches of the Dee in spring or autumn you are likely to find their larvae. Those of many Mayflies are flattened, to help them avoid the water current, and they scuttle across the stone to the underside, instinctively avoiding the light and the upper side, where they would be vulnerable to predators as well as the current. Mayfly larvae have three tails (although the flying adults may only have two), whereas the Stonefly larvae have two and are generally cylindrical. The adult Mayflies may swarm over the rivers in spring and summer, being snapped up by fish and imitated by the flies of fishermen.

Another inhabitant of Grampian's rivers is the Freshwater Pearl Mussel, which is black and grows to a length of 15 cm (6 in) and an age of up to 100 years. These mussels burrow into coarse sand and filter organic debris from the water for food. In the past they were more common but their numbers have been sadly reduced by pearl fishermen, who may collect and open hundreds to find each pearl. The mussels have a complex life cycle and release millions of almost microscopic larvae each summer. These are carried along by the water currents until they are inhaled by young trout and salmon, on whom they attach by "snapping" shut their hinged shells on the fish's gill filaments. The tiny proportion which succeed in this then grow slightly, before releasing themselves from the fish the following spring as young mussels. Infestations are usually so small that the fish are not unduly affected. Grampian's freshwater pearls have been harvested for many centuries but unfortunately the mussel has now become so scarce, in most rivers, that it will need some conservation measures to survive.

Amongst the largely ignored, but vital, decomposers of the "litter" layer beneath the live vegetation, are the many species of snails and slugs. Some of these also feed on growing plants, such as the slugs which decimate our lettuce seedlings each year, but many are the initial stage in the breakdown of the season's discarded leaves. These snails are largely sedentary, have low powers of dispersion to new sites and are usually very specialised in their habitat requirements. Consequently, they often act as excellent "indicators" of the habitat type. For example, it is usually possible to tell fairly reliably whether a wood is an ancient relict of Scotland's original forests by identifying the number and type of snails present. "Recently" planted woodland (perhaps only one or two hundred years old) may not yet have been invaded by these species. They may also indicate very clearly that the soil is lime rich, or conversely acidic, because certain species can only tolerate a specialised type of soil, regardless of the plants present. There is a fascinating wealth of information on the history and conditions of an area, which can be gained by studying its lowly snails, and this is being increasingly used by land managers who need to know such things in planning their activities. A study of almost any of Grampian's invertebrates involves consideration of the geology, land-use, climate and most other aspects of the environment, and our fauna ranges from the most extreme sub-arctic species to others found only where the conditions are mollified by the sea.

FRESHWATER FISH

In common with the rest of Scotland, the Grampian Region was completely covered by ice during the last Ice Age (see Chapter 2) and the present fish fauna (Table 6) started to come into the area only after the disappearance of the ice, some 10,000 years ago. Migratory fish, especially salmonids (Atlantic Salmon, Brown Trout and Arctic Charr) and lampreys, which had a marine phase, were able to move in readily from the sea and occupy all easily accessible waters. Some time later (probably several thousands of years) these were followed very gradually by a number of purely freshwater species from the south of Britain (e.g. Pike and Perch) which managed to move overland from one fresh water system to another. Thus, for historical reasons, Grampian has many more fish species than Shetland (Maitland and East 1976) or the Outer Hebrides (Maitland 1981), but fewer than the south-west of Scotland (Maitland 1970) or the Forth area (Maitland 1980). More recently, and particularly over the last few hundred years, Man has been responsible for moving many fish around the country and several of the species now established in the Grampian Region were introduced there (e.g. Tench, Gudgeon and Carp). The Humpback Salmon, which was introduced to rivers in the White Sea area of the USSR has appeared occasionally as a vagrant along the Grampian coast. Some species, especially perhaps the Arctic Charr, appear to have declined and are now present in only one or two waters (e.g. Loch Lee).

The commonest type of fresh water in the region is represented by the numerous fast flowing and rather poor burns and rivers which occur virtually throughout the area. The dominant fish in those waters inaccessible from the sea is the Brown Trout and this is usually the only fish found in some of the highest lochs in the region (e.g. Sandy Loch and Lochnagar). Where there are no waterfalls or other obstructions, the community includes this species (with its marine running form the Sea Trout) as well as Atlantic Salmon and Eels. In many places Minnows and Three-spined Sticklebacks are common too, whilst the Brook Lamprey and Stone Loach occur in some running waters. The status of the latter species is uncertain in a number of rivers. In several of the richer lowland lochs in the region Perch and Pike may be the dominant fish, though Eels too are often common here (e.g. these three species are the only fish found in Loch Kinord). There are no really well developed estuaries in the region, so most of the estuarine species (e.g. shads, mullets and Common Goby) occur only casually at the mouths of the major rivers or along nearby coasts. A few other species which also spawn in fresh water elsewhere occur only casually as vagrants along the coasts (e.g. Sturgeon, Smelt and Sea Bass). However, the Flounder, which is often thought of

TABLE 6. Freshwater fish species recorded from the Grampian Region. Closed circles (●) indicate that the species is: A. native; B. migratory; C. widespread; D. a breeding species in Grampian; E. angled; F. recorded by Sim (1903); G. recorded recently. Open circles (o) mean the opposite

COMMON NAME	SCIENTIFIC NAME	A	B	C	D	E	F	G
Sea Lamprey	*Petromyzon marinus*	●	●	O	●	O	●	●
River Lamprey	*Lampetra fluviatilis*	●	●	O	●	O	●	●
Brook Lamprey	*Lampetra planeri*	●	O	●	●	O	●	●
Sturgeon	*Acipenser sturio*	●	●	O	O	O	●	●
Allis Shad	*Alosa alosa*	●	●	O	O	O	●	O
Twaite Shad	*Alosa fallax*	●	●	O	O	O	●	●
Humpback Salmon	*Oncorhynchus gorbuscha*	O	●	O	O	O	O	●
Atlantic Salmon	*Salmo salar*	●	●	●	●	●	●	●
Brown Trout	*Salmo trutta*	●	●	●	●	●	●	●
Rainbow Trout	*Salmo gairdneri*	O	O	O	O	●	O	●
Arctic Charr	*Salvelinus alpinus*	●	O	O	●	O	●	O
Smelt	*Osmerus eperlanus*	●	●	O	O	O	●	O
Pike	*Esox lucius*	●	O	●	●	●	●	●
Roach	*Rutilus rutilus*	●	O	O	O	O	O	●
Minnow	*Phoxinus phoxinus*	●	O	●	●	O	●	●
Tench	*Tinca tinca*	O	O	O	●	O	●	●
Gudgeon	*Gobio gobio*	O	O	O	●	O	●	●
Carp	*Cyprinus carpio*	O	O	O	●	O	●	●
Stone Loach	*Noemacheilus barbatulus*	●	O	O	●	O	●	●
Eel	*Anguilla anguilla*	●	●	●	O	●	●	●
Three-spined Stickleback	*Gasterosteus aculeatus*	●	O	●	●	O	●	●
Thinlipped Mullet	*Chelon ramada*	●	●	O	O	O	●	O
Thicklipped Mullet	*Crenimugil labrosus*	●	●	O	O	O	●	O
Sea Bass	*Dicentrarchus labrax*	●	●	O	O	●	●	●
Perch	*Perca fluviatilis*	●	O	●	●	●	●	●
Common Goby	*Pomatoschistus microps*	●	●	O	●	O	●	●
Flounder	*Platichthys flesus*	●	●	●	●	●	●	●

as a purely marine species, penetrates quite far up some rivers and is common in a few lochs (e.g. the Loch of Strathbeg).

Several species are important commercially in the region, particularly the Atlantic Salmon for which there are a number of net fisheries along the coast and at the mouths of some rivers. This is also the major angling species but Trout (both Brown and Sea) are also very important in many rivers and lochs. These two species are of considerable significance in the tourist economy of the region. Rainbow Trout have been introduced to a number of lochs for angling but, as elsewhere in Scotland, appear unable to sustain themselves and the populations are maintained only by regular stocking. In a few places, Eels, Pike and Perch form the basis of angling fisheries.

The River Dee is probably the most significant running water in the region and is an extremely important river nationally. The North Esk is also of some importance and is now the northern boundary for the Roach, a species which made its first appearance there only a few years ago. Compared to the west Highlands and many of the islands there are relatively few lochs in the area. Among the most important is Loch Muick, one of the largest and deepest standing waters, containing an excellent mixed population of Atlantic Salmon, Brown Trout and Eels. The quality of the water in most places is excellent, thanks to the continued efforts of the North-East River Purification Board, but active conservation measures are required (as in other parts of the country) to ensure the future of several of the less common fish species.

Part two

PRE-HISTORY AND HISTORY

Chapter seven

THE EARLY PEOPLES

Mr Ian Shepherd

Following the Ice Age, the great forest that established itself over the river banks and hill slopes of Grampian Region in time provided a rich and useful range of habitats for the first inhabitants. Perhaps as much as eight thousand years ago small bands composed of several family groups from farther south began to include the coasts and rivers of Grampian in the territories whose game and other resources they exploited. These territories, over which the hunters and gatherers moved according to the seasons and the cycles of game, were vast, but the resources they could thereby command were substantial. In the forest the large mammals such as red deer or elk would provide not only an abundance of meat [one red deer stag at 165 kg (363 lb) clean carcase weight could have fed a family of five for more than 30 days (Champion *et al* 1984, 94)] but also skin for clothing and bone and antler for tools. In season the nuts and berries of the forest would have provided additional nourishment while the rivers were an ample source of fish.

Archaeological evidence for these earliest settlers is sparse in Grampian and conditioned by differences in the intensity of field-work between different areas. However, on the haughs of the Dee, between Banchory and Peterculter, substantial quantities of flint flakes, the waste from tool-making, have been found. One site, Nether Mills of Crathes, has been excavated to modern standards. It can be described as a major winter base camp, perhaps for a group of four or five nuclear families exploiting deer in winter and fish in spring (Kenworthy 1981). The flint industry is related to the rod-dominated industries of eastern England of c.4000BC. Approximately 0.5 km (0.3 miles) farther up the Dee is a site with evidence of earlier occupation in the form of larger obliquely truncated bladelets and isosceles triangle microliths, while nearer Banchory, at Birkwood, triangular rod-shaped implements related to narrow blade forms have been found (Paterson and Lacaille 1936).

The precise size of the territories exploited from such sites is not yet known; microliths have been found on the Feugh (Ian Ralston, pers comm), while several sites are also known on the Ythan. That the hinterland of the region was penetrated, at least on a seasonal basis, by hunter-gatherer bands is indicated by the barbed point or fish spear from Glen Avon, deep in the Moray hills (Morrison 1980, 164, pl xv).

The resources of the shoreline were also exploited. The flint-working floor (for the maintenance of hunting equipment) on what would have been the sandy flats at the mouth of the Denburn in Aberdeen (Kenworthy 1982, 212-14), the extensive flint collections from the coastal sand systems between the Don and the Ythan, some of which have been characterised as the residue of tool-kits for the manufacture of composite bone implements such as fish-spears (Hawke-Smith 1980, 501) and the microliths incorporated in collections from the Culbin Sands, Moray (Lacaille 1944, 13-15) all indicate that the fish, sea mammals, birds and shellfish of the coast would have been attractive sources of food.

There is no clear horizon between the hunter-gatherer way of life and the appearance of the first farmers. This is not merely a result of the paucity of radiocarbon dates for these periods in the region, but rather an indication that the two modes of subsistence could have co-existed, perhaps for many generations (until the forest-cover on which the hunter-gatherers relied for game had been reduced significantly by the farmers). Certainly it is possible that some of the earliest episodes of forest clearance identified in pollen analysis may have been either the result of fire-setting by hunter-gatherers in an attempt to increase the areas for browsing animals within the forest or the work of pioneering farmers intent on producing crops; equally, some of these indications may have been caused naturally (Edwards 1979; Edwards and Ralston 1984, 25; Ralston 1984).

Few settlements of the earliest farmers have yet been identified. The excavation of the complex timber hall at Balbridie, on Deeside, gives the clearest picture so far of their life (Ralston 1982). The hall, 26m by 13m (42.5 ft by 85 ft), and standing 8 m (26 ft) high at the ridge, was made by skilled carpenters. Here the community cultivated cereals, principally wheat and six-row barley, which was stored in one end of the building. Bone did not survive in the gravelly soil, but the pottery that was found consisted of carinated, round-based bowls related to the Unstan tradition of the west and north. It is difficult to imagine that the Balbridie farmers did not also make use of the fish in the Dee and the resources of the forest, now contracting, on the hill slopes behind (Edwards and Ralston 1984). Indeed, charred hazelnuts were found amongst the burnt material. The social group represented by the 320 m^2 (3445 ft^2) of the hall might be an extended family.

Other timber halls in Grampian, although not yet confirmed as Neolithic in date, are at Crathes, opposite Balbridie, and at Monboddo, in the Mearns (Ralston 1984, 74-5).

Elsewhere in Grampian evidence of Neolithic settlement has been found at Easterton of Roseisle in Moray (Henshall 1983; Walker 1968a) and beneath a burial mound at Boghead, Fochabers (Burl 1984).

By combining the distributions of Neolithic pottery and flint and polished stone axes (Plate 16) the primary areas of farming settlement can be seen to have been lower Deeside and Cromar, the Garioch, east Buchan and the Laich of Moray. If the distribution of long cairns and barrows is added, the gravel terraces of the south Mearns, the hill slopes of the central Mearns and the lower Deveron also come to prominence (Shepherd 1986b), [Fig 19].

The pottery of the first farmers in Grampian comprises well fired, plain round-based vessels, some with carinations and concave necks. A distinctive feature is the fluting of the necks, seen for example at Easterton of Roseisle, Boghead and Pitglassie (Henshall 1983, 31). Although this pottery falls within the 'Grimston/Lyles Hill' tradition of early Neolithic pottery from north Britain, it has been noted recently that the use of a description for these North-eastern pots comprising a Yorkshire and an Irish element obscures the significance of Grampian's own strong local Neolithic traditions (Kinnes 1985). There is in fact a greater range, with better contexts, of Neolithic pottery in Grampian than in Yorkshire *(ibid)*.

The polished stone axes are currently the subject of petrological study, revealing connections with Tievebulliagh in County Antrim. Equally important may be the identification of local factories and sources for the large number of stone axes in Grampian, such as Group XXXIII, on the Aberdeenshire/Banffshire border. The importance of the deposit of flint gravels which runs inland from Stirling Hill in east Buchan has still to be fully assessed (Graham Smith 1919; Childe 1946, 46-7). What is clear is the intensity of use of the flint deposit, not only at Den of Boddam itself, but along its 13 km (8 mile) length (Wickham-Jones and Collins 1978) and the existence of several important flint-working sites throughout the Garioch.

The major monument constructed by the early farmers is the long cairn or barrow, an elongated trapezoidal or oval burial mound, usually oriented E-W, with the higher, broader end at the east, located either in a

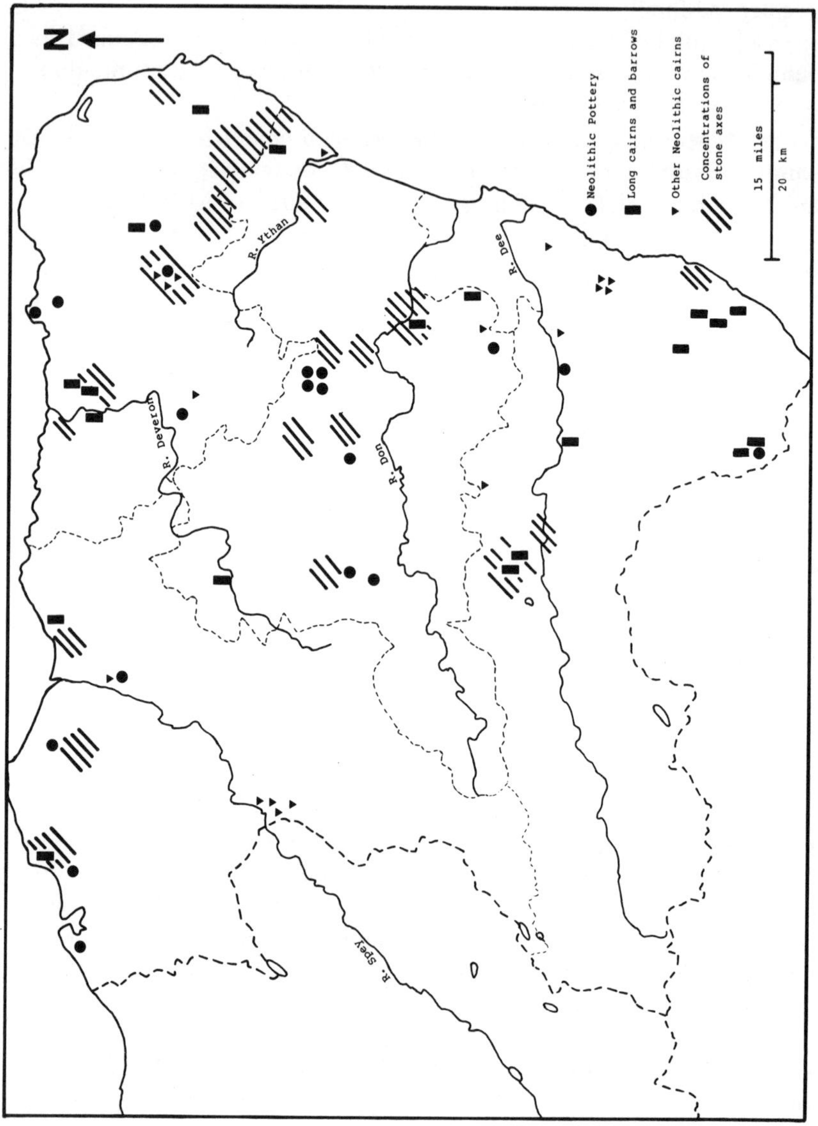

Figure 19 — Grampian in the third millennium BC.

prominent, skyline location or, more low-lying, on a terrace-edge (Henshall 1963; 1972). Other, less substantial burial monuments were constructed, such as the Yorkshire-type cremation mound at Atherb, Old Deer, or the non-megalithic embanked monument at Midtown of Pitglassie, Auchterless (Milne 1892; Shepherd, A 1986). Several of the skyline cairns could be taken to be performing as boundaries, perhaps, as at Finzean, between the territories of two river systems, the Dee and the Feugh, or perhaps, as at Gourdon or Longmanhill, even related to seaward approaches.

Of these large, prominent cairns a certain number show evidence of multi-period construction, usually in the form of a dip in the profile or a waisting or constriction in plan, eg Longmanhill, Balnagowan, and Knapperty Hillock. It is assumed at present that these cairns or barrows were unchambered, and certainly the only decently excavated example, the long barrow at Dalladies, Kincardine and Deeside, contained only a simple mortuary structure (Piggott 1972). Yet in the face of the sheer size of many, particularly Finzean and Longmanhill and the depressions in several (West Hatton, Finzean) that are usually interpreted as stone robbing but which could conceivably be chamber collapse, the question must remain open.

Although these skyline cairns are the most prominent in location and complex in structure, several of the terrace-edge ones would have been clearly visible to their communities, even, in some cases, from fields or settlements on slopes above, rather than below, the cairn (eg West Hatton, Bank of Roseisle, Balnacraig).

Finally, the distinct clustering of long cairns should be noted, the mid Mearns, Cromar, lower and mid Deveron being particularly well furnished. Whether this is a reflection of pressures of social competition in areas of less good land (cf Bradley 1984, 16-18) remains for the moment an open, though attractive, explanation.

The investment of community effort to build such shrines to their ancestors was considerable. Even the (comparatively) slight earthen long barrow of Dalladies required 6000 man hours and the sacrificing of 0.75 hectares (1.9 acres) of cleared land for the turves (Piggott 1972, 45).

No less impressive communal monuments of the third millennium BC are the recumbent stone circles, Grampian's megaliths. They are concentrated in areas with strong Neolithic presence, but in groups separate from the concentrations of long mounds. The recumbent stone circle consists of a circle of standing stones, whose two tallest members are in the south-western arc, flanking a massive slab (average weight 24 tons), laid on its side (Plate 22).

Although some commentators have viewed the recumbent stone circle as essentially second millennium in date, the product of beaker-related (Plate 20) activity and in a secondary relationship with the Clava cairns of the Inverness area (eg Kenworthy 1975; Burl 1976), there is no good reason to maintain this position. First, no beaker or beaker artefact has been found in an unequivocally primary context on a recumbent stone circle: at Loanhead of Daviot the sherds were in disturbed contexts (Kilbride-Jones 1935, 172); at Old Keig most sherds came from just below the topsoil while the one beaker sherd from beneath the recumbent cannot be accepted as *in situ* in view of the tree roots that passed right under the recumbent (Childe 1933, 42, 45, 48; *pace* Burl 1976a, 172); at Candle Hill, Old Rayne, the archer's wristguard came from a pit in the centre of which there are no details of its stratigraphical position (Coles 1902, 530); at Berrybrae the N3 beaker was inserted in the bank as a final act (Burl 1976b). Such beaker-finds are at any rate rare at recumbent stone circles (five out of 74, if Corrie Cairn is included: Shepherd 1986a, 34). Of the other pottery found at the circles, the Grimston/Lyles Hill ware from Loanhead, although also in disturbed contexts, would now be placed early in the third millennium (Henshall 1983, 32), while the 'flat rim ware' from the same site and from Old Keig could equally be third millennium in date (Piggott and Simpson 1971, 10-11). There are very few radiocarbon dates from recumbent stone circles; those from Berrybrae relate to the last phase of use (Ritchie and Ritchie 1981, 60).

Several other factors indicate a third millennium context for these monuments. There is general agreement that the recumbent and flankers commanded the greatest attention from the circle builders and were probably the first elements to be erected. (This is related to a subsidiary possibility that at some sites the recumbent and flankers were the only elements ever erected, eg Leylodge or Stonehead: Ruggles and Burl 1985, S30.) Certainly, although the recumbent and flankers were carefully placed, the alignment of the stone circle itself was often haphazard (see plans in Ruggles and Burl 1985, Fig 8). As for the primary purpose of these monuments, there is no clear evidence that it was funerary. Although several recumbent stone circles now have ring cairns within, these relate to the final use of the monument: only 12 out of the 74 confirmed recumbent stone circles still have recognisable cairns within (Burl 1976a, 168), while such modern excavations as have been carried out suggest that the building of the cairn was late in the use of the circle: it was seen as the final act at Loanhead and at Old Keig.

Rather, the emphasis on the south-west in the positioning of the recumbent suggests the monument's primary function. The bulk of the declinations of the recumbents and flankers fall exactly within the southerly band between the rising and setting of the major standstill moon, that is to say the recumbents are oriented on the rising and setting of the moon in the local southern sky (Ruggles and Burl 1985, S34). The recumbent and flankers form a frame in which to view or 'catch' the moon when viewed from the centre of the circle. It follows that the centre of the circle, for the monument to fulfil its primary function, would have had to be unencumbered by cairns.

Furthermore, the nature of these observations, of broad, seasonal events, can be seen to be adapted to the needs of a small farming community, which agrees with the description of them as communal creations, requiring between 30 to 100 adults (Ruggles and Burl 1985, S30), for the purposes of fertility rituals (Burl 1976a, 87-9). Their relative uniformity speaks of small egalitarian groups (Ruggles and Burl 1985, S27).

The positioning of cupmarks on recumbent stone circles is important for a discussion of the dating of these and related monuments. The 12 recumbent stone circles which have cupmarks are confined to the central area of Grampian (Ruggles and Burl 1985, S55). At these sites (of which the most profusely marked are Loanhead, Balquhain, Sunhoney and Rothiemay) the cupmarks are always located very precisely, either on the recumbent or on the flankers or the adjacent stone, nowhere else (barring the small displaced slab at Strichen: Hampsher-Monk and Abramson 1982). At Cothiemuir the cupmarks cluster at the end of the recumbent at the spot where the moon disappears (Burl 1976a, 178; Ruggles and Burl 1985, S54-6). That is to say, the cupmarks group at the points marking the rising or setting of the major standstill moon.

The use of quartzite, which is an important feature of recumbent stone circles, being broken on site and strewn around at Strichen and Castle Fraser or forming the recumbent itself at Auchmaliddie and North Strone, is very rare elsewhere, other than at Clava tombs (Burl 1976a, 164). Its use has been imaginatively linked to milky moonlight (Burl 1981, 192).

Given that the core area for the development of this type of monument, unique to Grampian, is the inland basin of the Howe of Alford (Burl 1976a, 172) there would seem to be no good reason to attempt to derive it from outside the area. Furthermore, a range of collateral types is also to be found within the region, to the west and south-east of the main recumbent stone circle areas, which could be seen to be influenced by the recumbent tradition. To the south-east are ring cairns with an emphasis on the SW in their perimeter stones (Raedykes: Henshall 1963, 401-2), while to the west, on the Avon, is a group of Clava cairns (Lagmore: *ibid,* 389-90).

There are strong links between Clava cairns and recumbent stone circles: the emphasis on the south-west, the grading of the heights of the

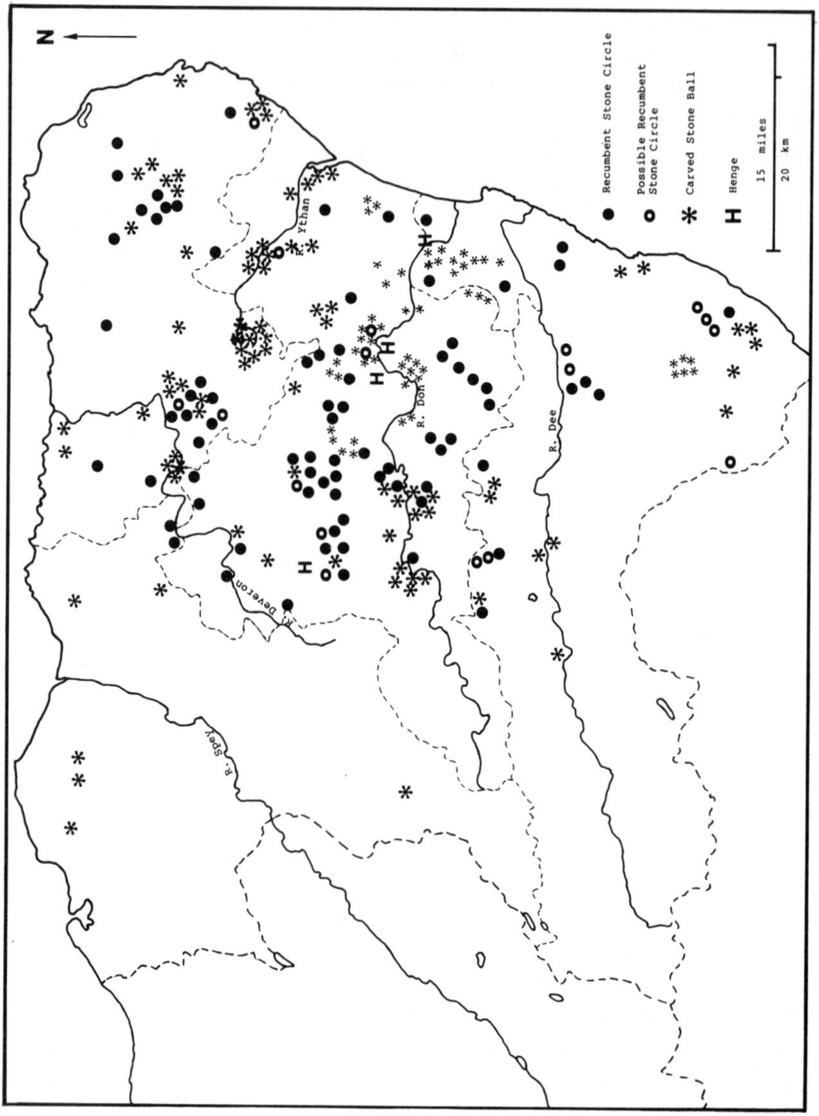

Figure 20 — Grampian in the later third millennium BC.

stones of the surrounding circle, the use of the circle itself, a very rare addition to a chambered tomb (Burl 1976a, 162) and the use of quartzite and cupmarks. The haphazard positioning of cupmarks on Clava cairns [where they are found 'almost indiscriminately' (Burl 1976a, 178)] may indicate the borrowing in the Inverness area of an imperfectly understood feature from the pre-existing recumbent stone circle tradition to the east. Similarly, features such as the cupmarked boulder positioned in the south-west of the Croft Moraig circle, the quartzite at the same Perthshire site (Piggott and Simpson 1971, 9) and the grading of the timber circle at the Balfarg, Fife henge monument (Mercer 1981, 150, 154) show the influence of the strong North-eastern tradition of recumbent stone circles spreading south.

Of henge monuments, ceremonial enclosures of the later third and early second millennia, there are only four definite examples in Grampian, all in or on the fringes of the Garioch (Whitestripes, Oldmachar; Dilly Hill and Broomend, Inverurie and Wormy Hillock, Rhynie: features such as Quarry Wood, Elgin, which has been claimed as a henge, would seem to be later in date and related to defensive enclosures such as Caysbriggs, Spynie: *pace* Henshall 1976, 111). The henge at Broomend of Crichie was part of an elaborate ritual monument that included a form of recumbent stone circle and an avenue of standing stones (Dalrymple 1884; Burl 1981, 183).

The large central shaft grave containing an individual inhumation and the prestigious stone battle axe deposited in a pit within this henge are both indications of the growth of individual, as opposed to group, approaches to authority. Such statements had been preceded by such late third millennium finds as the possible single grave from Greenbrae, Cruden, which was accompanied by jet and amber beads and a rare type of stone axe, all probably from Yorkshire (Clarke *et al* 1985, 66). The enigmatic carved stone balls, of which a substantial proportion come from Grampian, may have been early symbols of authority (*ibid,* 59), [Fig 20].

The deposition of beaker pottery at certain recumbent stone circles has already been noted. These characteristic pots, highly decorated and with an S-profile or everted necks, are found in Grampian in considerable numbers, usually accompanying single inhumation burials in short stone cists. Their use appears to have been as a symbol of prestige associated with the new knowledge of metalworking acquired from the beaker-using groups of the Netherlands. In Grampian, beakers seem to have been adopted most readily in Buchan, where the new skills of metalworking were also beginning to be established. The unusually high concentration of moulds for early metalworking in the far North-east has

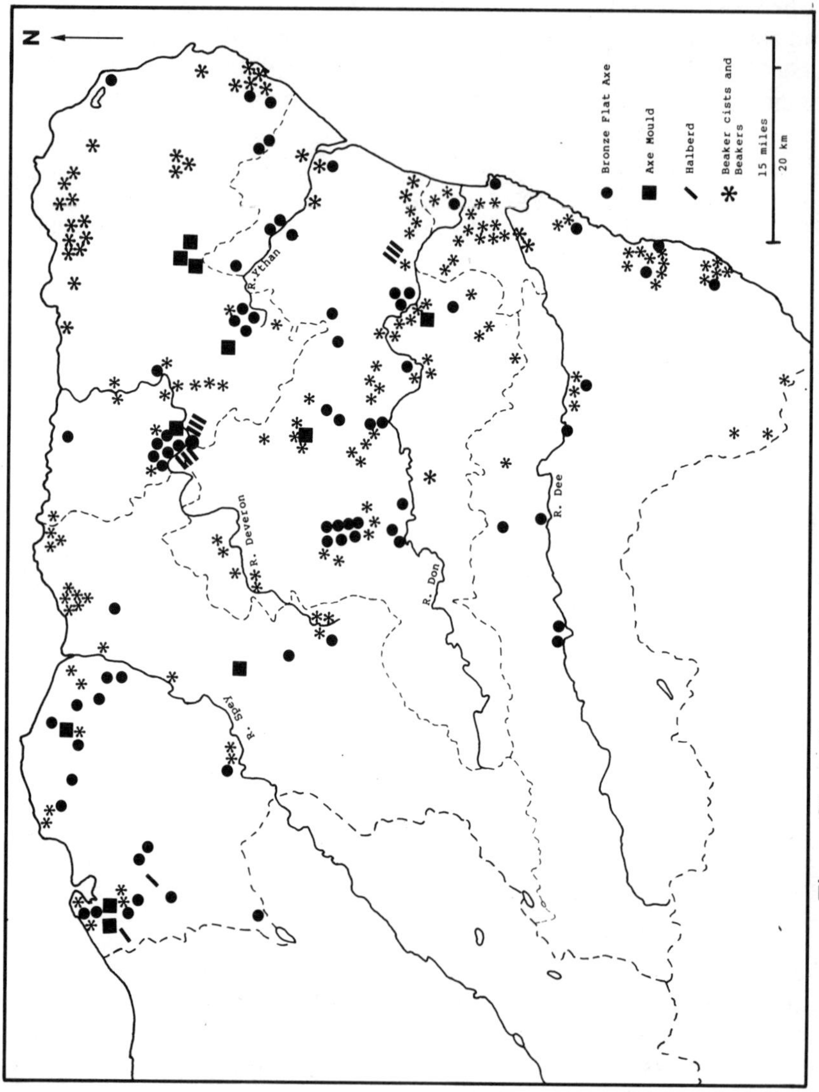

Figure 21 — Grampian in the early second millennium BC.

long been recognised (Piggott 1962, 88). In particular, evidence of metalworking occurs in the Auchterless, Inverkeithney, Fyvie, Aberchirder and New Deer areas (eg Inglis and Inglis 1983), coinciding with the distributions of early beakers (Shepherd 1986a, 7). The Laich of Moray, in particular the Culbin Sands, became an important area not only for metalworking, but also for the production of faience (Clarke *et al* 1985, 217; Aspinall *et al* 1972). The large numbers of late beakers from the Garioch and elsewhere in Grampian may be taken as emulation of the prestige symbols of Buchan (Shepherd 1986a, 10).

The short cists containing beakers are often grouped in small cemeteries such as at Buckie (Walker 1968b), Borrowstone (Plate 20) Kingswells (Shepherd 1986a, 12) or Leslie, Premnay (Callander 1912.) By contrast with Angus and much of Scotland south of Grampian, food vessels are rare in Grampian; however, the cinerary urns of the second millennium BC, containing cremation burials, are well represented. Enlarged food vessel urns, cordoned and collared urns have been discovered as single chance finds (eg Shepherd and Cowie 1978), grouped in open cemeteries, as at Easter Culbeuchly, Banff (Walker 1961), or deposited in more formal contexts such as in the enclosure at Loanhead of Daviot (Kilbride-Jones 1936) or beneath a cairn at Beattie Lodge, Laurencekirk (Shepherd 1984).

Important evidence of the disposal or destruction of wealth, in the form of high-status bronze axes, comes from several sites in the region. Hoards such as the seven flat axes found in a pot at Colleonard, Banff (Clarke *et al* 1985, 103, 300-1) can be closely paralleled in two upland sites. At Finglenny, Rhynie, a similar number of axes was found in an escarpment adjacent to a small henge (Stevenson 1948), while at the Pass of Ballater, on Deeside, a pair of flat axes was recovered from high on a scree (Ralston 1984, 77), recalling the dramatically situated site at Dail na Caraidh, near Fort William (Gourlay and Barrett 1984).

The second millennium saw a reduction in the size of ritual monuments such as stone circles. The little six-stone setting at South Ythsie, Tarves, is typical of this development (Coles 1902, 524-6; Keiller 1934, 6, 7), into which the more irregular ovals of Glassel, Banchory or Image Wood, Aboyne (Thom and Burl 1980, 212-13) also fit. The sequence concludes with the tiny 'four-post' settings such as Templestone, Rafford, in Moray (Shepherd and Ralston 1979, illus 10; Burl 1976a, 361) and North Burreldales, Alvah, in Banff and Buchan (Thom and Burl 1980, 236-7), [Fig. 21].

Although many round cairns of simple, hemispherical shape were built during the second millennium, the ring-cairn tradition appears to diminish in size to the kerb cairn (Plate 24; *pace* Lynch and Ritchie 1975, 33). One of a group of three kerb cairns has been excavated on the Sands of

Forvie (Ralston 1980). It was 4.4 m by 4.05 m (14.5 ft by 13 ft) and covered a cremation deposit. Similar cairns are at Logie Newton, Auchterless (Shepherd 1986b) and within the boulder circle at Cullerlie, Echt (Kilbride-Jones 1935).

Evidence of settlement is still sparse, although many of the as yet undated upland systems of stone clearance heaps and hut circles could reasonably be expected to date from the second millennium BC. For example the 1000 year long period of clearance and cultivation which has been identified in the pollen diagram from Braeroddach Loch in the Howe of Cromar was surely not unconnected with the extensive field system of Balnagowan on the hill above (Edwards 1975; 1979). However, coastal sites do preserve some evidence of second-millennium settlement, principally in the middens of Culbin (Coles and Taylor 1970) and Forvie (Ralston 1980), the latter site with evidence of ploughing.

Chapter eight

IRON AGE TO MIDDLE AGES

Dr. Ian Ralston

The beginnings of metalworking in iron, traditionally marking a major change in the later prehistoric record, occurred during the last millennium BC. Whilst the use of edge-tools and weapons of this material probably became increasingly widespread thereafter, the advent of iron technology was not accompanied by other readily-perceivable changes in the archaeological record, particularly of settlement sites. There is thus no radical break with the preceding "Bronze Age", except in terms of the assumed socio-economic consequences of the demise of the bronze industries. Similarly, several centuries later, the appearance in the Grampian area of Roman armies on more than one occasion, did not lead directly to any radical changes in the lifestyles of the native populations. In a very real sense, then, the "Iron Age" may be taken to embrace the last millennium BC and the first thousand years AD, a principal difference being that the latter thousand year span is at least partially illuminated by written sources. Thus, we know that the inhabitants of this area were Picts, first so named in 297 AD and the direct successors of the tribes initially recorded in Classical sources.

The inhabitants of the north-east knuckle of Scotland at this period inherited a set of landscapes that had already been modified by human actions over several thousand years. The prevailing climate during our span would probably not have differed much from that of more recent times, and already was markedly worse than it had been when the area was first colonised. During the last millennium BC, inroads continued to be made into the forest cover, though such clearances, if irreversible in terms of detailed vegetational composition, were not so in more general terms: if woodland could be felled, it could also establish itself afresh in some areas at subsequent stages. Rainfall and earlier human mismanagement probably rendered parts of the lowlands unsuitable for agricultural use; and it is likely that there, and on parts of the upland edge, peatlands were expanding. We should picture the Iron Age inhabitants settled in a landscape that offered a mosaic of woodland, moorland, pasture and tilled areas, linked by a network of routeways that in subsequent time could be used by the advancing Roman armies, and by the chariot force, so remarkable to Tacitus, assembled by the natives before the battle of Mons Graupius.

The clearest indications of the scale of human impact on the natural environment of the North-east are recorded in research on the Howe of Cromar on middle Deeside. Pollen and other analyses combine with radiocarbon dating to provide a guide to landscape use around Loch Davan and the nearby upland Braeroddach loch. Sustained activity from a little before 1000 BC almost to the end of the millennium is indicated; apart from the recent past, this period witnessed the most intense use of that landscape for agriculture, including barley growing, and for stock-raising; the volume of soils carried into the lochs at this stage indicates erosion related to these activities. The first millennium AD sees the continued use of this landscape for farming but, it would appear, less intensively.

Elsewhere, the imposition of Roman temporary camps, to accommodate the tents of the army in the field, is testimony to the existence of tracts of country over 50 ha (125 acres) in extent unencumbered by substantial woodland cover — the more so since such quickly-constructed camps will have been surrounded by uninterrupted views, to minimise the risks of ambush. At Portknockie (Moray District), the marks of a primitive form of plough, underlying a Pictish fortification on a coastal headland, indicate that even such windswept locations were, on occasion, cultivated. Such evidence, taken with the indications of storage capacity on some settlement sites, contrasts markedly with the words, implying the absence of arable lands, Tacitus puts into the mouth of the native leader in his speech before the battle of Mons Graupius (Agricola 31). Against the backcloth of a diverse landscape, part farmed, but part still the haunt of wild beasts and the domain of the huntsman, the story of Iron Age Grampian must have unfolded. Some indication of the utilised portion of the landscape towards the end of the first millennium AD is offered by placenames with the Pictish element "Pit-", meaning a parcel of land; the correspondence between the distribution of such names, and the better agricultural land in the North-east, is noteworthy.

In this summary account, only certain themes can be picked out. Survey evidence is most plentiful for the settlement record, and this seems the best set around which to frame this essay. Consideration of this range of material allows us to touch on the development of the kingdom of the Picts; and consideration of the sculptured stones attributed to these people brings into focus the question of the arrival and development of Christianity. The establishment of the Church and the increasing scale of political units are two themes that continue to attract attention in the medieval period.

THE PEOPLE

Our direct knowledge of the people of the North-east during this long period is restricted to two sets of evidence: depictions of human figures on sculpture; and skeletal remains, recovered from burials. Evidence from the latter source is not plentiful. Although a set of burials in square, ditched enclosures and likely to belong to this period has been recognised through oblique aerial photography, no such burial has yet been excavated in Grampian.

Ten inhumations, found in superficial positions in a much older burial mound in Speymouth Forest, Fochabers, are hardly likely to represent a "typical" Iron Age population, insofar as only two females were definitely recognised: they do, however, suggest that survival to the age of 40 was exceptional. Some sculptured stones of the later first millennium AD include human representations: whilst these may well be symbols, as the stereotyped character of some examples suggests, details of dress and appearance provide intimations of a ranked aristocracy, engaged in the fitting pursuits of warfare and the chase. Observable details include the wearing of tunics and pointed shoes (or leggings); pointed beards are frequently represented, along with long, if not elaborate, coiffures: all these details can be noted on the remarkable incised stone recently recovered at Barflat, Rhynie.

Much debate over the years has focused on the question of the language and cultural traits of the Picts, characteristics that must have continued from those of later prehistory. At least in the earlier, but still historically-secure, period of the Pictish kingdom, succession to the kingship appears to have been through the female line; the testimony of the Venerable Bede has been added to this, to suggest that Pictish society was matrilinear, a trait which would have distinguished the inhabitants of northern Scotland from other peoples in early medieval Britain. This proposition has recently been called into question, but the prevailing view has not been overturned.

It appears likely that two languages were spoken in the Grampian area during the first millennium AD: one, Pictish, is distinctive to the extent of being incomprehensible, with the exception of a few words. The other is a member of the Celtic languages, the dominant speech of much of the British Isles at this time. Such a linguistic pattern need not trouble us unduly; it is conceivable that the Pictish language, non-Indo-European in character and sometimes related to Basque (although there are manifest problems in so doing), was retained for commemorative or ritual purposes after its replacement by Celtic as the medium of everyday communication.

THE SETTLEMENT RECORD

Visually the most spectacular, but by no means the most numerous, of the settlement sites of these millennia, are the enclosed works which crown inland hill-tops and coastal promontories. There is every reason to believe that these forts span almost the entire chronological period with which we are concerned, without us being able to demonstrate phases when such fortifications were abandoned, as can be suggested for other areas of Scotland where excavation evidence, backed by radiocarbon dates, is more plentifully available. These sites are complemented by others, either unenclosed or apparently less-heavily defended; their range of locations extends from the shallow waters of some of the lochs, where a few crannogs have been reported, to the upland moors.

Amongst other types attributable to this chronological bracket we may include: sets of circular stone-walled foundations, often termed hut-circles, and for which a wide date range may be proposed (perhaps beginning, as in Atlantic Scotland, in the second millennium BC); souterrains, underground stone-lined passages, probably used for storage (of cereals?), with which above-ground structures are sometimes associated; some of the ill-dated enclosures; and, as a result of a programme of aerial photography, an increasing array of traces from the present-day croplands, where no surface indication of the former presence of habitation survives, but where the airborne observer can detect the positions of pits and ditches, many of which relate to the former existence of elements of timber architecture. Interpretation of this last mentioned evidence is not straightforward, the more so in the absence of supporting excavation evidence. Nonetheless, the "cropmark" record can be seen to include: further examples of enclosed sites, including some examples defined by stockades or palisades; a range of circular house types, including one distinctive variant, marked by the presence of a penannular ditch, which excavation evidence from Angus southwards suggests enjoyed a floruit in the mid- first millennium BC; souterrains and less-formal, smaller-scale related features, of which one set has been examined at Dalladies in Kincardine and Deeside District; and, lastly and entirely speculatively, timber halls. Whilst this final category certainly belongs to the first millennium AD farther south in Britain, the only excavated example in Grampian is attributable to the Neolithic period: nonetheless, certain recently-discovered examples, as at Monboddo in the Mearns, may have been the establishments of Pictish landowners.

Distinct from these native works is the suite of Roman temporary camps, which extends northwards from the most northerly permanently-inhabited fort, at Stracathro near Edzell. It is habitual amongst Romanists to associate these works with various of the historically-documented campaigns in eastern Scotland north of the Forth. Their temporary nature means that these sites produce little or no artefactual evidence to assure their dating, which is therefore advanced on the basis of size and proportions, and details of entrance arrangements, where possible fixed by stratigraphic relationships to other recognisably-Roman works. The temporary camps of Grampian have been attributed in recent years to both the campaigns of Governor Agricola in the first century AD; or to the advance of Emperor Septimius Severus about 130 years later. It is not inconceivable that this set of camps includes testimonies of both these campaigns and, arguably, others as well. The known series of Roman works meantime extends no farther than the Spey, but energetic work in the lowlands of Moray may yet carry the distribution northwards.

The most recently proposed site for the battle of Mons Graupius, at which Agricola inflicted a severe defeat on the assembled native army in 83 or 84 AD, lies on Bennachie; supporting evidence consists of the proximity of the largest Roman camp in the area, at Logie Durno. Nonetheless, such is the vagueness of the location of the battlefield and the characteristics of its terrain, that there seems no compelling reason to accept this particular site; the battle need not have taken place within the confines of Grampian. Unfinished native forts have traditionally been ascribed to the period of the Roman advance; but there is no chronological evidence to support this view.

Both the scale of the Roman works and the burgeoning, if ill-dated evidence of the cropmark record, point to the existence of substantial cleared areas in the landscape; and perhaps, to a rather higher population figure during this period than used to be surmised.*

It is, however, the native forts which, in the present state of our ignorance, provide the clearest intimations of co-operative effort, whether enforced or not, and, by extension, of the existence of sizeable socio-political units, including the precursors of the Kingdom of the Picts. This monument type probably originated in the Late Bronze Age,

* Interim statements (by I. Keillar, C. Daniels and B. Jones) on the recent work west of the lower Spey can be found in *Popular Archaeology,* Vol. 7 No. 3, April 1986, 2-16. (Published by Carphone Consultants Ltd., Vallis House, Frome, Somerset).

as indicated by radiocarbon dates from outwith the region; among early variants of the class we may include the series of oblong timber-laced forts, often displaying substantial signs of vitrification, as at Dunnideer Hill, Insch, Gordon District. The conspicuous use of timber in fortifications continued into the Pictish period, as the defences of the Moray Firth promontories of Burghead and Green Castle, Portknockie (Plate 17), illustrate. The latter site, in common with the excavated promontory at Cullykhan on Troup Head (Banff and Buchan District), displays long use beginning in the later part of the Bronze age.

Only one site in the region may be directly related to the Annal evidence of the Pictish period; Dun Foither may be equated with the site of Dunnottar Castle (Plate 28) on the coast south of Stonehaven, and is documented under attack, on separate occasions, by the Angles and the Norse. Unfortunately, recent excavations failed to produce archaeological evidence of Pictish settlement or fortification, a fact that may be attributable to medieval and later alterations at the site.

The construction of fortifications enclosing extensive areas may be attributable to the coalescence of the native tribes beyond the frontiers of the Roman Empire; such developments would form a logical precedent for the subsequent emergence of the Pictish kingdom. If such a view is accepted, and it has not gone unchallenged, the major fortification on Tap o' Noth (Plate 18), near Rhynie (Gordon District), enclosing over 20 ha (49 acres), and showing signs of dense occupation, may represent a "central place" for the early tribes of Grampian, despite its high altitude (563 m; 1847 ft). Another high-altitude, but much smaller fort, on the Mither Tap o' Bennachie, may also be suggested as being of Pictish date on the basis of architectural details.

Artistic Achievement

The Iron Age witnessed the development of a local variant of Celtic Art around the 2nd century AD. This was distinguished by the relative massiveness of its bronze products — armlets and rein-rings, suitable for use on chariots. Other products, like the bronze mouth of a war-trumpet, fashioned in the shape of a boar's head, and recovered from a bog at Liecheston Farm, Deskford, Moray District, date to around the first century AD, but may have been crafted farther south. While metalworking continued into the Pictish period, and included items made in silver, as in the surviving elements of a silver hoard from Gaulcross, Fordyce, Banff and Buchan District and a set of chains, similar to an example from Parkhill, Newmachar, Gordon District, the most substantial quantity of surviving art is found on sculptured stones.

Traditionally subdivided into three classes, such stones in the region share traits with others from much of Scotland north of the Forth-Clyde isthmus. The most recent of these products display influences from both the Anglian area to the south, and the Scotic west of Scotland and Ireland. These stones, with the likely exception of the earliest class, were produced in a Christian milieu: Classes II and III bear crosses, carved in relief on shaped slabs. Numerically the largest set in the North-east is however the Class I stones: these lack overt Christian imagery, are carved by incision, and include three principal suites of symbols including animal designs and geometric forms. The chronology and meaning of these Class I stones are both disputed: some see the origin of the symbols in the art of the late Roman world, or even in older Eurasian animal art; others hold to a derivation from the symbols presented in later, Christian illuminated manuscripts. Views of their purpose have ranged from grave markers (for which a few examples, such as the Picardy stone near Insch, have produced some evidence), to territorial markers, to indicators of lineage relationships amongst the Pictish aristocracy. Neither of these problems is readily capable of solution. For our purposes, the significance of these carvings lies in the appearance of symbolic sculpture, with shared traits over a considerable area of northern Scotland; this provides archaeological support for the emergence of patrons and artists, capable of commissioning and executing work with similar artistic canons over a wide area — no mean achievement.

It is often suggested that the Pictish stones of the Grampian area do not include either the finest, or the earliest of the tradition, although the related carvings on the walls of the Sculptor's Cave, Covesea, Moray, have been put forward as early examples. To some extent, quality is circumscribed by the geology of the available stone — granites, for example, in much of our area. Nonetheless, the Pictish stones of the North-east area include some imposing monuments, such as Sueno's Stone at Forres, Moray District, and the Maiden Stone (Plate 14) at Pittodrie on the skirts of Bennachie (Gordon District).

Reformationary zeal and sundry other vicissitudes (as the individual histories of certain stones make plain) have disrupted the pattern of these stones in the landscape. There is, however, evidence for: some remarkable groupings of stones, as in the eight examples recovered from Mains of Rhynie and Barflat farms, and perhaps associated with a complex crop-mark enclosure enveloping the Craw Stone, near Rhynie (Plate 19); an association with elaborate monuments of substantially earlier date, as at the henge monument of Broomend of Crichie, near Port Elphinestone, Aberdeenshire; and a more general association with water. Class II and III stones, the last-mentioned set bearing solely Christian iconography, may be considered along with the recently-named Class IV stones (sometimes termed "primary grave markers", bearing simply an inscribed cross, and often considered Irish/Scotic in inspiration) as the best archaeological evidence for Christian communities in the region.

THE ESTABLISHMENT OF CHRISTIANITY

There is no surviving religious architecture of first millennium AD date in the Grampian area. Early churches, of wood, have not been recognised, and the formation date of the early graveyards in the North-east has yet to be tested archaeologically. The spread of Christianity is thus presently best approached by asscssing the available written evidence in relation to the distribution of the surviving sculpture. It is fair to say that this method leaves some areas, such as the lowlands between Deveron and Spey, devoid of information.

Present opinion suggests that it is unlikely that Christianity reached our area as a result of the activities of Ninian, bishop of Whithorn in Galloway, whose activities appear to have been restricted to the Southern Picts (around the Tay). The first Christian communities in Grampian were probably established after the mission of Columba to Bridei mac Maelchon, King of the Picts, somewere in the Ness Valley, in 565 AD. The 6th and 7th century developments were thus in accord with the Celtic tradition of Christianity, and led to the formation of monastic communities, at Turriff and elsewhere. The landing of St Augustine in Kent in 597 AD, however, began a chain of events which was to see Iona's influence wane. In 663 AD, the Northumbrian Angles adopted the Roman form of Christianity; two generations later, in 710 AD, it was to the Anglian monasteries of Northumbria that Nechtan mac Derile, King of the Picts, was to turn for help in doctrinal matters, despite the fact that a generation earlier he had checked the expansion of Anglian temporal power in battle at Nechtansmere, near Forfar (685 AD). This doctrinal re-orientation did not, however, eradicate the West's influence on sculpture, the more so after the accession of Kenneth mac Alpin to the joint kingship of the Picts and Scots in 843 AD. Later sculpture, as in the surviving fragments from Kineddar, Drainie, Moray, displays continuing Irish influences.

The general distribution of this early Christian sculpture betokens the presence of Christian communities during the period from about 600 AD; in some cases, it is possible to match the sculpture with literary tradition, as in the case of the record of Nathalan in the *Aberdeen Breviary*; incised crosses of Class IV type have been found in the churchyard at Tullich, near Ballater, a foundation attributed to him.

With the advent of the Roman form of Christianity, it is likely that Pictland was remodelled into a series of territorial sees, each the responsibility of a bishop. Such an organisation would have had the potential of complementing the territorial holdings of a number of secular land-owners.

CONCLUSION

The establishment of the joint kingdom of the Picts and Scots in the middle 9th century, and the development of Church-State relations, mark major achievements, not least in terms of the territorial extent of the kingdom. The evidence for unity should not be over played, however, and in the 10th century kings met their deaths in our region with some regularity. If the possibility of northern control over the south of the kingdom ultimately died with Lulach, Macbeth's son, at Essie in Strathbogie in 1058, 30 years later Lulach's son, Maelsnechtai, was still styled "King of Moray" at his death. The Pictish endowment to the making of medieval Scotland was blotted out by the time of the writing of the Declaration of Arbroath in 1320, but their contribution to the seedbed from which medieval developments ensued may now begin to be reassessed.

Chapter nine

THE MIDDLE AGES

Dr. John S. Smith

THE DARK AGE LEGACY

The environmentally favoured North-east lowlands which the Romans despite their victory at Mons Graupius, [recently argued to have been fought on the skirts of Bennachie (St. Joseph 1983)], failed to occupy, was to become the northern heartland of the Picts in the period up to the mid 9th century. With the foundation of Iona in 564 AD, any rudimentary Christian organisation which may have been established through Ninianic activities, was consolidated and expanded by the mainland missionary activities of Irish-Columba clerics. Their Celtic organisation was based on monasteries with no specific territorial commitment for spiritual ministration. Celtic monasteries were founded at Turriff, Old Deer, Mortlach (Dufftown) and at Aberdour — all associated with standard foundation legends. In the case of Aberdour, the story of the foundation siting is recorded in the Book of Deer, which specifies a fortified place (Dundarg), the stronghold of Bede the Pict, mormaer of Buchan. The tradition recorded by the scribes is of the landing of St. Drostan in company with Columba, and the gifting of Dundarg promontory for the establishment of the Christian community. A small rectangular building set within the foundations of the 14th century castle has been suggested as the chapel of 7th century date, but the walls could equally be medieval in origin and excavation has revealed no significant finds to tie in with the primary monastic phase implied by the records. The Book of Deer, which consists of illuminated Gospels augmented by 11th century notes in Gaelic added to its margins, was compiled at least in part in the Celtic monastery of Deer, whose site is generally believed to underlie the old parish church on the south Ugie river. Even in peripheral Grampian, the expanding Columban Church was eventually to feel the effects of the irresistible force of an equally vigorous and expanding Roman missionary church based in the kingdom of Northumbria. Following the Synod of Whitby (664 AD), first Northumbria and then Pictland opted for the diocesan structure of mainland Europe and Rome rather than the monastic Celtic structure of the Atlantic west and Ireland. In any case, the increasing Scandinavian raiding activities along the west coast of Scotland effectively ended the missionary activities of the prime Columban foundations, and with the Union of Picts and Scots politically under Kenneth Macalpine in 843, Dunkeld became the main ecclesiastical centre of the united kingdoms. Communities of Culdees[1] settled themselves as clergymen within the secular communities at Brechin, Monymusk and at Mortlach, while other ongoing centres of religious activity at this time included Clova, Kinkell and Tullich. At the latter site near Ballater on Deeside, a pre-Reformation church of the 13th century date is associated with a remarkable collection of early Christian crosses and gravemarkers related to a still older church with a St. Nathalan foundation legend. Kinkell — in the Gaelic *Caenn Cill* meaning 'head church' — appears to have been the organisational centre for a group of subordinate churches which included Dyce, Kintore, Kemnay and Skene. Over the period up to the 11th century, the church in Grampian, although peripherally located in the then Scottish body politic, moved steadily towards its medieval territorial diocesan organisation, becoming in effect increasingly European mainstream, writing in Latin, and sending its bishops periodically to Rome.

THE SCANDINAVIAN RAIDING AND THE TAMING OF MORAY

The coasts of Grampian were periodically raided by Scandinavians, with the Irish Chronicles recording battles possibly near Cruden Bay in 954 and 962. In 1004, the Vikings unsuccessfully raided Gamrie on the north coast, the skulls of three of the defeated leaders being by tradition buried in or around the walls of Old Gamrie Kirk. In 1012, a further attack on Cruden Bay was beaten off by Malcolm Mackenneth (Malcolm II, King of Scots, 1005-1034) here operating in the old Pictish province, far from his home base. In the 9th century Moray looked across the Breidafyord (0. Norse — The Broad Firth), now known as the Moray Firth, towards a powerful Norse earldom established in Caithness and Sutherland. From there, Norse political and military influence extended on occasion across the firth into the southern coastlands, where Sigurd may have established a temporary foothold in the old promontory fort of Burghead. Hints of conflict on a substantial scale appear in the battle-scene depicted in Sueno's Stone near Forres. A series of coastal strongholds stretching eastwards from Burghead to the extreme knuckle of Grampian seem likely to have been periodically occupied during this period of political uncertainty. Only when the Scandinavian raiding in Moray and Buchan ended, was it possible to begin to visualise Mar and Buchan as potential springboards from which Scottish Kings might attempt to incorporate the recalcitrant province of Moray into the Scottish medieval kingdom. Until such effective control was achieved in the 1160's, Moray operated as a semi-independent 'kingdom' under its Pictish line of mormaers, which included one Macbeth Macfinlay[2]. Macbeth defeated and killed Duncan I of Scotland in battle near Elgin in 1040, and subsequently became King of Scotland for a period, basing his political and military clout on an alliance with Thorfinn, greatest of the Orkney Earls. In 1054, Macbeth, despite including in his forces the first Norman mercenaries seen in Scotland, was defeated by an English-supported invading force led by Duncan's son Malcolm at Dunsinnan, north east of Scone, and eventually killed near Lumphanan in Mar in 1057. His body was subsequently taken to Iona for burial. Despite a shrewd marriage alliance between Malcolm III and Ingibjorg, the widow of Thorfinn, aimed at eliminating potential intervention from the Norse north, Macbeth's descendants in Moray were to retain a foothold there until 1130 when David I defeated Angus of Moray in battle,following up with an effective punitive campaign along the southern coastlands, and an eventual 'settlement' of Moray. The last claims for an independent Moray were effectively ended in 1187 when William I killed Donald Macwilliam, Moray-based pretender to the Scottish throne, in the vicinity of Inverness.

The Feudalisation of Grampian

From 1066 onwards, the Scots were dealing to the south with a Norman England. Within two years, the advent of Norman influence in Scotland was encouraged by Malcolm's new marriage to Margaret, a daughter of the Old English Royal Saxon line. The effects of this marriage were quickly seen in church affairs, particularly in church reform, although military pressures, notably in Northumbria, took up much of Malcolm's energies. Nonetheless, his name is associated with a church built at Monymusk on Donside. Monymusk illustrates the complexity of church sites in early medieval Scotland. In the 1120's, a Culdee community is documented here; in 1179 a church was built in association with a priory, and in 1245, the Culdees were replaced by Augustinian canons, as a result of complaints made by the Bishop of St. Andrews, to whom Monymusk was then subordinate. The Norman church tower at Monymusk was built under the aegis of Gilchrist, Earl of Mar, a descendant of the original line of Pictish aristocracy. The main flow of Norman ideas into Grampian dates from the reign of David I (1124-1153). He introduced feudalism by inviting leading Norman and Saxon families to settle in Scotland. In the very first year of his reign, David granted the lordship of Annandale to Robert de Brus, and, as noted by Barrow (1981), of the nine charter witnesses, eight were incoming Normans. In Grampian, the 'white settlers' included the De Lesselyns at Leslie, Balliols at Dunnideer, the Bissets at Aboyne, the Comyns in Buchan and the Durwards at Lumphanan and Strachan. Castle mounds (mottes) of generally natural origin originally surmounted by a timber tower and perimeter palisade are the classic early indicators of the arrival of feudal land tenure and law. A recently excavated example near Strachan in Feughside has confirmed their essential features. Here a natural gravel mound was flattened, utilising as exterior defence an old stream channel. A more sophisticated example with enclosure ditch and counter-scarp is the Doune of Invernochty near Strathdon — perhaps amongst the early examples in Scotland of a Norman earthwork castle. These essays in carpentry, strikingly depicted in the Bayeux Tapestry, were rapidly constructed to provide secure bases from which incoming barons could exercise local law and order, and provide the sort of conditions which encouraged market and trading opportunities.

BURGHS AND MARKETS

It may be assumed that settlements of some significance existed in early medieval times, at river and estuary crossing points, for example, but the royal identification of settlements with potential for commerce with the aim of burgh designation post-dates 1100 and appears to have been initially associated with David I, a monarch with quite exceptional energies. Burghs were small mercantile communities where burgh law, the granting of trading monopolies and the provision of a strongpoint created a central place where producers and consumers could meet and transact their business. The royal motive behind burgh creation lay in the diversion of a proportion of the trading profits (or goods) to the Exchequer to supplement the basic income derived from royal estates. Encouragement was often given to the establishment in the royal burgh of specialist craftsmen. Frequently, as in the royal burghs of Aberdeen and Elgin, the king would own property in the burgh, some of which could be subsequently given to establish friaries. Within defined rural territories, eventually to be policed as sheriffdoms, goods were collected and set out for sale in strictly controlled burgh markets. Coastal burghs with a likely potential for harbours and a productive hinterland attracted Flemish craftsmen encouraged by royal offers of low rents or even rent-free periods during which they could establish themselves. Protection was provided through a royal castle. These burgh castles, as in Elgin on the Ladyhill and Aberdeen on the Castlehill, generally stood on the periphery of the medieval burgh, perhaps for the strategic reason of maintaining open ground around them. In peripheral areas like Moray, the royal burghs of Forres and Elgin were envisaged as 'civilising' elements, rather on the line of the bastide settlements of the north Wales coast. Once established by royal charter, subsequent growth depended on the amount of trade they could capture, both in terms of drawing on the products of their own hinterlands, and also in terms of high value imports from the international North Sea trading theatre. The basic requirements for entry into the premier league of Scottish medieval trade were a productive landward area and a port of sorts. The three primary royal burghs of Aberdeen, Elgin and Forres, all in existence and trading by the early 12th century, were to be supplemented by a further clutch of foundations by the early 13th century — Cullen, Banff, Inverurie and Kintore. The last-named pair of inland royal burghs acted as collecting centres but their activities were curtailed not only by the primary privileges of Aberdeen but also by their lack of direct access to the sea. Aberdeen, with the best access to markets and goods furth of Scotland, prospered steadily, enjoying a succession of further charters which by 1222 permitted the establishment of a merchant guild, and by 1273, the establishment of provost, baillies and elected council.

CHURCH ORGANISATION

Over the same period, the church continued to improve its organisation and increase its influence in medieval Grampian. By the 12th century, sees were established for Moray and Aberdeen. The delimitation of the territorial diocese and the siting of cathedral and bishop's palace were tangible evidence of the drawing power of the new breed of royal burghs. David I re-sited the diocesan administrative centre from Mortlach in Banffshire to the St. Machar site in Old Aberdeen in 1137. The Moray bishopric, which was founded in 1107, initially employed a peripatetic centre shifting between Birnie, Kineddar and Spynie[3] before eventually settling in Elgin, where the splendid cathedral was completed by the 1270s. The 12th and 13th centuries were also notable for the foundation of monasteries and abbeys within Moray: the Cistercian foundation of Kinloss in 1150, and the Valliscaulian foundation of Pluscarden in 1230 (it became Benedictine in 1454). In 1218, William Comyn who had married into the old Pictish aristocrary of the province of Buchan, founded the Cistercian abbey of Deer. Feudalism and church organisation spawned the parish system, centred on the parish kirk, a building usually of simple rectangular design, as displayed in the original fabric of the old kirk of Kinneff. These early churches were simply furnished and characterised by thick rubble walls, an earthen floor and thatched roof. The boundaries of the early Scottish dioceses were on occasion tortuous including outliers — the product of land grants by men of substance who had an eye for their ultimate salvation. Medieval Kinneff, for example, was a part of the extensive diocese of St. Andrews which included parishes within the North-east of Scotland as well as in Fife, the Lothians, Kincardine and the Borders. The neighbouring parish of Catterline fell into the diocese of Brechin. As a measure of church-building activity in the 13th century, Bishop de Bernham of St. Andrews consecrated no less than one hundred and forty churches in the period 1240-1249, including Kinneff in 1242. The parish ministries were supported by teinds, one tenth of the annual produce within their catchment. The burgh charters of the 13th century which specify trading privileges on named goods enable the identification of the main marketable countryside commodities. In Aberdeen's case, these were hides, dyes, corn, meal, salt and fish. Luxury imports from the Low Countries included spices, wines and fine cloths, the wines particularly, if the itinerant royal household was paying a visit to the royal burgh or destined for a sporting sojourn in upper Deeside or the Mearns[4].

Developments in Castle Architecture

The early timber towers sitting on the motte became redundant in the face of the twin demands to increase strength and provide a better range of accommodation. Faced with these needs, the castle had to quit the mound and stand on more stable ground for wallbase stability and to provide security from the possibility of organised siege. The stone counterparts springing up in 13th century Grampian were the tower house and the concentric ring castle. In the latter, the domestic buildings were entirely surrounded by strong stone walls to create an inner enclosure. The curtain walls were punctuated by salient towers which individually formed potential centres of resistance in the event of the overwhelming of the outer walls. In Grampian, a rather simplified version of the Edwardian North Wales castles was in vogue, characterised in its essentials by a single curtain wall, partly salient towers and a strong gatehouse unit. Kildrummy in Strathdon and Coull in Cromar are examples of this style, and arguably a third may underlie the fabric at Fyvie (see Chapter 10). The idea of the single dominant tower implicit in the motte timber tower was retained in the form of the donjon occupied by the constable of the castle. The salient towers allowed the flanks of the castle to be swept by crossbow fire.

Kildrummy Castle was built during the reign of Alexander II in the first half of the 13th century. Its location strongly suggests that it was envisaged as the first in a chain of royal castles designed as spring-boards for controlling the formerly recalcitrant province of Moray. The man responsible for its primary construction was Bishop Gilbert de Moravia, and his role in its design is clearly seen in the eastern projecting chapel gable which violates the normally strict military principles of castle perimeter strength. During the Scottish Independence Wars, Edward I visited Kildrummy and his keen eye appears to have led to a number of modifications to the original design, including an uncompleted salient tower base cloaking the chapel gable. Very few large royal castles were built in Grampian. They must have been expensive in labour and materials and by the time Kildrummy was being built, the idea was already outmoded. Nonetheless, castles of this scale created major problems for invading armies. Although armies could easily bypass such a castle, by doing so it became possible for the large garrison to sally forth and harry the advancing troops in the rear where the supply lines lay. As a general rule, medieval castle architecture favoured the stone tower houses. These rather primitive towers reflected the lean purses of the majority of the barons and a royal discouragement of large castles especially following the Scottish Independence Wars. The standard medieval tower house, exemplified at Hallforest Castle, Kintore, took the form of a set of superimposed vaulted stone cells, set within a rectangular tower. Entry was by mobile ladder to the first floor level. The materials were almost entirely local in origin — before enclosure of fields by clearance walls, surface gatherings would provide a nucleus of accessible material — and such primitive towers relied for security on thicknesses of wall. They should be regarded as the secure homes of local barons designed to cope with the sudden raid rather than the formal siege. The internal domestic arrangements were no more than adequate.

The Succession And Independence Wars

Lean times for Grampian followed the death in 1286 of Alexander III. The death of the female heiress en route from Norway for crowning left the Scottish kingdom with neither a monarch nor an obvious successor. There were no less than 13 claimants, with Robert Bruce and John Balliol the leading contenders. Both men had their supporters in Grampian, with the Earl of Mar and the burgh of Aberdeen soundly pro-Bruce, while the Earl of Buchan — the Comyn family — was firmly pro-Balliol. English intervention in support of John Balliol led to an invasion into the heart of Grampian, with the occupation of Aberdeen and the castles of Kildrummy, Fyvie and Elgin. In the period between this invasion and Bannockburn in 1314, Grampian played a substantial role in the settling of the succession argument with Robert the Bruce (the grandson of the original claimant) gaining support and significant victories in the area. In 1307, battles fought at Barra and Aikey Brae (on the flanks of the aptly named Bruce Hill within sight of the Abbey of Deer) eliminated the Balliol challenge in the area, and were followed up by the harrying of the extensive Comyn estates in Buchan. The slighting of the Comyn strongholds of Slains, Rattray, Inverallochy, Cairnbulg, Dundarg and Kelly (Haddo) would inevitably follow as standard Bruce policy.

Robert the Bruce was quick to reward his supporters in Grampian, while also filling the void left by forfeiture of Balliol-supporters' lands through the introduction of new families. The action of the citizens of Aberdeen in capturing the burgh castle from the English garrison led to a succession of Bruce-inspired charters, the most important of which were issued in 1314 (within a month of his victory at Bannockburn) and in 1319. In the 1314 charter, Bruce granted the burgh, through its council, the office of Keeper of the Royal Forest Stocket excepting the "vert and venison" which he retained for the royal sport. In 1319, a second important charter granted the burgh and Stocket Forest in *feu-ferme*, that is effectively giving the town total control of lands which latterly became known as the Freedom Lands in return for an annual payment. This meant that Aberdeen could retain many of the dues previously collected expressly for the royal coffers. The town was the first of the Scottish burghs to gain this status. Effectively Aberdeen had achieved burghal self-government, which led to the setting up of a Common Good Fund, the Council right to "stent" its burgesses for special purposes e.g. repair of the Town Kirk or shoreworks, and eventually the burgh was to lease out its Freedom Lands to prominent merchant families.

The reapportionment of estates in Grampian following the battle of Barra brought new families to fill the power vacuum left by the demise of the Comyns and their supporters. The lands of Cruden, Slains and Rattray were granted to Sir Gilbert Hay of Errol, while Sir Adam Gordon of Huntly (taking his title from Huntly in Berwickshire) was granted the lands of Strathbogie (the castle there being subsequently re-named Huntly!).

The Keith family, a member of whom had led the decisive cavalry charge at Bannockburn, gained lands in the Kincardine and Peterhead areas, as did the Irvines and Burnards in lower Deeside at Drum and Leys respectively. The death of Robert the Bruce in 1329 unlocked a further set of problems for Scotland, which in Grampian, culminated in the memorable raising of the siege of Kildrummy Castle and the battle of Culblean in 1335, as well as in the burning of the burgh of Aberdeen by English sailors in 1336. The return of David Bruce to Scotland in 1341 ended the problems of succession, and led locally to the granting of the lands of Balquhain to the Leslie family, but found no solution to the potential for future trouble hinted at by the pattern of a group of powerful "super-nobles" now strongly ensconced in the kingdom in general. These new families who were represented in Grampian sought more comfortable defended houses for themselves and their retainers. Thus new castles eventually were to spring up in the North-east, with changes in groundplan to provide private accommodation for the laird and his family. The passive strength of old tower houses like Drum and Hallforest were replaced in these new structures by provision for active defence. In the first instance a wing tower was added to the central block, and improved access to the higher floors provided by mural staircases. The L-plan favoured by most masons provided a couple of rooms at each floor level, and turrets pierced with shotloops provided the flanking fire both downwards and laterally along the wall base, in particular to the major weak point of the doorway which now conventionally opened at the ground-floor level. Variants of the same theme continued to be in use right through until the end of the 15th century, by which time the primitive tower house had run its logical course, and new designs were being sought which incorporated the desire for decorative and often superfluous detail in the upper elevations of the exterior, perhaps paralleling the ostentatious dress characteristic of the period.

Military threats to the peace of the North-east remained notably from the west with, in 1390, Alexander Stewart, Lord of Badenoch ravaging Elgin and Forres, including the large scale destruction of Elgin cathedral described in contemporary writings as "the ornament of the realm". In 1411, Donald of the Isles leading a body of men said to have numbered nearly ten thousand, invaded the Garioch and was only defeated at Harlaw on the outskirts of Inverurie by a defending body led by representatives of the landed families of Mar and Buchan. The inscription on Harlaw monument erected by the Town Council in 1914 records the death of Aberdeen provost Robert Davidson and several town burgesses on the battle field. A rather more contemporary memorial to Harlaw is the grave slab known as the Greenlaw Stone which stands in Kinkell church. The slab carries the armour clad figure of Gilbert de Greenlaw who also fell defending the western approaches to Aberdeen.

Burghal Trade

Despite the interruptions wrought by military affairs, the trade of the burghs in Grampian prospered. Amongst these, Aberdeen remained preeminent by reason of its prime geographical location and the energy of its burgesses. A steady supply of wool and hides flowed from its rural hinterland to be exported through the Dee estuary to England and the continent. The burgh's medieval street pattern of Castlegate, Broadgate, Upper and Netherkirkgates, Shiprow and Green was firmly established by the early 14th century, and recent excavations associated with central city redevelopment have revealed evidence of the nature of the buildings, economy and trading links, the latter derived principally through pottery finds. The wealth of Aberdeen burgesses was reflected in the various works accomplished in the church of St. Nicholas, both in altar foundations and in the furnishings. The three town friaries in existence in the 14th century were also recipients of citizen piety. Port works in an estuary which remained geomorphologically dynamic were rudimentary, although the French chronicler Froissart mentions a jetty in the 1360's. Excavations in 1975 revealed a granite pier at the foot of the Shiprow, which yielded pottery appropriate to the period. Aberdeen's trading prosperity extended beyond its energetic burgesses to encompass the landed gentry in the surrounding countryside. The Earl of Mar and the Earl Marischal, for example, built town houses in the more fashionable parts of medieval Aberdeen, and analysis of the burgh property records has shown that these families also invested their profits in urban property and land. A large slice of Grampian's land wealth remained in the hands of the Church and the monasteries and abbeys also had their ample estates.

Successive bishops of the diocese of Aberdeen accomplished great works for the commonweal. Amongst these, Bishop William Elphinstone is perhaps the most prominent in a distinguished line. His works include the foundation of the university of King's College (1495) in Old Aberdeen, the construction of the great central tower of St. Machar cathedral, and the planning and assembly of materials for the first stone bridge across the Dee (1530) on the southern approaches to Aberdeen. The vigorous drive of Elphinstone and his colleagues also resulted in a superb set of early 16th century sacrament houses set within parish churches, notably at Kinkell and Auchindoir.

Looking Ahead

Although the period under discussion witnessed considerable cultural and commercial development, Grampian did suffer on occasion from periods of economic setback through attacks from land and sea. Thus the royal burghs of Aberdeen, Elgin and Forres were furnished with "ports" or entry gates, but not with walls — the "ports" being principally designed to control the flow of goods to the market and to control movement of people during times of plague. The burgh records reveal more than a hint, at least in Aberdeen's case, of attempts by the landed gentry to impose their will by force in the matter of election of provost and council. The rising stars of the Gordon and Forbes families took a prominent part in these skirmishes, as they relentlessly clawed their way up the pecking order of the landed aristocracy in Grampian. Increasingly as the old earldoms became broken up through the decline in the power of the old-established families, so the new gentry spawned a rash of fortified mansions which remain a major element of the landscape. Many of these families were to benefit from the major redistribution of wealth and property which followed the events of the Reformation when the lands and buildings of the old church "came up for grabs" in the middle decades of the 16th century. One of the fruits of the Reformation was a Protestant rival university in New Aberdeen founded by the 5th Earl Marischal in the last decade of the 16th century. Increasingly, the hegemony of the ancient royal burghs was to be challenged by the new burghs of barony founded by bishops and barons in an attempt to develop local markets. The increasing establishment of markets, large and small, testifies to the growing quantities of raw materials provided by the countryside, although the staples of wool, hides and fish remained the dominant items.

FOOTNOTES

1. The name Culdee seems to have originated in 8th century Ireland, derived from the Irish *Cele-de*, meaning a servant of God or God-fearing man. Culdees occupied an intermediate position between monks and secular priests, adopting the discipline, without the vows, of the monastic system.
2. Any resemblance between Shakespeare's Macbeth and historical fact is only coincidental. Macbeth was killed not at Dunsinnan but in the Wood of Lumphanan, the spot where he was killed being marked by a cairn.
3. Culdee foundations at Birnie, Kineddar and Spynie were converted into the expanding Roman church by nominating a prominent Culdee named Gregorius as first Bishop of Moray — a device aimed perhaps at absorbing the older religious traditions.
4. Kindrochit Castle at Braemar (Castleton) and Kincardine Castle in the Mearns were frequently visited by Scottish monarchs for deer hunting and fowling.

Chapter ten

CASTLE COUNTRY

Dr. Cuthbert Graham

Over a quarter of a century ago it was observed by Dr. W. Douglas Simpson that there were just under 1000 castles of stone and lime still surviving in whole or in part throughout the length and breadth of Scotland, apart altogether from the remains of our earliest castles, which were made not of stone and lime but of timbered earthworks. Of the numbers of these, no census is available.

Out of this total Grampian Region can claim, to put it very modestly, at least a tenth. It is particularly rich in the castles of a range that extends over 500 years from 1150 to 1560. In this chapter the object will be simply to direct the attention of any visitor or student to castles which will repay inspection by reason of their special history, beauty or glory of interior spectacle.

Let us begin with the castles which were timbered earthworks — the Norman keeps or "mottes". In Scotland there was no Norman conquest in the English sense but under the Canmore kings from David I onwards there was a Norman penetration of which the outward and visible sign was the motte — a moated mound crowned by a palisade enclosing a wooden tower. Often there was a banked and palisaded courtyard sheltering the household buildings, which were also made of wood.

It so happens that in Grampian Region one of these wooden stongholds was eventually succeeded by a stone structure repeating all its original features. This is Duffus Castle, lying to the north-west of Elgin, a great Norman mound rising from the Laich of Moray "like a boss on a buckler". The immense stone castle was preceded by a very large motte and bailey castle of timber and earthwork. This was created during the Plantation of Moray around 1163 as a royal stronghold and given as a fief to Freskin de Moravia, a Flemish soldier of fortune who was rewarded for his service to the Scottish crown by an estate in West Lothian. From there the family moved north, obtaining the Lordship of Duffus as the base of what came to be known as "the House of Moray".

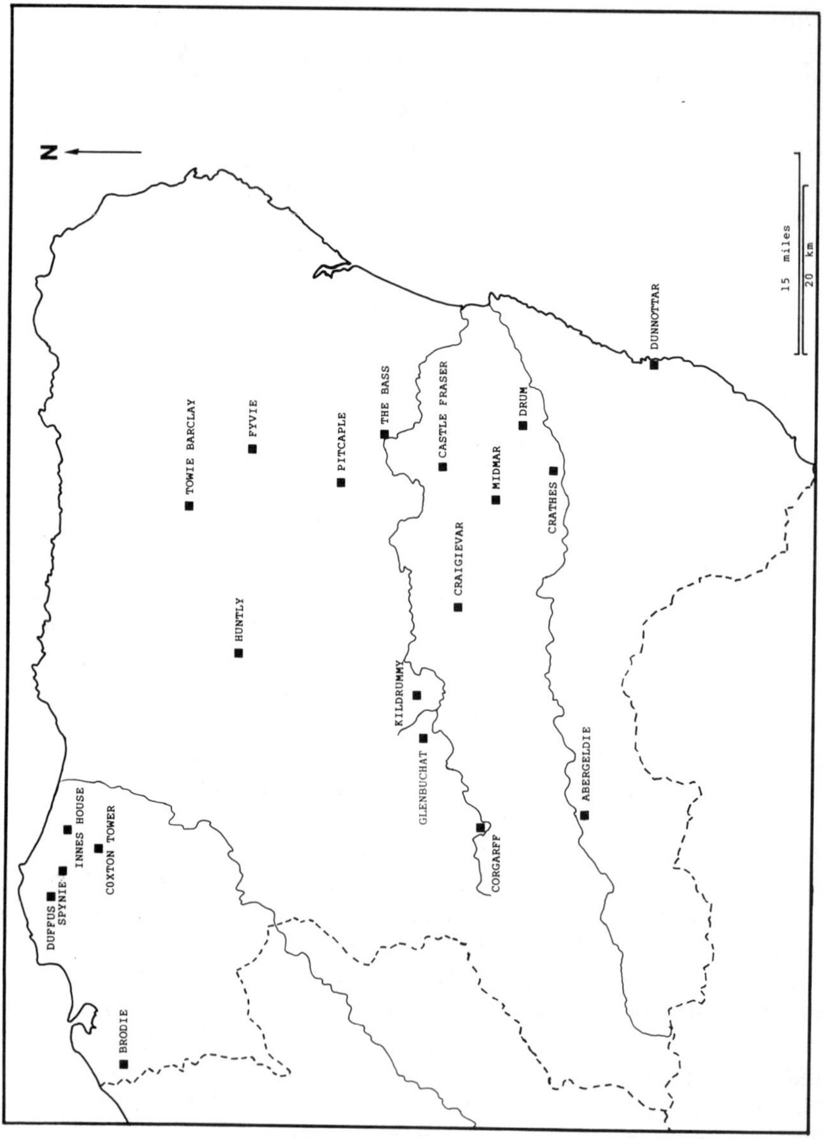

Figure 22 — Some Grampian castles.

By the 13th century it had become the most influential family in the whole of the north of Scotland.

The line of Freskin ended in three heiresses, and Duffus itself passed by marriage to the family of Cheyne. During their overlordship the motte and bailey castle, in 1290, harboured the English commissioners sent by Edward I of England to receive the hapless Maid of Norway, both on their way to Kirkwall, where she was expected to land, and on their "dolorous return" to report her drowning at sea. The Cheynes took the English side in the wars that followed and the castle was burned when harried by patriotic Scots rebels. In the middle of the 14th century the last of the Cheynes died and his heiress Mary brought the barony of Duffus to her husband Nicholas, a son of the 4th Earl of Sutherland. It was he who built the great stone castle of today. The castle stands on top of an isolated gravel mound in the centre of a flat plain and is still surrounded by a wide ditch on the level ground beyond the base of the hill, enclosing about 3.7 ha (9 acres) of ground. The mound itself was surrounded at the top of the slope by a high wall of enceinte, some portions of which still remain and may possibly be older than the keep. This keep occupies the highest point of the site, but, unfortunately, the foundations on the north side have slipped and large masses of the north wall have slid, almost in one piece, down the slope. More recent than the keep is a large range of domestic buildings, built after 1452.

The motte and bailey castle of Duffus was an exceptionally large one. In the outskirts of Aberdeen itself there were also Norman mottes at Nigg, Ruthrieston, Banchory-Devenick, Gilcomston and Tillydrone. The mound on which stood the Motte of Tillydrone is a feature of the riverside park west of the Brig o' Balgownie, leading eventually to a castle of much later date, the Wallace Tower, originally built in 1616 as Benholm's Lodging, a Z-plan house in Netherkirkgate, Aberdeen, which was transferred to Tillydrone in 1963. But perhaps the most familiar and useful Norman motte site not too distant from Aberdeen itself is the Bass of Inverurie (Plate 26), close to the River Don, just east of the Garioch capital. Here we can examine and climb the grassy mound on which the wooden castle stood and alongside it the subsidiary mound sheltering the household buildings. From the Bass we can obtain a much clearer idea of the domestic intimacy of most of the motte and bailey strongholds that were the first castles of Grampian Region. Other motte and bailey castles in Aberdeenshire were the Doune of Invernochty in Strathdon and the Peel of Lumphanan. In its very earliest stages, from which it went on to much greater glories, Huntly Castle was also a motte and bailey.

As Dr Simpson has pointed out, the stately buildings erected by the Gordons at Huntly stand amid the earthworks of a Norman motte and bailey castle on a grand scale, and the whole group of structures in earthwork and in stone, presents an epitome of military construction from the 12th to the 17th century. The story ends in earthwork as it began; for the latest addition to the defences, still well preserved, is a ravelin (outwork) of the Civil War period.

If the 12th century was the age of the motte and bailey in Scotland, the 13th was the age of the great courtyard castles built to command and dominate a territorial region. The finest of them are beautifully built of dressed ashlar and have large round towers flanking curtain walls enclosing a courtyard. The walls and towers together are known as the *enceinte*; normally, one tower is larger than the others, and forms the keep or *donjon*. Usually this tower is placed at the remotest corner of the courtyard, within which are the domestic buildings — hall, kitchen, solar (or lord's suite) and chapel. The perfect place within Grampian Region to see all of these features is Kildrummy Castle, the most complete example of an elaborately constructed castle of enceinte in Scotland.

Dr W. Douglas Simpson, who carried out excavations there over a long period, wrote of Kildrummy Castle: "In every detail of its architecture and masonry it is a masterpiece of the highest merit; as a ruin it is grandly picturesque and on all accounts . . . truly described as 'the noblest of Northern castles'." It was begun in the reign of King Alexander II as a fortress intended to secure lines of communication to the turbulent province of Moray, and modelled on the mighty Chateau de Coucy near Leon in France, with a massive curtain wall surrounding a very large courtyard and defended by five projecting round towers, the largest of which, known as the Snow Tower, was the donjon. Not later than the middle of the 13th century there was added a stately chapel with three great windows of equal depth in the east gable. They remain the artistic glory of the castle today and have been imitated in modern churches such as Craigiebuckler in Aberdeen.

The castle's history is part of the national history of Scotland. The siege of Kildrummy in 1306 when Nigel Bruce defied the English might was the most famous incident but the ultimate eclipse of the castle's overlords, the Earls of Mar, is one of the main reasons why so many rival castles built by lesser lords are scattered throughout the Grampian area.

It was the English who gave Kildrummy its two great gatehouse towers (now virtually reduced to their foundations), but when they were complete they must have been almost identical with those of Harlech Castle in Wales. They are attributed to Edward I's military engineer Master James St. George. In August and September 1306, while held for King Robert the Bruce by his brother Sir Nigel, the castle was besieged by Prince Edward of Carnaervon, the future Edward II. The Scots defenders fought off every attack until treachery betrayed them. Osburn the Smith, bribed by the promise of as much gold as he could carry, fired the castle with the red-hot blade of a plough-coulter. The defenders were then compelled to surrender. Sir Nigel was beheaded, and the English poured the gold they had promised down the treacherous blacksmith's throat.

Behind the castle is the Back Den of Kildrummy, now converted into a garden, overlooked by Kildrummy House Hotel and spanned at one point by a modern replica of the medieval Brig o' Balgownie at Aberdeen.

Coull Castle was built by the Durward family in the 13th century as a rival to and in imitation of Kildrummy Castle. It had five circular towers defending an extensive curtain wall. In the Wars of Independence it was garrisoned by the pro-English faction and was attacked and damaged by revolting Scots. In 1304 it was handed over to Alexander Comyn, Sheriff of Aberdeen, to hold for the pro-English establishment. In March 1307 Edward I of England sent urgent instructions that with other Scottish castles it was to be garrisoned in view of Robert the Bruce's activities. No written account of its subsequent fate survives but excavations have shown that it was set on fire and then deliberately demolished. "I for one" wrote Dr. Douglas Simpson "can never visit these grey ruins without picturing . . . a wild night when the farmers of Cromar rose to expel the hated Southron."

Two more structures of the 13th century may be mentioned. Although there is no written evidence of stone building at Fyvie Castle before 1385, when Margaret Keith, wife of Sir James Lindsay, was besieged there by her nephew James Lindsay, there is some evidence that a castle of enceinte existed there nearly 200 years earlier.

In the beginning Fyvie, a royal property, was the capital Messuage of the Thanage of Fermartyn, the area between the Rivers Ythan and Don, and played its part in housing the largely peripatetic medieval monarchy. William the Lion was there in 1214 and Alexander III granted a charter at Fyvie on February 22, 1222, while Edward I of England was at "Fyvie Chastel" on Saturday July 21, 1296. The really interesting building at Fyvie Castle took place centuries later and will be dealt with in due course.

One fascinating building which does survive and can be examined today is the stern and massive keep-tower of Drum Castle, built around 1286 to keep watch and ward over the Royal Forest of Drum. That it was the handiwork of Richard the Mason, Richard Cementarius, the first-known Provost of Aberdeen, there is little doubt and its connection with the Brig o' Balgownie is clear from the fact that the construction and dimensions of the great stone vault in the top storey at Drum are identical with the Brig's massive arch.

Drum as a Royal Forest is first mentioned in 1247. The keep, a simple rectangle with battlements and rounded corners 21 m (70 ft) high and 16 m by 12 m (53 ft by 40 ft) in area, with walls at basement level 3.7 m (12 ft) thick, was completed before the Wars of Independence. In February 1323 King Robert I bestowed upon his armour-bearer and clerk-register, William de Irwin, the lands of Drum by a Royal Charter still surviving in the house, with characters as clear as on the day a medieval scribe formed them. The Irwins or Irvines of Drum continued to hold these lands and the castle down all the intervening centuries until in terms of the will of the 24th laird, H. Q. Forbes Irvine, they were handed over to the National Trust for Scotland on 28th May 1976. The castle and its policies were first opened to the public by the Trust on Friday 16th July of that year.

The Keep of Drum is linked to a Renaissance mansion built in 1619, with a sunny south front topped by dormer windows and crow-stepped gables. You can leap across the three-and-a-half centuries by passing through an internal door from one to the other. In 1411 "Good Sir Alexander Irving", the third laird, fell in the battle of Harlaw fighting side by side with the Provost of Aberdeen, and in 1439 his successor, another Sir Alexander, held the unique and never-to-be-repeated office of Captain and Governor of the town.

In its original form the Keep of Drum contained three great vaulted chambers placed one on top of the other. The two upper floors were later subdivided by timber floors, thus providing a total of five flats. The basement contained kitchen and cellarage, the first floor the great hall, with the solar or lord's private room above it, while the upper vault contained two more big rooms.

Today the Great Hall has had the timber floor removed to provide a lofty room with the arms of the families linked with the Irvines on the ceiling. The visitor now ascends to the turnpike stair in the tower by an outside stair and by means of the turnpike to the great Upper Hall, from whence he can ascend by another wooden internal stair to the battlements, with a magnificent view over the surrounding country.

Owing to the de-stabilisation brought about by the Wars of Independence the 14th century was a fallow period in castle construction in Scotland, but interesting and important developments were taking place in the second half of the century at Fyvie.

In 1391 the lands of Fyvie were re-assigned by Robert III to Sir Henry Preston, in redemption of "Ralph de Percy, English Knight", captured at the Battle of Otterburn in 1384. This was a business transaction in which Robert III bought out Sir Henry Preston's interest in the ransom of Ralph de Percy. Preston's son-in-law Alexander Meldrum inherited the castle in 1433. These two owners provide the first two of the series of names given to the great towers of the castle in the Victorian era along with the myth that each tower was built by successive dynasties as the castle was shaped, that is the Preston, Meldrum, Seton and Gordon towers. Nowadays, thanks to the researches of Dr. Simpson and more modern successors, we do know that the spectacular south front of the castle embracing the Preston Tower on the east, the great double gatehouse known as the Seton Tower in the centre and the Meldrum Tower at the west end were all given their spectacular modern form by Sir Alexander Seton, first Earl of Dunfermline, in the closing years of the 16th century, all having a medieval castle of the 14th century, which still survives, under the Dunfermline masterpiece, as their basis.

The evidence uncovered in a re-harling operation in 1962 showed that this "hidden ancestor" was represented by the lower 5.5 m (18 ft) of the Preston Tower, the lower 7.6 m (25 ft) of the curtain wall between the Preston and Seton Towers, complete to a wall-head of embrasures (gaps in the battlements) and merlons (the "teeth" of the battlements). Between the Seton Tower and the Meldrum Tower the early curtain wall was discernible up to a height level with the third-floor window lintels. The Meldrum Tower contained early work up to 4.6 m (15 ft). It was established that Fyvie Castle during the period of the Meldrum occupation had an almost comical resemblance to a child's toy fort.

When Alexander Seton and his architect, William Schaw, took over in 1598 they rebuilt on a narrower plan the whole of the south range between the Preston and Meldrum Towers. It was four storeys high across the front, topped at the centre and at the end with an icing of bartizans and carved dormer heads. At the centre the drum towers were bridged with a gabled oversailing arch . . . The great symmetrical palace front at Fyvie is without precedent in the canon of Scottish tower houses.

To the interior of the house Seton added what is undoubtedly its most spectacular feature, the great stair in the west wing. Entered at the north-east corner, a small lobby gives immediately into a vast turnpike stair. With a radius of 3 m (10 ft) about a central newel (spiral stair) which is carved in a belt of ornament with Seton's arms, the stair rises not only to the Great Hall but continues to the second floor. In 1690 the Setons' connection with Fyvie ended when the 5th Earl of Dunfermline fled to France after the Battle of Killiecrankie and the estate was forfeit to the Crown. In 1733 it was bought by William, 2nd Earl of Aberdeen, who died in 1745. His young widow's eldest son William Gordon became at the age of nine the possessor of the castle.

The addition of the Gordon Tower at the north end of the west wing and alterations in the south front, which was deepened in plan and reduced in height from four to three floors, were Gordon's chief external changes in the castle. The Gordon Tower closely matches the Meldrum and Preston Towers in detail. This determined and largely successful attempt to repeat the old work in the 1790s was, says Richard Emerson, an astonishingly early essay in the Baronial Revival. After visiting Rome and sitting for his portrait by Pompeo Batoni, Gordon began the process by which Fyvie (Plate 27) was to become a treasure-house of art. In 1889, house and estate were bought by Alexander Leith and the fourth great dynasty took over. It became the nation's property in 1984 when the National Trust for Scotland acquired it from Sir Andrew Forbes-Leith with assistance from the National Heritage Memorial Fund.

Before we now pass on to the climax of the Grampian castle-building story with an account of the great tower houses of the 16th and 17th century, the most spectacularly sited strongholds on the coast call for mention. Dunnottar Castle (Plate 28) stands on a stupendous isolated rock south of Stonehaven with Castle Haven on the north and Old Hall Bay on the south, and with the defile called St. Ninian's Den at its base. St. Ninian, Scotland's first evangelist, is said to have set up a cell on Dunnottar and in 1276 the Bishop of St. Andrews dedicated a parish church on the rock. Twenty-four years later Sir William Wallace set it on fire and burned to death the English garrison who had taken sanctuary there in the hope of escaping his wrath. But part of the stonework survived and two pointed windows in the existing chapel, itself of much later date, are believed to be survivals from this period.

Sir William Keith, Great Marischal of Scotland, built the Great Tower or Keep of Dunnottar at the end of the 15th century. A hundred years later William the 4th Earl Marischal began building the first range of the renaissance wings grouped round the central quadrangle of the castle, a work which was continued by his successors, notably the 5th Earl, George, who also founded Marischal College in Aberdeen. The two most famous incidents in the castle's history were the siege of eight months' duration from September 1561 to May 1562, and the imprisonment of the Covenanters in the Whigs' Vault in 1685. During the siege, by Cromwell's army, Sir George Ogilvy of Barras secured the safety of the State papers of Scotland and the Scottish Regalia (smuggled out with dulse in a creel to be buried in the parish kirk of Kinneff) before surrender with "all the honours of war". It was in 1645 that the 7th Earl Marischal built the oblong block, running out from the north-east corner of the quadrangle to the extreme point of the rock plateau that contains the Whigs' Vault, where, in May 1683, 122 men and 45 women,

Covenanter internees of their day, were herded indiscriminately and kept in "durance vile" until the end of July. A text from Revelations is inscribed beneath the list of their names in nearby Dunnottar Churchyard:

"And they heard a great voice from heaven saying unto them: Come up hither. And they ascended up to heaven in a cloud; and their enemies beheld them."

The Whigs' Vault is an eerie place which should on no account be missed. Neither should the visitor fail to see the drawing room so finely restored by Lady Cowdray. Another beautifully restored and furnished room is Benholm's Lodging.

Of the superb ruin of Findlater Castle on the cliffs 3.2 km (2 miles) west of Sandend it was said a century ago: "The outer walls of several parts of the building are so founded on the cliffs as to correspond with the face of the precipice so that the principal tower seems to hang over the sea, and from the windows of several apartments a pebble may be dropped into the waves." The licence to build Findlater Castle was issued by James II to Sir Walter Ogilvy of Deskford in 1455. Briefly held by the Gordons, the castle was defended against Mary Queen of Scots but it surrendered and was reoccupied by the Ogilvys, who, when they moved to their new home at Cullen House in the 17th century, left it abandoned. The third great coastal stronghold in the region was undoubtedly the castle of Ravenscraig, west of Fraserburgh, begun in 1640.

Much older than that was Balvenie Castle, Dufftown. It began its career as a castle of enceinte, with the form of a quadrangular court 45 m by 40 m (150 ft by 130 ft) enclosed by high curtain walls 2.1 m (7 ft) thick. In the 13th century, when it belonged to the Comyns, the living quarters were at the north-west and south-east sides of the courtyard. From the "Black Douglases", who owned it after the Comyns, it passed in 1455 to John Stewart, 1st Earl of Atholl and it was the Stewarts who, in the 16th century gave Balvenie the shape it has today by demolishing the south-east front and building in its place a three-storey Renaissance tower house known as the Atholl Building.

For three centuries Spynie Palace, some 3.2 km (2 miles) north of Elgin played a part in the history of Scotland. Over 18.9 m (62 ft) long and 13.4 m (44 ft) wide, its walls which are 3.4 m (11 ft) thick, rise 30 m (75 ft) to the parapet walk. It was defended at basement level by enormous gunloops. This structure, only one part of the palace, was begun by David Stewart, Bishop of Moray from 1461 to 1476. The more outlying parts of the palace were earlier in date, having been begun by John de Winchester, who held the See of Moray from 1437 to 1458. One of the smaller but more attractive tower houses of the 15th century was Pitcaple, a Z-plan baronial tower house with a 19th century wing attached.

The old house is believed to have been built shortly after 1457 when James II granted the lands of Pitcaple, 32 km (20 miles) from Aberdeen, to David Lesley. Mary Queen of Scots dined at Pitcaple in 1562 and danced under a thorn tree which survived until 1856. One of the most touching sights in Pitcaple is the grim little shaft in the thickness of a wall. Its facilities were offered to the Marquess of Montrose during the night he spent at Pitcaple in 1650 as a prisoner labelled by his captors "James Graham, a traitor to this country". The Lady of Pitcaple, who happened to be his cousin, lodged him in the room and in the middle of the night she came and showed him this painfully narrow secret way of escape. He looked at the aperture and said: "Rather than go down to be smothered in that hole I'll take my chance in Edinburgh." He was beheaded on the 21st of May, and in July of that same year Charles II landed at Garmouth and came to Pitcaple.

That poetic quality so characteristic of Grampian castles in the 16th and early 17th centuries makes itself felt as early as 1538 in Corgarff. No fancy turrets here, simply a grim keep within star-shaped battlements, beautifully restored by the Ministry of Works and Lady Stockdale of Delnadamph. In 1571 it was the scene of the tragedy recounted in the ballad "Edom o' Gordon" (see Chapter 23) when Captain Ker burned alive Margaret Campbell, the wife of John Forbes of Towie, with all her family and servants to the number of 27. It was burned again in May 1607. It served as Montrose's headquarters in 1643 and it was put to the flame a third time by the followers of "Bonnie Dundee" in 1689.

Abergeldie on Deeside dates from 1550. In Moray it is now thought that 1567 is the most likely date for the building of the existing Brodie Castle, a simple vernacular tower-house but displaying the ornate corbelled battlements and bartizans (overhanging corner turrets) of the period. It was opened under the National Trust for Scotland in 1980. Between 1587 and 1593 there was completed Towie-Barclay Castle, the most spectacular of the Buchan group which also includes Craig, Gight and Delgatie. The first floor contains the Great Hall, reached through a window bay by a flight of steps up from the main newel just as at Craig and Gight. The hall, as Stewart Cruden puts it, "enlarges upon the medieval atmosphere to which the vestibule has already introduced us. It consists of a single high rib-vaulted chamber, 9.1 m by 6 m (30 ft by 20 ft) with the ceiling in two bays, having ridge and transverse ribs, diagonal ribs, sculptured corbels and heavy pendant bosses, also sculptured. But the most remarkable feature is a small oratory above the entrance to the hall. Being entirely open and separated only from the body of the hall by its elevation and traceried parapet wall, it would have been used not only by the laird and his family at their private devotions, but also at more

. The Maiden Stone at the chapel of Garioch *(J. Livingstone)*

. Polished stone axes, Pond Croft, Keig and Auchterless *(Royal Museum of Scotland)*

15. The Brandsbutt Stone with ogam inscription, Inverurie *(J. S. Smith)*

17. A timber-framed wall of Pictish date excavated at Green Castle promontory fort, Portknockie *(Aberdeen University Geography Department)*

18. Tap o' Noth hill fort, near Rhynie. Clearly visible crowning the hill is the oblong vitrified circuit of the inner defence *(Aberdeen Archaeological Surveys)*

19. The cropmark trace of this complex enclosure envelopes The Craw Stone, a Class I Pictish stone on Barflat Farm, Rhynie. Some eight Pictish stones have been recovered from the vicinity, supporting the idea of a major centre of post-Roman activity here *(Aberdeen Archaeological Surveys)*

20. A beaker from Cist 3, Borrowstone Farm, Kingswells, Aberdeen
(Anthropological Museum, University of Aberdeen)

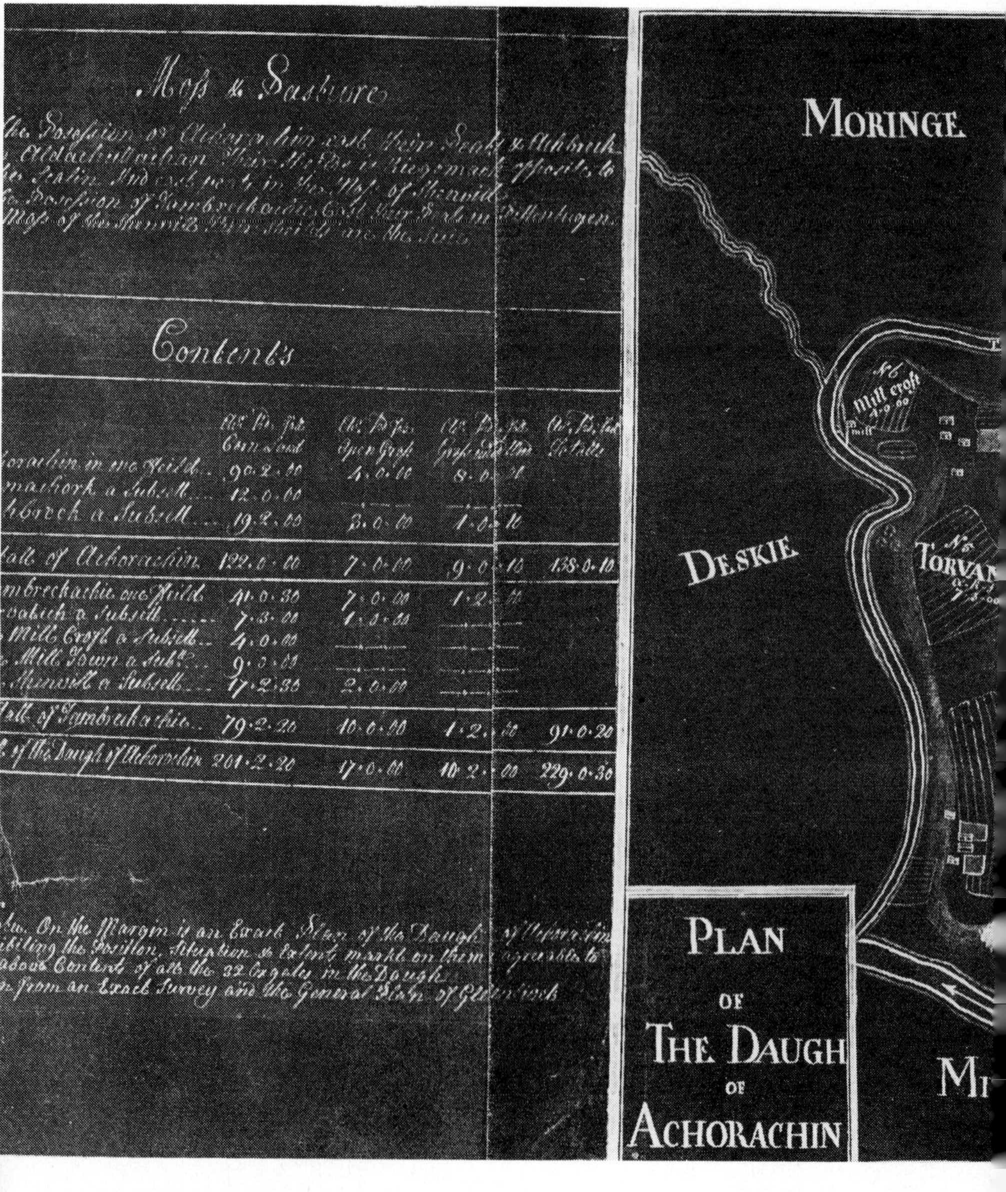

21. Plan of the Daugh of Achora

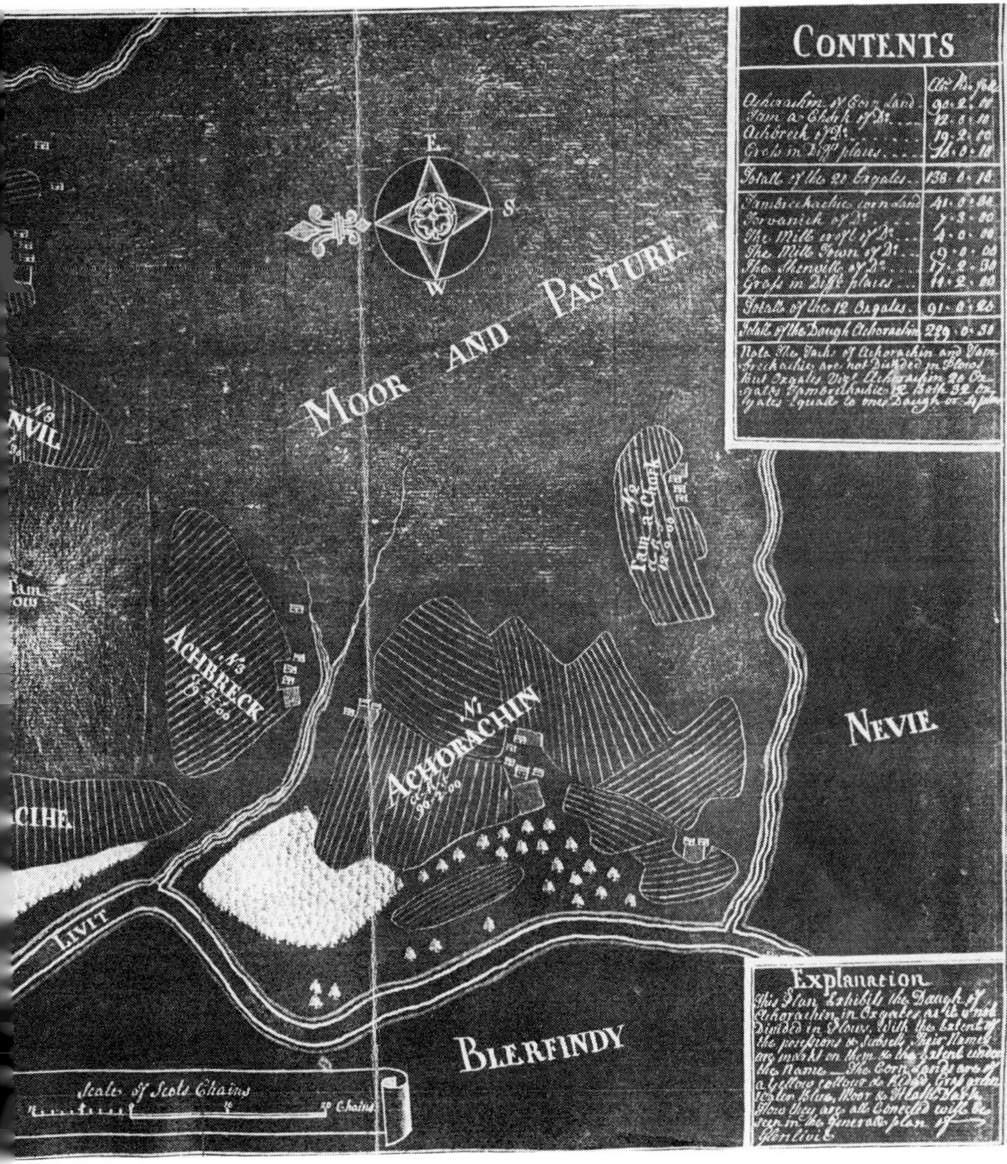

(Scottish Records Office)

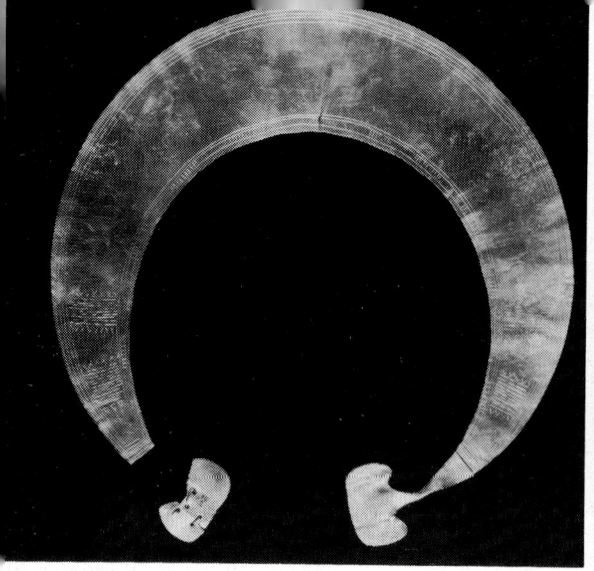

22. Gold lunula from Orton, Fochabers
(Royal Museum of Scotland)

23. A megalithic monument showing a recumbent stone with tall flankers at Cothiemuir Hill
(I. Shepherd)

24. Kerb cairns within a boulder circle at Cullerlie, Echt
(I. Shepherd)

25. Craigievar Castle, an etching of 1852 *(R. W. Billings)*

26. The Bass of Inverurie: two mounds that formed the basis of a medieval motte and bailey castle *(J. Livingstone)*

27. Fyvie Castle, architecturally one of the most satisfying built in Scotland *(The National Trust for Scotland)*

public services at which the tenantry mustered in the hall below." Built by John Gordon in 1590 on upper Donside was Glenbuchat Castle, a Z-plan structure unique in the north-east in that the two stair turrets are carried not on corbelling but on "trompes" or bold squinch arches. The castle, now a ruin, is under the care of the Scottish Development Department.

It was in this same decade, between 1597 and 1602 that the first Marquis of Huntly built his Renaissance palace at Huntly Castle. It is a large oblong building 23 m (76 ft) long with a round tower at the south-west corner and a smaller tower opposite it at the north-east angle carrying the grand stair. Above the entry on this tower is carved what has been called "the most splendid heraldic doorway in the British Isles. Achievement after achievement stretches up the side of the tower connected with delicately moulded panels in a series that symbolises first human and then divine authority — first the lord of the castle and his lady, then the King and Queen, then the Passion of Christ and the Resurrection. Above all is the figure of St. Michael, the warrior Archangel triumphing over Satan." Huntly Castle was the home of the chiefs of the Gordon family from 1376 to 1752.

But it is time now to turn to the Castles of Mar, for which the whole region is chiefly renowned. These ornate castellated mansions with their regal coronets of pointed turrets and their riotous profusion of corbelling form a group of buildings unique in Europe.

Although still in private ownership Midmar Castle displays the elaborate and beautiful castle-building style of the Bell family, who also worked at Crathes, Castle Fraser and Craigievar. This stronghold of the Gordons is thought to have been built by George Bell who was buried in Midmar Kirkyard in 1575. Midmar is built on the Z-plan, so popular in the north-east that it might almost be called an Aberdeenshire patent. Castles on this plan consist of a central block with flanking towers, either round or square at diagonally opposite angles. Through carefully sited gunloops on the flanking towers defenders could cover with cross fire every possible approach to the building.

At Midmar, one of the flanking towers is round and the other is square and the design of the building is a veritable symphony in stone. On the main building are crow-stepped gables and large rectangular gabletted turrets resting on elaborate tiers of key-pattern corbelling. The square tower has circular corbelled turrets with conical roofs, and the round tower is finished with an open battlemented parapet. In the re-entrant angle between the round tower and the main block a staircase turret soars upwards and overtops the whole of the rest of the building being capped by a graceful ogee roof. (Ogee is an architectural term meaning S-shaped in profile — that is having a graceful double curve). In the past few years, Midmar's owner has had the castle re-harled, refurbished and restored.

Not far from Midmar, and a short distance south of Banchory, Crathes Castle was the first of the Castles of Mar to be opened to the public by the National Trust for Scotland. It is an L-plan tower house begun in 1553 and finished in 1596, though it is not now thought that it took 40 years to build. The later date appears to mark the remodelling of the upper parts of the structure by masons of the Bell family mentioned above. On the wallheads of soaring perpendicular towers they made sprout corbelled turrets, both round and squarc. Thc Great Hall or Tower Room recovered its original austere dignity when in the '30s of this century the walls were stripped back to the naked stonework by the late Sir James and Lady Burnett of Leys. Here beside the Horn of Leys are works by Jamesone and a portrait of Bishop Burnett, aider of Dutch William and author of "A History of My Own Times". On the second and third floors are bedrooms with famous painted ceilings that were uncovered in 1877 after over a century under concealing lath and plaster. The Chamber of the Muses and the Nine Worthies' Room on the second floor, and the Green Lady's Room on the third, had each been decorated by Jacobean artists on the same principle. On boards between joints are gaily painted symbolic figures and on the side of the joints themselves are inscribed wise saws and descriptive jingles explaining the pictures and delivering little homilies in the manner beloved of James the Saxt and his contemporaries. At the top of the house is the Long Gallery traversing the whole building from east to west. On its oak ceiling delicately carved heraldic shields form the centre pieces of the panelling. Crathes also has a magnificent 18th century formal garden enclosed by massive Irish yew hedges 260 years old.

One of the grandest examples of castellar construction in Scotland, Castle Fraser was presented by its owners, Major and Mrs Michael Smiley to the National Trust for Scotland in 1976. Although an old tower no doubt existed here from the middle of the 15th century, the present Z-plan structure began to be shaped when the Michael Tower, the square tower at the south-west corner, was built about 1576 by a well-known local master mason, Thomas Leiper, for the laird Michael Fraser. When the laird died there was a halt to operations, but in 1600 Leiper's plan was completed by the building of the lower part of the main block and a round tower at the south-east corner. But that was not the end. Between 1610 and 1620 I. Bell (who had already built Crathes and was yet to build Craigievar) was called in. He added a new storey and a garret to the Michael Tower and the main block, and to the round tower he added three more storeys. On the north wall, facing the main approach via a broad walk sheltered by stately sycamores, he placed an armorial frontispiece carved in deep red freestone bearing the Royal arms above those of the Fraser family, while inset on the base of a modest tablet he placed the inscription "I. Bell 1617". Later in the 17th century low cottage-like wings projecting to the north and forming a courtyard were added.

The decorative features of Castle Fraser are outstanding. The dormer windows on either side of the frontispiece are sculptured with cyphers and heraldic devices and dated 1616. The corbelling, a bold cable moulding, steps up and down to meet that of the angle turrets just like a hem of lace. Bell's masterpiece, despite his superb accomplishment at Castle Fraser was yet to come. Exactly a decade later he was at work for Willie the Merchant, William Forbes, on the completion of Craigievar Castle (Plate 25) which stands at a height of 255 m (838 ft) on the eastern slope of the Hill of Craigievar. As Douglas Simpson put it: "The tall six-storeyed tower-house of Craigievar seems to grow like a giant tree out of the braeside upon which it is set". At Craigievar I. or John Bell decided to have it both ways. On the front of the building (which is simply a rectangular tower-house with a jamb or wing and a square tower set in the re-entrant angle) he gave us soaring turrets. At the back he showed gables triumphing over turrets.

The turrets on the south front are plump, aggressive and two storeys high. They reduce the gable between them to a mere strip, little more than a chimney stack; on the north front the crow-stepped gables are virtually smothering the turret.

Inside, the house also has its wonders. The Great Hall is one of the most perfect examples of its type. Its groined vault is covered with relief plaster surface decoration of raised panels, heraldry, foliage, classical portrait medallions and elaborate pendants. "One thing," observes Douglas Simpson, "that will forcibly strike the visitor as he mounts from floor to floor is the surprising spaciousness of the house. From the outside it may have appeared a tall narrow tower, crossing its arms over its chest and hugging itself together in jealous isolation. In sharp contrast, the internal impression is one of mounting amplitude. This is partly due to the encorblement which carries out the area of the building in its upper storeys, and partly to the decrease, by successive internal offsets, in the thickness of the walls."

Stewart Cruden attributes to Craigievar "a sort of sublimity, a serene assurance not communicated by any other tower-house, however pleasing. Quite perfect, lightly poised upon the ground, it is the apotheosis of its type."

After Craigievar there is nothing comparable to add to the story of

Grampian castle-building as the 17th century advances. We may say farewell to it with just a passing glance at two Moray phenomena — Coxton Tower (1644) which looks as if it came straight out of the middle ages and Innes House (1640 - 1653) which is a small Renaissance masterpiece. Instead of being allowed to fall into ruin like its twin, Leslie Castle in Aberdeenshire, it has been considerably extended and modernised.

Chapter eleven

EARLY MODERN TIMES

Dr. David Turnock

This is a time of transition from a medieval to a modern way of life. Prospects of economic growth became brighter and the people of Grampian found several ways of participating in the drive for modernisation which was sweeping across most of Scotland, especially in the late 18th century. Agriculture and fishing were becoming more productive and an important industrial sector arose through the encouragement of textiles, especially linen. There was a progressive outlook, above all in Aberdeen, where the schools and universities trained a remarkable number of talented people whose skills were deployed to advantage both in the region and farther afield. And the involvement of all parts of the region, not simply a handful of burghs, in a more comfortable and prosperous life-style was facilitated by enlightened attitudes among feudal landowners and by a significant improvement in communications which stimulated a market-orientated economy. Yet little of this was evident at the start of the period, in the aftermath of the Reformation, for this religious trauma saw Grampian in a somewhat ambivalent position between the south, the stronghold of the Covenanters, and the conservative north where loyalty to the old church frequently remained strong (Muir 1970). The historic dichotomy between Celtic and Anglo-Norman cultures was deepened by the religious divide so that 'the Highlands in the 16th century became more anarchic and more hostile to the Lowlands than they had been before' (Smout 1969; p.44). The deposing of James VII in 1688 also sent shock waves through the north and loyalty to the Stewart cause was expressed in two major rebellions which served to perpetuate the military ethos of the feudal estate in the second half of the 18th century (Daiches 1964).

It has been asserted that there was a measure of indifference to the Reformation so that 'there is no sign of the rabid fanaticism which was so conspicuous to the sunward side of the Mounth' (Simpson 1963; p.73). However, there was some 'casting down of images' in country churches like Auchindoir, Banchory Ternan and Midmar. The mob was responsible for some damage to the church of St. Nicholas in Aberdeen (Hunter 1972-4) and over the years there was a solemn campaign of official destruction of incalculable proportions. Valuables removed from St. Nicholas and taken to the Town House of Aberdeen for safe keeping were rouped and the proceeds used to repair the harbour and the bridge of Balgownie; while alterations to the church, converting the small chapels into two 'preaching kirks', involved the removal of carved woodwork (1574 and 1596) and finally the decision in 1640 that the crucifix should be 'dung doon' (Nicol n.d.). Then there was the failure to keep buildings in repair so that the roof of the West Kirk of St. Nicholas collapsed in 1698 (leading eventually to the opening of a new church in 1755 using plans drawn up by the eminent Aberdonian James Gibb). Even worse was the neglect of the cathedrals (Lindsay, 1926). Despite some mob damage, St. Machar's Cathedral at Old Aberdeen was saved from complete destruction by the Earl of Huntly (who took the precious possessions into safe keeping), yet the building was neglected and the central tower collapsed in 1688, destroying surrounding parts of the building (White 1985). Fortunately, much of the nave escaped and after several renovations the old cathedral served as the parish church for Old Machar. Deterioration also followed at Elgin after it was decreed in 1567 that lead should be stripped from the cathedral roof. The central tower, 60 m (197 ft) in height, fell in 1711 and the entire complex became derelict. Only in 1825 was a custodian appointed to look after the substantial ruins of the 'Lantern of the North'.

The Reformation was not accepted passively by all the influential people in Grampian, for it served to deepen the traditionally difficult relations between two leading families with extensive estates in the old Lordship of Mar: the Forbeses who embraced the Protestant cause and the Gordons who, for the most part, adhered to the ancient faith (Simpson 1944, 1949). 'The civil war between the rival factions took on an aspect of peculiar savagery' (Simpson 1963; p.84) as the Earl of Huntly, Cock o'the North, miscalculated in supposing that Mary, Queen of Scots, would launch a Counter Reformation. She found it expedient to accept the *status quo,* in view of her aspirations towards the throne of England, and her attempts to contain the House of Gordon initiated a series of events which culminated in the death of Huntly at Corrichie in 1562. The depth of bitterness is also revealed in two battles which occurred later in the century: Craibstone (1571) and Glenlivet (1594), and in the burning of Corgarff Castle and its inhabitants in 1571 (Imlach 1868).

The struggle was perpetuated through strife between supporters of the two rival versions of the reformed faith since the Forbeses supported the Covenant while the Gordons were champions of Episcopacy. And it could be said that Grampian was involved in the first and the last incidents of the wars waged between 1638 and 1655 through the 'Trot of Turriff' in 1638 and the submission of Dunnottar Castle to Cromwell in 1655, though the period was also punctuated by two notable victories for the Royalists by Montrose of Aberdeen in 1644 and Alford in 1645.

Grampian also saw much of the marching and countermarching by Claverhouse and Mackay during the revolutionary campaign of 1689, while considerable support was given to the Jacobites between 1698 and 1745 (McLynn 1985). Gestures of support for James in the year of the Glencoe massacre, like the one at Fraserburgh by Charles Fraser of Castle Fraser and the Laird of Inverallochy, led to a government decision to increase the strength of the armed forces and the consequent tax assessments led to the drawing up of the Poll Book which remains a valuable source for population and settlement studies in Aberdeenshire. There was strong support for the Jacobites with the planned French landing in Buchan in 1707 (which did not materialise) and the launching of the 1715 rebellion at Braemar, supposedly after the leaders had gathered for a hunting party with the Earl of Mar at Kildrummy (Simpson 1925). The Old Pretender eventually arrived at Peterhead and journeyed south through Aberdeen to join his army at Perth while several of the leading figures escaped abroad from Grampian ports after the rebellion collapsed. The estates of the Earl of Mar and the Earl Marischal were forfeited. Although there were no major incidents in the region during the 1745-6 rebellion there was again strong support. Local men moved first south and later north to Culloden, the decisive engagement which brought the Jacobite rebellions to an end. Moreover, with this crucial battle and the subsequent scouring of the countryside for fugitives (most of whom were able to make good their escape), the long history of civil strife in the North was brought to a conclusion (Buchan 1961).

Under the circumstances it is hardly surprising to find that rural buildings continued to be heavily fortified during the period. Only in the 18th century were large houses built without concern for defence: for example, Duff House near Banff, William Adam's baroque-style house for Lord Braco, later Earl of Fife (1725) and Haddo House, by the same designer, for the 2nd Earl of Aberdeen (1732). To be sure there were smaller buildings without substantial defences, like the new house at Monymusk built from the priory ruins after Duncan Forbes of Corsindae acquired the estate c. 1584, and also Fettercairn House in 1666, but the three-storey house built by the Irvines at Drum in 1619 was merely an extension of the medieval tower house of 1286 while the substantial extensions at Fyvie, including the gatehouse in 1599 by Lord Seton (Earl of Dunfermline) and the Gordon Tower by General Gordon in c.1777, showed a continuing appreciation of the need for security (Hill 1943). Damaged castles were still being renovated, like Huntly Castle which suffered in the revolt of the Catholic Earls: the rebuilding included a row of oriel windows, apparently inspired by the Chateau of Blois where the Marquis of Huntly is reputed to have been governor for a time. Several entirely new castles were built, like the small 16th century castle at Westhill near Oyne, including an L-shaped parapeted tower which was extended eastwards in the 17th century, and Leith-Hall where the original fortalice of 1650 grew into a complex of four wings grouped around a wholly enclosed courtyard by 1800. At Gordonstoun (Plewlands) however, a new 18th century mansion house by Sir Robert Gordon (1704-1772) replaced an older building, presumed to have been a tower house and, more remarkably, some rather unconventional outhouses were built, notably the Round Square, conceived by the previous Sir Robert Gordon ('The Wizard') as a magic circle: 'a scientific sanctuary for his soul, capable of defying the Devil himself' (Brereton 1968; Keith 1975).

More notable still was the turreted L-plan castle at Braemar built for the Earl of Mar in 1628, following the return of the estranged estates of the Earldom to the Erskine family by Mary Queen of Scots in 1565. A replacement for the ruinous castle of the Kindrochit was needed to guard the Cairnwell and Tolmounth routes (Smith 1980). The castle was burnt by the Farquharsons in 1689 to deny access to government forces but it was subsequently renovated as a Hanoverian garrison in 1748 (with a wall and other alterations entrusted to John and Robert Adam who were working for the Board of Ordnance in Scotland) and it was eventually returned to the Farquharsons after the garrison left in 1797. But most remarkable is the work of the Bel family: George who died in 1575 and his son John. Midmar and Crathes were 16th century creations, though an 18th century wing was added in the latter case, while at Castle Fraser a four-storey fortalice of 1617 rounded off the earlier work by another local mason, Thomas Leiper, who started on a simple tower house (Michael Tower) in 1575 (Slade 1977-8). However, the gem must surely be Craigievar (1610-1626), the new home for Aberdeen merchant William Forbes ('Willie the Merchant'). The great walls seem to shoot out of the earth like an organic growth and there is a subtle modulation of style as height increases: all is severe and unwelcoming at ground level but there is more embellishment higher up until the roof bursts into a harmonious blend of cupolas, balustrades, pinnacles and gables (Simpson n.d.). And S. Cruden writes (1960; p. 173) in measured terms how 'no infelicity of style or exaggeration of detail suggests room for improvement'. There was some attention to gardens at these great houses; notably Crathes where the famous yew hedges were planted in the 17th century. But the outstanding example is Pitmedden where the gardens were started by Sir Alexander Seton in 1675: his years in Edinburgh would have made him familiar with the enclosed garden laid out at Holyrood-house and similar gardens at Pinkie, Seton and Winton (Prentice 1965). Elsewhere, gardening was not a major preoccupation and at some of the great houses landscaping was a 19th century improvement, as at Haddo where land reclamation and tree planting was eventually put in hand.

If the Reformation stirred up controversy that was sometimes expressed through violence it also stimulated intellectual activity. One notable initiative was the founding, in 1593, of Marischal College in Aberdeen by George Keith, 5th Earl Marischal. This university remained separate from the existing University of Aberdeen (at King's College, Old Aberdeen) until the merger of 1860 (Rait 1895). The idea was probably to set up a Protestant rival to King's, known to be loyal to the ancient faith and hence supported by the Earl of Huntly, the leader of the Counter Reformation. Enthusiasm seems to have been infectious because in 1597 Parliament ratified the charter granted to Sir Alexander Fraser of Philorth in respect of a university at Fraserburgh, but this institution fell into decay 'owing to the troublesome times' (Walker 1897; p. 258). Nevertheless, the surviving universities 'gave a tone to the whole district' and enabled pupils from the parish schools to go to university courses (Walker 1897, p. 259). In turn rural education was enriched by the locally trained graduates. Even in the 17th century there were schools in a quarter of the parishes of Aberdeenshire, as well as the burghs, although there was still room for considerable improvement in the 18th century when the principal academies began to appear, for example Elgin Academy in 1791.

These education facilities generated a flow of talented researchers who contributed to the life of the region and the country generally. 'It is striking how often, in the 17th century, work of really worthwhile academic stature came out of Aberdeen' (Smout 1969; p. 187). Pride of place must go to the hereditary genius of the 'Academic Gregories', mainly doctors and mathematicians over nearly three centuries. This remarkable family descended from Rev. John Gregory of Drumoak, and included the astronomer James Gregory (1638-1675), educated at Marischal College and Padua, who forged a link with the work of Isaac Newton whose mathematics was being taught in Scottish universities by the early 18th century. Then John Gregory (1724-1773) was a famous doctor but it was another Aberdonian physician, Archibald Pitcairne, who helped found the Royal College of Physicians in Edinburgh in 1681. Again worthy of mention are the cartographers Robert Gordon of Straloch and John Gordon of Rothiemay (Straloch's son) who continued the work of Timothy Pont in mapping Scottish counties (Emery 1958) and the doctors Sir William Fordyce and Alexander Gordon. Also Robert Brown (botanist), John Clark (animal breeder), William Davidson (chemist), John Forbes of Corse (theologian), George Jameson (artist), George Low (natural historian) and Duncan Liddel (mathematician). Learned societies contributed to an appetite for enquiry and innovation. The Aberdeen Philosophical Society was a small scholarly circle which survived only for fifteen years (1758-1773) but the Aberdeen Medico-Chirurgical Society of 1789 had a longer life as did the early farming societies: Gordon's Mill Farming Club (1758), a small group of professors, farmers and lairds (Smith 1962), and Morayshire Farmers' Club (1799). The latter organised modest monthly dinners to discuss the agricultural history of the district: 'the cost was never to exceed eighteen pence per head and no member was permitted to spend more than another two shillings on drink' (Rampini 1897; p. 304).

The intellectual activity of the 18th century may be seen in the context of the wider national movement known as the 'Scottish Enlightenment'. It is possible that the dreadful conditions of the 'ill years' of the 1690s inculcated a desire to modernise and secure both material and moral advancement. The Aberdonian James Dunbar (1742-1798) did much to point out that the prospects for growth were real and that people had the capacity to improve their lot. While the physical conditions of the region were of fundamental importance their value was not fixed but varied according to technology and human perception: the 'moral' causes were all-important in effecting change (Berry 1970). The mood for change was most clearly demonstrated in Grampian by transformation of agriculture. The traditional system (Dodgshon 1973) was by no means inflexible (Smout and Fenton 1965) and there is a substantial amount of research, contributed by Dodgshon (1981), Whittington (1973) and Whyte (1979), which suggests a progressive adaptation to changing circumstances. But now the landowners took a firm lead through the consolidation of farms, eliminating the joint-farms with their run-rig system, and the introduction of new crops and methods (Campbell 1977). Production for a wider market grew in importance, relative to local subsistence, and regional specialisation became gradually more evident (Handley 1953).

The landlords had the advantage of 17th century legislation allowing for enclosure at will, without the need for any formal procedure, and also for division of *commonties* (areas of land common to several owners) by private agreement or by simple legal process (Smout 1964). When the lairds were ready to move, change could be accomplished at remarkable speed: over as little as a decade estates might be totally replanned so that old settlements and boundary lines might disappear to be replaced by the familiar landscape of regular square or rectangular-shaped fields (Symon 1959). There was plenty of work for the surveyors and it was largely from the more mathematically-minded of the parochial schoolmasters that a native group of Scottish land surveyors emerged. Some surveyors, however, came from England, along with the basic technology for Scotland's agricultural revolution: in 1726 Thomas Winter was brought to Monymusk by Sir Archibald Grant and Peter May came north in 1754, eventually taking up permanent employment with the Earl of Findlater at Cullen. There was also work for labourers by the thousand, draining recalcitrant sections of boggy ground which had previously been allowed to break up the continuity of the old infields; clearing the enlarged fields of rocks and boulders and building sometimes elaborate 'consumption dykes' out of such materials; paring, burning and liming to extend cultivation to the higher ground where hungry soils could be cultivated thanks to the new grasses and roots; and raising the new housing required for the consolidated holdings and for the surplus population removed to the towns and villages.

The new farming pattern was first exemplified at Monymusk where Sir Archibald Grant took over the management of the estate in 1716 (Hamilton 1945, 1946). There was then an archaic run-rig system with low output arising out of the practice of continuous cultivation of the infield without any fallowing. Grant's youthful energies were stretched to the full in encouraging tenants to enclose fields, clear boulders and drain the damp patches. Better cultivation involved keeping the ground free from weeds and this was achieved initially by fallowing and later by the introduction of turnips into the rotation: for turnips (sown in drills) needed careful weeding and this served to clear the ground as effectively as fallowing while the roots also provided a valuable feed crop which offered a solution to the age-old problem of keeping stock through the winter. The increase in livestock meant copious quantities of manure to boost the harvests of corn, straw and turnips. The new rotation usually involved the alternation of oats, easily the most popular cereal, with turnips one year and grasses another, though the grass and clover ley might often be maintained for three years to rest the land more fully and at the same time ensure adequate grazing for cattle in summer. This simple Monymusk formula was evolved on the home farm but once the best solution had been found it was applied elsewhere on the estate where suitable tenants were encouraged by low rents and long leases. Subtenancies disappeared but some of the people displaced could move to new holdings carved out of the waste or else occupy crofts where work on the smallholding could be combined with casual employment on the larger farms (Kay 1962). Others could find a place in the cottar houses attached to the principal farms, perhaps with a vegetable patch thrown in. Under such conditions there were improved prospects for all concerned (Turnock 1976).

The experiments by Grant came at a time when the Society of Improvers was trying to diffuse the principles of Jethro Tull and others north of the border. The first experiments made on the home farm seemed to have little relevance to everyday farming because of the great expense in relation to prevailing commodity prices. But rising prices later in the century, associated with population growth, and a brief encounter with famine (in 1782) made the Monymusk package of improvements quite irresistible. As J. R. Allan put it, 'the northern farmer discovered a law of increasing returns: the more stock the bigger the midden; the bigger the midden the better the crops; the better the crops the more stock' (Allen 1952; p. 75). Grant's methods were taken up in Banffshire and Morayshire by leading landowners like the Duke of Gordon and the Earl of Findlater and much new land was broken in now that the colder and heavier soils could be brought into production (Turnock 1977, 1980). In Kincardine, improvers like Barclay of Ury and Silver of Netherley transformed the stoney and ill-drained plateau land between Maryculter and Stonehaven. Attention could be given to stock breeding once adequate fodder supplies were available, although many farmers had to drive their beasts to market until the railway age and therefore hardy animals were still needed. The black horned cattle were highly favoured as good drovers well suited to the northern environment, but with winter keep more widely available some farmers could envisage fattening cattle for despatch to market by boat. A solution was found in the introduction of Teeswater stock for crossing with the horned cattle. Barclay of Ury played an important part in the import of these animals from south of the border but further progress was made by Amos Cruickshank, an Aberdeen hosiery merchant, and William Duthie of Collynie who produced the strong, vigorous and rapidly-growing Shorthorn. Even where cattle had still to be driven over long distances improvements were feasible (Haldane 1952). In Tullynessle, Leith of Whitehouse was the leading stock breeder at the end of the 18th century and the minister records how 'most of the gentlemen and substantial farmers in the neighbourhood have thought it worthwhile to possess themselves of a few of his breed which are of a pretty large size, very handsome and remarkably well horned' (Old Statistical Account IV 28). There were good prices from the drovers 'who begin to pick them up early in spring and continue buying through the summer' *(Ibid)*.

There were far-reaching changes in industry, especially textiles. The production of coarse woollen plaiding was traditional but there were some notable 17th century improvements arising out of the immigration of Flemish weavers into Aberdeen which 'provided the foundation on which factory textile industries were built after the Industrial Revolution' (Coull 1963; p. 86). The combination of local raw material and Flemish weaving and dyeing skills produced a successful industry in the area, with organisation provided by Aberdeen merchants (Barnes 1977; Grant 1921). Plaiding and stockings were exported to Germany and the Low Countries and in the next century, with more use of imported wool, the local product sold more widely from the Mediterranean to Scandinavia. However, other branches of the textile industry made a powerful impact in the 18th century. There was a cotton mill built at Woodside (now part of Aberdeen) in 1785 but, more importantly, the linen industry was promoted widely in Scotland after the Union because there appeared to be good prospects in the English market. A Board of Trustees for Manufacturers, based in Edinburgh, helped to provide instruction in spinning and other processes with the result that a substantial industry developed in the second half of the century. Once again the Aberdeen merchants played an important part in organising the distribution of flax imported from the Low Countries (though some was produced locally) and the circulation of semi-finished goods.

The manufacturers also pioneered the factory system because of the convenience of centralisation for the preparatory and finishing processes, restricting the domestic workers to spinning and weaving. The first factory was built in 1779 in Woodside but ten years later a mill was built on the Don using water-powered machinery for carding and spinning, and later weaving (Shaw 1984). By 1800 there were three other mills on the Don, including a seven-storey building by Leys, Masson & Co. (1797) standing beside their bleachfield, and another using the dammed-up waters of Gallowgate Loch. There was a close link (through the supply of rags) between the linen industry and the paper mills built near Aberdeen in 1751 (on the Culter Burn at Peterculter) and in 1771 (on the Don at Stoneywood). And there was further industrial development through brewing and distilling, brick and nail making, as well as shipbuilding: the famous firm of Alexander Hall & Co. was founded in 1790. The granite industry of Aberdeen has essentially 18th century origins and the well-known Rubislaw quarry was being worked by 1741 (Trail 1930).

Granite had previously been used for a number of buildings in the town, like St. Machar's Cathedral and the town houses of Provost Skene and Provost Ross: and for various castles in the country, including Crathes, Drum and Midmar. But there was now more widespread use of granite for building: the Town House of Old Aberdeen (1721), Robert Gordon's College (1732) and Union Bridge (1803).

Industry was also developing in other parts of the region, particularly the linen industry, although there was a lot of emphasis on the processing of flax and the spinning of yarn for weavers on Tayside (Durie 1974). Developments were also taking place in forestry, initially by the Commissioners of the Forfeited Estates. Continental practices were being widely copied in the later years of the 18th century when some of the more famous forests of the region were being established, Darnaway for example (Anderson 1967). Whisky distilling was another expanding industry, for with rising demand for the product local grain surpluses could be efficiently utilised. However, the inappropriate legislation in the 1780s resulted in widespread illicit distillation, especially in parts of the Grampian Uplands (Devine 1975; Sillett 1975). Reference might also be made to lime working, for example at St. Cyrus where there were kilns at East Mathers and, more importantly, at Miltonhaven where the sea ultimately broke into the quarries to destroy both the industry and the village (Fraser 1970). However, the most widespread non-agricultural activity was fishing. By 1800 virtually every coastal parish had at least one 'fishing toun' but during the next hundred years there was a great increase in the number of such places. Some villages founded late in the century had a regular plan, like Macduff and St Combs, whereas in the older settlements houses were huddled together on the seashore. Some of the new settlements were replacements for places abandoned due to the accumulation of sand e.g. Corsekelly, Rattray and Sandend, for there seems to have been a process of natural selection with 'the open shores and points liable to sand accumulation being rejected in favour of those with better landing places and harbours' (Coull 1969; p. 21-2). The fishing was organised on a family basis and activities were related closely to a seasonal cycle (Coull 1977). Much of the effort went into white fishing in local waters but before 1800 Fraserburgh and Peterhead were fitting out boats to go to Barra Head for the cod fishing in summer (Cranna 1914; Findlay 1933). Salmon fishing was locally important too. There was a considerable measure of self-sufficiency in the fishing villages and it was common for fishermen to work smallholdings in their spare time. However, it was generally accepted that 'the cod and the corn dinna mix': farming and fishing were both specialist crafts supporting separate communities and while the fisher folk would go inland to sell their produce there was little social intercourse and intermarriage was virtually unknown.

The development of the region's economy rested on an improvement of communications. Strategic considerations made it imperative to provide new roads for military purposes in the middle decades of the 18th century (Haldane 1962; Mathieson 1924). Grampian was affected by the road which was started at Blairgowrie in 1749 and extended north to the Well of the Lecht (1754) and Fort George (1763) (Graham 1963-4; Taylor 1976). The castles of Braemar and Corgarff were refurbished for use by local garrisons looking out for cattle thieves and whisky smugglers. Various landowners were able to put improvements in hand: thus the enthusiasm of the Earl of Kintore stimulated sufficient public support to bridge the Don at Inverurie while the first bridge across the Dee at Ballater owed much to the interest of Farquharson of Monaltrie (Fraser 1913). Other notable achievements were the bridges over the Deveron at Banff (1763, replacing the old bridge swept away in the flood of 1768) and the North Esk at Kinnaber, south of St. Cyrus (1775). Bridges were of great significance for coach traffic and for the marketing of local farm produce. Thus the Kinnaber bridge helped to simplify the coach journey from Edinburgh to Aberdeen and enabled St. Cyrus folk to sell their produce in Montrose. The bridges over the Spey date to 1798 (at Fochabers) where work arose out of a fund launched by the Duchess of Gordon and 1812 (at Craigellachie) where Thomas Telford was responsible for the construction of the most architecturally distinguished bridge in the region (Rolt 1958).

However, comprehensive road improvements were needed and the foundation of a modern network of radial roads for Aberdeen was laid by the act of 1795 (Patrick n.d.). By the end of the century the Deeside road had passed Drum, the Inverurie road was nearly complete, the Banff road was approaching Newmachar and the Fraserburgh/Peterhead road had reached Ellon. These roads were all finished by 1810, as was the Alford road sanctioned in 1800, while an extension from Inverurie to Huntly was finished in 1820. There was a great increase in carts where wheeled traffic had previously been almost unknown. Not that the old trails and droving routes were immediately superseded, for cattle droving continued into the railway age and it is still possible to follow sections of these routes such as the trail from the Braes of Glenlivet up the precipitous slopes of the Ladder, thence by the Nochty to Donside and by Deskry Water and Tillypronie to Logie Coldstone and Deeside with the Mounth passes beyond (Fraser 1920, 1980; Kyd 1958). Reference should also be made to road building in the burghs, notably Aberdeen where Charles Abercrombie suggested in 1796 that new access routes be built from both north and south. The work was put in hand and the new streets, King Street and Union Street respectively, were opened in 1801. The latter scheme involved an impressive bridge over the Denburn which was a stimulus to the development of the West End for 'if you had been able to look down on the Castlegate of the 1790s you would have seen little further than the square itself, for Aberdeen consisted of a tightly packed little town concentrated mainly around the ancient St. Katherine's Hill and separated from the country to the west by two defiles', the Putachie and Den burns (Graham 1972 p.21). Then there were the harbour improvements (Graham, 1976-7), best exemplified once again by Aberdeen where the clearance of the harbour channel in 1610 was followed up by the North Pier (1775-81) and even more substantial improvements in the 19th century; the canals, most notably the Port Elphinstone Canal which was opened in 1806 and played an important part in the development of the Garioch (Graham 1967-8); and the major drainage schemes, most notably the Brander Drain of 1780 which emptied the water from the Loch of Spynie into the Lossie and so yielded almost 430 ha (1060 acres) of new agricultural land (Brereton 1968).

The commercial life of the region focused on a number of local centres where services were provided for the rural population, quite apart from the kirktouns and milltouns found in virtually every parish (Paddison 1969). This is evident from the 1696 Poll Tax returns which are particularly useful in the case of Aberdeenshire (Stuart 1844; Walton 1950). However, the privileges of the royal burghs were only slowly eroded (Gibb and Paddison 1983). Aberdeen was particularly important and the strategic rôle which emerged in medieval times was complemented by a growing economic function as the merchants extended their overseas contacts and mobilised the rural hinterland over the production of textiles (Keith 1972; Wyness 1966). This can be seen in the growth of the town, expressed in the map of John Gordon of Rothiemay (1661) and in the improvements made to the harbour to accommodate the increase in ships owned by Aberdeen merchants: just two vessels of some 30 t. each in 1700 but 150 with an average tonnage of 115 about the year 1850. It can also be seen in the domestic architecture for the fine Provost Ross house in the Shiprow was built in 1594 for the merchant Alexander Farquhar and the house associated with another civic leader, Provost Skene, was started in the fashionable Guestrow in 1545 (Meldrum 1958-9). Several other burghs, including Banff, Elgin (Mackintosh 1914), Forres (Forbes 1975) and Stonehaven, were flourishing centres of commerce and administration even though they were in no position to challenge Aberdeen's primacy (Cramond 1888,

1893). The 18th century growth of Banff has left a particularly rich architectural legacy through the excellent Georgian buildings in High Street, Low Street, Carmelite Street and also close to the harbour which was improved in the 1770s. The growing prosperity of the coastal markets (Geddes 1945) towards the end of the century would have seemed remarkable to those who, a generation earlier, had been plagued by a band of several dozen 'gypsies' under the leadership of James Macpherson and the protection of the Laird of Grant: many of those seen receiving money at the markets of Banff, Elgin and Forres were later robbed and it was only after numerous depredations that Macpherson was brought to justice. But there is always the maverick. Rattray was erected as a new royal burgh in 1564 but, planted in an unstable coastal environment, it failed to maintain its harbour and the town prospered for only a century (Cumine 1887-90). It is reported that burgesses were selling land to outsiders in the 17th century and less than a score of adults were left in 1696. The town was completely derelict by 1750 (Walton 1956).

However an outstanding feature of the settlement geography of Grampian in the 18th century was the building of new settlements — the planned villages — which served as resettlement centres for families displaced by the agricultural improvements (Lockhart 1975). Reclamation of land for smallholdings could go hand in hand with rural industry and local marketing, thereby stimulating the farm population (Smout 1979). The model was formulated in the south (for John Cockburn rebuilt the village of Ormiston in Lothian in 1740) but was given considerable impetus in Grampian in the 1770s. James Anderson moved north from Hermiston near Edinburgh to take over the farm on Monkshill on the Udny estate where he threw his youthful energies into the task of breaking in the Aberdeenshire moorland. Anderson was knowledgeable as well as energetic and the laird hoped that other tenants would seek to emulate his successful methods. But Anderson was also a keen author and in his writings he went to great pains to stress the need for urban markets as a stimulus for increased agricultural production. Aberdeen's demand could stimulate local farmers into clearing land at such places as Echt and Skene but estates situated far from a burgh might benefit from the planting of a small industrial community concerned with linen, for which high hopes were expressed in the late 18th century. The idea had already been taken up at such places as Cuminestown and New Keith (Walton 1963) but further schemes were now implemented. The Duke of Gordon was responsible for the rebuilding of Fochabers in 1776, which provided extra space for the gardens at Gordon Castle and simultaneously gave better housing conditions and services with building related to a regular plan involving a main street and square (Slater 1980). In the Mearns Lord Gardenstone, who purchased the Johnstone estate in 1762, was busy with the rebuilding of Laurencekirk, erected as a Burgh of Barony in 1779. Laurencekirk was a community of linen weavers with a spinning mill processing locally grown flax (plus some material imported through Aberdeen) and a bleachfield. Subsequent ventures were started in the 1780s at New Pitsligo and Tomintoul (Gaffney 1960, 1976). Later on developments occurred at Aberlour, Dufftown, Lumsden, New Deer and Rhynie.

With the emergence of so many new market centres and the demise of some long-established burghs, changes in the local settlement pattern could be quite profound (Coull 1984). Perhaps the greatest changes occurred in the Mearns. Here there was the demise of Kincardine, accelerated by the removal of the county seat to Stonehaven in 1607. The castle at Kincardine had been important for controlling the land route across Cairn o'Mount, like the old Pictish fortress of 'Green Castle' nearby, but it was abandoned in the 16th century and was probably last used by Mary Queen of Scots during her expedition against the Gordons (Tranter 1972). Meanwhile the commercial decline of the burgh was hastened by the realignment of the Cairn o'Mount road around the northern side of Hunter's Hill. This meant that the rôle of local market centre passed to Fettercairn, where Kincardine's mercat cross now stands, and Auchinblae (Cameron 1899). The markets date back to 1504 and 1554 respectively and Fettercairn was erected as a Burgh of Barony. 'In both cases it appears that the local nobleman was taking advantage of declining royal interest in Kincardine to establish a market village within his own lands' (Small 1966; p. 25). Both places benefited from the droving trade because Fettercairn was conveniently situated in relation to the Cairn o'Mount route to Banchory while Auchinblae was useful for the Craigincrosse route to Drum. Elsewhere in the Mearns there were developments in the shape of the handloom weaving settlements of Laurencekirk (already noted) and the rather less accessible Luthermuir (Feus of Caldhame) while St. Cyrus developed from the roadside community by the Kinnaber Bridge and expanded to incorporate the kirktoun standing on the higher ground to the south.

The early modern period witnessed a radical transformation of the region and the laying down of firm foundations for the modernisation which is outlined in the next chapter. Civil war ceased to be a means of resolving disputes and a generally more peaceful society set to work to improve the material conditions of life, especially in the last years of the 18th century. The Scottish economy as a whole began to 'take-off' in the 1780s with the cotton boom following the American War of

Independence (Hamilton 1963), and in the predominantly rural Grampian Region there was a powerful consensus in favour of agricultural improvement with a reorganisation of farming under the powerful leadership of the landed proprietors: 'the snowy hairst of 1782 brought famine conditions approaching the scale of the 1690s and marked the culmination of the stubborn opposition of the tenant farmer to change' (Godsman 1958; p. 276). There was of course a powerful demographic pressure for a more productive economy (Macdonald 1937) with a generally upward trend between the Webster census of 1755 (Youngson 1961-2) and the first official census in 1801 (Walton 1961). Death rates were still high among young children for the availability of the potato and the reduced incidence of plague, typhus and malaria, was balanced to some extent by the rise of smallpox and an ambivalent attitude to inoculation. But earlier marriage seems to have resulted in a higher birth rate although there was also a theory that luxury 'discourages marriage until persons acquire an income adequate in their estimation to that state' (Old Statistical Account V, 22). But when we are reminded of the ever-present risk of low cereal yields through heavy rainfall or low temperatures and note the observation of Rampini (1897; p. 319) that 'kail nettles and mugwort boiled together and thickened with oatmeal was a favourite soup' it becomes apparent that the quest for luxury was a minority interest (Lindsay 1976). Yet if the people were disposed to work hard for modest improvement they also maintained the traditional pleasures of cock fighting, shinty and bowls. There was considerable mirth and jollity and 'none of the old festivals of the church had so strong a hold on the affections of the people as had that of the essentially pagan festival of Hogmanay' (Rampini 1897; p. 326). The reformed church tried to oppose such traditions as 'lyke-wakes' (following a bereavement) and 'penny weddings' because of the scandalous and unseemly behaviour associated with such legacies of Roman Catholicism. But old habits were not to be easily disturbed by legislations such as the Synod of Moray's prohibition of 'all piping, dancing and fiddling at pennibridells within doors' (1676) and the Elgin authorities' stand against the participation of citizens in any lyke-wake 'unless they be in relation to the defunct or called by his friends under the pain of ten pounds Scots' (*Ibid* 314). Game poaching was more effectively controlled but was by no means completely eliminated (Watson and Allan 1986).

It would be dangerous, however, to suppose that the region was a homogenous one in terms of cultural and economic conditions (O'Dell 1951, 1953). Plainly town and country could be almost different worlds and there was a strong cultural distinction within the rural districts between the Highland fringes, where Gaelic was still spoken, and the Lowlands (Withers 1982). But local variations were also significant on account of different levels of implementation of agricultural improvement policies (Godsman 1970; Simpson 1942). This comes out from some very substantial writings on farming conditions commissioned by the Board of Agriculture: James Anderson's *'General view of the agriculture of the county of Aberdeen'* (1794) was followed up in 1811 by a study of G. S. Keith, for many years the minister at Keith Hall and Kinkell, on *'The agriculture of Aberdeen'*. But the most valuable material comes from the parish reports of the *Old Statistical Account,* a mammoth questionnaire exercise carried out among the Church of Scotland ministers by the famous improver Sir John Sinclair (Morgan 1968). There is no space to do justice to this invaluable source, though much of the literature quoted in this essay includes substantial references to it. The ministers supported the process of improvement almost without exception and most criticism was applied to cases of failure to implement improvements. There was concern over moral questions at a time of rapid change in many parishes, especially in the context of underemployment in some of the villages and increased addiction to spirits, but on the whole the region was successful in providing new jobs for its people and in maintaining a strong community spirit.

Chapter twelve

MODERN TIMES

Dr. John S. Smith

Towards the end of the 18th century, the pace of agricultural improvement accelerated. Enclosure, drainage and apportionment into individual farms resulted in immense landscape change, reclamation of the waste and village foundation. The drive to win land from the stony interfluves and lowland peat mosses was checked by a series of famine years in the 1780s (notably 1782) which resulted in declining populations in the decade prior to the descriptions of the Old Statistical Account (1792). In the lowlands of Buchan and Moray, parish totals continued to increase, in part the result of successful foundations of planned villages with their domestic textile and agricultural servicing bases, and in part because of continuing land reclamation, probably led by colonists from the famine-hit interior areas. The end of the 18th century and beginning of the 19th century was a fluid period of migration and movement, often to the New World. Those who remained on the land benefited from the decrease in numbers as farm servant wages increased. Longer leases encouraged greater tenant attention to the land. Within the lowlands, only a few core areas of difficult waste land remained as unimproved rough grazings or peatlands — a reminder of the previously inhospitable nature of much of the countryside. Despite later farm amalgamations, the proportion of small farms and crofts remained high into the 20th century, although amalgamation has increased markedly in the last 20 years. Although the main phase of reclamation was accomplished by the early 19th century, in Kincardineshire, the cultivated area increased again in that century by over 50%. Increases in arable land were greatest in the vicinity of Aberdeen where manure, imported lime and a ready market for agricultural produce were freely available. In the 1870s, throughout the Grampian lowlands, but particularly in Buchan, beef prices were high and Aberdeenshire beef was much in demand for the London market. The costs of transport fell markedly with the infilling of the rail network, making the livestock fattening enterprise extremely profitable. Centres like Maud became extremely large cattle-marketing nodes. In many parts of the region, the winning of the agricultural countryside had been achieved by immense human toil — one small farm recording the wheeling of over 15,000 cartloads of stones off the ground within a 30 year period. Such labours produced a hardy farming stock closely associated with their land, which must have helped many to weather the difficulties of the agricultural depression in the 1930s.

In the present century, the contrast between upland and lowland Grampian has strengthened. Upland areas — west of Kincardine O'Neil on Deeside, and west of Alford on Donside — have limited cropping potential and the emphasis is on beef cattle and sheep, while in the lowland parishes, which occupy roughly 46% of Grampian, the emphasis is more on cash crops, although lowland grazings support over half of Grampian's breeding cows and ewes. The hill and upland farms are extensive low out-put systems and many experience winter keep problems especially in severe weather. In contrast, the lowland enterprises are relatively intensive with varying combinations of arable and rotation grasses. In the post-war period, mechanisation has meant the continued shedding of farm labour — employed farm labour in Grampian falling from 18,296 in 1955 to around 6000 in 1980. Other changes in farm size, and the nature of the enterprise have resulted from new agricultural legislation regarding incentives and subsidy patterns, plus the increasing involvement of farmers in borrowed capital. From the 1950s onwards, oats have been almost universally replaced by barley, and the traditional root crop of potatoes has declined, in part because of high labour costs. Silage and beef production increased markedly in the period 1950 - 1970. Dairying has become increasingly concentrated in large specialist units, while pork production was encouraged by the presence of Lawson's of Dyce on the outskirts of Aberdeen. The decline in the number of small units was particularly marked in the 1960s — the number of farmers (including farm managers) falling in the period 1961 - 1966 from around 11,000 to 6800. The same period witnessed considerable and often heated discussion over the merits of the afforestation of agricultural ground, notably in Strathdon. The technological innovations of combining, silage towers and improved machinery which enabled the lowland farms to improve production vastly and shed labour were not extended to the hill and upland farms (see Chapter 13).

Since 1973, agricultural strategies have been tied to the Common Agricultural Policy involving annual reviews of Community Policy and fairly frequent changes in direction of support for particular products, each of which encourages farmers to tool up by investment in the appropriate machinery or buildings. Generally the period has been characterised by the search for crops with high profit margins, the abandonment of the traditional rotation, and greater inputs of fertiliser. The balance between livestock and cereal has changed in favour of the latter, although at present the Community overproduces in beef, milk and cereals, thus severely curtailing the options available for Grampian farmers. Oilseed rape has appeared as a colourful and popular crop in the last five years, and production seems set to expand until the inevitable quotas are imposed. Changes in public preference in terms of "healthy" foods are also registered in the Grampian landscape as there has been a swing away from the traditional beef cattle breeds towards the leaner Limousin and Charolais. In economic terms, farming seems to mean the survival of the largest, and thus many lowland rural parishes combine a measure of prosperity with quite marked rural depopulation.

In the upland areas, the collapse of the clan system after Culloden left these parts of Banffshire and Aberdeenshire temporarily without leaders, and with a reduced and somewhat chastened population. Significant changes in landownership and in land use patterns were to follow. The new landlords, and those of the old lairds who survived, began increasingly to realise the potential of moorland and deerforest as commercial assets. Although a few of the upper Deeside glens were cleared of population for sheep farming in the 1780s and, despite the fact that the wool and mutton market retained its rising prices until the 1860s, upland glens briefly turned over to sheep stock in Deeside were quickly returned to the sporting land uses of deer and grouse. In those areas where sheep farming survived, it was eventually to suffer decreased stocking due to declining pasture quality. As early as 1800, a sporting consortium led by Sir John Maxwell took a ten-year lease of the Deeside estate of Abergeldie, a system which was to become extremely popular in the uplands of Dee, Don, Spey and Avon. Although the limited accuracy of the rifles available required hounds to be held in reserve to bring down wounded deer, a strict etiquette and tradition grew up around the sport which greatly appealed to the Victorians with their staunch belief in the health-giving properties of fresh air. The traditional lowlanders distaste for all things Highland following the events of the early 18th century was to be totally reversed in favour of a sometimes over-romantic perception and delight in the craggy scenery and "faithful Highlanders", well conveyed in the journals of H.M. Queen Victoria. By the first 30 years of the 19th century, the number of advertised deer forests had trebled, and much of the ground above 300 m (985 ft) was under sporting land uses.

The essentials of the present estate pattern crystallised with the ground parcelled up into units of varying size according to the nature of the terrain, but with limited valley or basin floor in proportion to mountain and moorland. The lower the productivity of the ground, the larger the estate unit — varying from perhaps 4000 ha (9880 acres) in the hill edge zone to over 40,000 ha (98800 acres) beyond the glen heads. Although the process of deforestation initiated in prehistoric times meant that stalking took place on open ground, the deer stock, although smaller than their woodland habitat medieval counterparts, began to increase in numbers with conscious efforts being made to improve stock and often to provide a measure of winter feed. Access to the hill for stalking and keepering purposes was provided by major capital investments in roads, shooting lodges and game larders, and there were job opportunities for domestic staff and ghillies in relatively remote areas, thus locally reversing the process of retreat from the hills. Deer parks, woodland shelter belts and arboreta produced distinctive land use elements where the individual taste of the new laird, who clothed his staff in distinctive tweeds, became paramount in moulding the cultural landscape as in Glen Tanar, Deeside.

The Royal interest in Deeside in the middle 19th century confirmed the already well-established fashion for game sports and the publication in 1834 of William Scrope's *Days of Deer Stalking* together with the paintings of Landseer, combined to further the commercial value of sporting lets. The growing demand for the sport which continued to create substantial seasonal employment and rateable incomes in remote areas until the First World War was often fuelled by fortunes made in industry. The old Gordon lands of Glenbuchat on Donside, for example, passed first to Lord Braco, then to the 4th Earl of Fife, and he subsequently let the glen to Lord Craven. The succeeding tenant, Lord Buckingham, built the lodge, and was himself followed by a succession of shooting tenants, several of whom were cotton tycoons. This pattern of constant change in ownership and occupancy was typical of many estates although some, like the Farquharson estates in Upper Deeside, remained with the same family throughout the period. Small estate villages developed around the laird's house and home farm, with game larders and kennels as at Glen Tanar or Delnabo, Tomintoul. Although the decline in the sport in terms of estate revenue continued in the inter-war and post-war periods, the letting of stalking rights and, more recently, venison sales remain significant components in estate revenues. The key to success of red deer management remains the availability of winter feed and shelter. Several estates and upland or hill farms have developed deer farming in a paddock situation, as the work of the Rowett Institute in Aberdeen has revealed that red deer are by far the most efficient convertors of fodder to meat — beating sheep, cattle and pigs.

The grousemoors, also ranged by red deer, occupy the dry moorlands in the altitudinal band between 400 m and 700 m (1310 ft and 2300 ft), particularly in upper Banffshire and Strathdon. The management of this resource is rather more intensive than that of the deerforest, as the grouse relies for its food on young heather shoots, the availability of which are dependent on recurrent firing (muirburn) of moorland over a fifteen year rotation. Reasonably intensive management of this type is well exemplified in upper Strathdon and in Glen Gairn and is responsible for the mosaic of different colours on the moor, reflecting varying stages of recolonisation following muirburn. Research work undertaken to discover the reason for fluctuations and overall decline in grouse numbers has revealed that grouse densities closely relate to the quality of the ground and moorland community. The better moors include green flushes where nutrient is washed out from localised areas of base-rich soils and where concentrated by natural drainage, it provides useful trace elements for grouse nutrition. In general terms, assuming uniform management practices, grouse bags are significantly higher on the base-rich schists of Glenshee than on the poorer acidic granites of Lochnagar. On the best moors where burning is consistently operated over the fifteen year cycle, and where base-rich localities occur, grouse densities may be five pairs per 2 ha (4.9 acres), but a more generally applicable figure might be five pairs per 8 ha (19.8 acres). Grouse moors are, however, subject to fluctuations in crop according to weather conditions during the nesting season, the relative severity of the preceding winter, as well as the ability to burn in the spring which is much dependent on weather conditions. Management aims at the maintenance of a heather monoculture (any trees regenerating are carefully burnt out) with the young heather shoots for feeding, and the older mature heather providing cover for nesting and from predators. The small and carefully controlled fires necessary to achieve an optimum mosaic require considerable resources in keeper control, and in many areas of low productivity and extensive land uses, the number of keepers employed has markedly declined in the post war period. The result is that many Grampian moors carry lank old heather of knee-height or higher, quite incompatible with even modest grouse densities. Thus the scenic heather moors enjoyed by visitors and locals alike are basically fire-climax communities with periodic burning generally preventing the re-establishment of native pine and birch woodland, on the assumption that there are nearby seed sources. This can be clearly seen on the moors of the Lecht and Glen Cairn where scattered open copses of native pine which have reached an age sufficient to survive the rapidly moving moorland fire are a feature of the moor. On the burnt patches, stone clearance heaps and hut circles intermingle with clachans and shieling foundations, all indicating settlement and subsistence activities in the past. On the flatter interfluves as in the Ladder Hills of Strathdon, the wetter moors developed on these peaty surfaces were drained in the early 20th century in an attempt to improve heather growth and thus grouse densities, but these efforts have proved ineffective.

Increasingly the upland areas of Grampian have been subject to afforestation, both of grouse moor and marginal agricultural land (see Chapter 14). The relatively tree-less nature of the uplands has been transformed in the last two hundred years by plantations of pine and larch initially, and in the present century, by faster North American conifers such as Sitka and Lodgepole Pine. In the large private estates, forestry has long been practised as part of the diverse estate land use pattern, and replantings quickly followed the extensive fellings of the World Wars — often producing a varied landscape in which both coniferous and broad-leaved species have a role. Particularly since the Second World War, the Forestry Commission, and since the early 1970s, several Private Forestry enterprises, have planted land in the higher and poorer areas — the extensive planting of Glenbuchat in Strathdon is an example of how the agricultural frontier has retreated in the face of commercial forestry. The upper limit of tree growth for commercial purposes has risen with new species, improved provenance and better planting techniques, and may be as high as 500 m (1640 ft) in some localities, but is governed in detail by wind exposure, decreasing growing season temperatures and thin soils. The costs of forestry establishment are high in these upland areas because of the need to drain, fertilise and enclose plantations with deer and rabbit-proof fences. Such constraints tend to promote large forest blocks where establishment and fencing costs are relatively low by comparison with a mosaic of smaller enclosures, but the potential for forestry-hill farming integration through shelter and road access benefits is reduced. In Glen Livet the signs of such integrated designs implemented in the 1960s are still evident. Where such integrated schemes are feasible, they at least in theory help to slow down the inexorable retreat of permanent settlement from the upland but deserted steadings and cottages are eagerly sought after as second homes by urbanites. The deep bite of upland depopulation is well shown by rural school closures — in the upland parishes of Glenbuchat and Strathdon, there were six schools in the late 19th century, three by the 1930s, and now only two, with secondary education served from the lowland centre of Alford. Such examples could be repeated from many parts of both upland and lowland Grampian and clearly highlight the considerable population redistribution from countryside to town which has been ongoing for the last hundred years. No satisfactory palliative, if indeed one is desirable, has yet been identified and proven successful.

Around 60% of rural Grampian is designated a "less favoured" area under the Council of Europe Directive of 1975 characterised by "mountain, hill farming and farming in less favoured areas". Within such areas specific policies exist to sustain agricultural activities in the form of grant aids, some to ensure the continuation of farming and hence a minimum population threshold, others more concerned with the conservation of the countryside. In the future, because of immense EEC surpluses in agricultural products, it seems likely that hill farming support may be broadened to include grants aimed at the conservation and management of wildlife and landscape within a broader-based uplands policy. Common Agricultural Policy limitations on production in meat and cereals mean that farmers will be looking at cost reductions rather than increased production as a means of balancing their books. In this context attention may be drawn to the iniquity of "headage payments" on sheep stock which encourages heavy stocking, but with no penalty for stock in poor condition and low lambing percentages. The expansion of forestry is viewed with alarm in certain quarters. About 15% of Grampian Region is currently under commercial forestry, mainly conifers. With the exception of lowland Moray with about 30% woodland cover, the commercial woodland tends to form a band along the hill edge and middle slopes, with fingers up the major valleys of the Dee, Don and Spey. In the lowlands, woodland may double up as game cover, shelter and stock grazing in winter. In the remote inaccessible upland glens of Deeside there are important native woodland remnants. The extent of future planting for commercial purposes depends on levels of government funding and grants and also on the possibilities for land acquisition, the latter depending on the value in market terms of the land in question, and also on the flexibility of the statutory bodies in their decision-taking. In Grampian, the Forestry Commission has identified a number of upland areas as potentially suitable for planting. These include the upper Dee and Clunie catchments [up to 500 m (1640 ft)], Glen Dye, the Ladder Hills and the Moors of Troup in Banffshire. In recent years private forestry companies are playing an increased role, competing with the state forest enterprise for ground, and this seems likely to increase in the future. In remote areas, where effects on population are relatively small because of low densities, plantings nonetheless appear to conflict with deer sports, chiefly deer movements and wintering grounds, with nature conservation interests (effects on moorland bird habitats) and with landscape, although conceivably planting might locally benefit hill farming activities. In addition, extensive afforestation of river catchments is viewed with suspicion by water engineers and fishermen alike. An increasingly important land use dimension to be superimposed on existing upland land use systems is recreation and the demands of nature conservation. Although largely without the Grampian Region yet close enough to excite controversy and generate access patterns from Grampian are the Cairngorm Mountains. These have merited over 40 years of identification and designation as an area of outstanding scenery and nature conservation interest. In 1954, some 250 km^2 (96 $mile^2$) became designated as a National Nature Reserve, and National Scenic Area status came into operation in 1979. In addition to these nationally awarded designations, the Cairngorms have been singled out as special by bodies like the Council of Europe and by several International Conservation Bodies. Yet most of the area remains under private ownership. As a Less Favoured Area — remote and with very low resident populations — there is clear potential for conflict between the conservation lobby and those whose job it is to supplement the declining job opportunities in forestry and farming with the promotion of further tourist-related economic growth, both in summer and winter. The Lecht and Glenshee winter sports centres have both expanded their uplift facilities in recent years. In these superb upland areas of Grampian, while all might agree that the resources are "outstanding hills, good snow for skiing, scenery, wildlife and wilderness", the last two decades have seen a hardening attitude by most of the interested parties, to an extent that any development or extension of an existing facility is viewed as deleterious to the interest of at least one group — thus multi-purpose land use is not always feasible, or indeed desirable. At present, agriculture and related industries account for about 8% of employment in Grampian (the comparative Scottish figure is 6%). Any decline in agricultural productivity would have knock-on effects in industries such as food processing.

In modern times, the city of Aberdeen has increasingly dominated its geographical hinterland. The seeds of its success were sown in the Victorian and Edwardian period when a new breed of industrialists and traders, bankers and lawyers combined highly successful business careers with the highest burgh offices. Notable amongst these were Alexander Anderson, the Hadden family and George Thompson, respectively lawyer, millowner and shipowner. Amongst the four Scottish cities, Aberdeen was consistently the most versatile and varied in its economy, avoiding excessive specialisation and hence narrow market dependence. Although the important 18th century textile industry was seriously affected by the financial crisis of 1848 (all but three mills then in existence going under at that time), the city displayed an economic resilience which in a laissez-faire situation was presumably quite fortuitous, and new investments were made and jobs created as the older enterprises declined or folded. As textiles declined, shipbuilding, engineering, granite and eventually fishing filled the gap and increased urban job opportunities. The railway network and the developing port were vital struts in the growth. Aberdeen recruited its growing population almost exclusively from Grampian, hence reducing the intensity of the social problems felt in Glasgow, for example. High density populations were nonetheless crammed in accommodation close to factories, and while there were gutters and pavements, indoor sanitation was limited even in the upmarket residences in upper Union Street. As the century progressed, and particularly in the last decades of the 19th century, there was increasing municipal enterprise and involvement in sanitation, public water supply, electricity, tramways, refuse disposal, and eventually, in the 1890s, a modest investment of funds in council housing. Eventually the Town Council was to become a significant employer in its own right, in a situation where the Victorian profit motive was considered less important. Aberdeen's thirst for water illustrates the growth of the city over the last hundred and fifty years. The 1829 Act drew on the Dee for domestic supplies — from the vicinity of the Bridge of Dee at a rate of 4600 litres (1000 gallons) per minute, and fed to the Waterhouse at 478-484 Union Street, providing 9.52 million litres (1.2 million gallons) per day. In the 1860s, a lawyer's house at 233 Union Street had no bathroom, no hot water in the kitchen, no water at all above the first floor level, and a dry privy. In 1866, the Cairton Scheme including Invercannie near Banchory, was opened with storage at Mannofield, demand then being envisaged at 9.2 million litres (2 million gallons) per day, freeing the Waterhouse for other purposes. By 1885, Aberdeen's demands had increased to 27.6 million litres (6 million gallons) per day, requiring further Dee abstraction and additional storage at Mannofield, Slopefield and Cattofield. By the 1950s, daily consumption stood at 46 million litres (10 million gallons) per day, and at present is nearer 92 million litres (20 million gallons) per day, necessitating a new reservoir at Cults in lower Deeside. Efficient urban sewage systems awaited the last decades of the 19th century, with the major outfall at Girdleness, fed by a tunnel passing under the harbour — which took seven years to build and was only completed in 1907. A new offshore sewage outfall at the Bay of Nigg is currently nearing completion. The first Gaslight Company began operation in 1824, and the gasometer, by then under municipal enterprise, dates from the 1890s. The first public lighting by electricity appeared in Union Street and Castle Street in 1894, and the Millburn Street Station was opened in 1901. In the matter of prisons, Aberdeen was remarkably advanced — the West Prison or Bridewell opened in Rose Street in 1809 including the first steam-fired central heating to be installed in the city.

In the 1840s, around 14,000 out of a then burgh population of 63,000 were employed in the textile industry. At the same time, there were no less than six shipbuilding yards active around the estuary of the Dee, as well as major comb and paper manufacturers. The main concentrations of millworkers and artisans were in the old weaving districts of Jack's Brae, Short Loanings and Leadside Road in the Lower Denburn, while a further concentration was housed at Woodside and Cotton near the clutch of Donside mills. Other incomers found accommodation in the Gallowgate-George Street areas and in Putachieside, the latter wiped off the face of the city by the construction of the New Market in 1842. Much of the local capital for investment in textile mills came from the landed gentry who formed business and marriage alliances with merchants already involved in the business. The main families were the Haddens, Leys, Milnes and Bannermans, and all were also active in local politics. As the century proceeded, there was increasing competition from southern textile mills who shared the twin advantages of local coal supplies and nearness to markets. The Aberdeen mills suffered greatly in the depression of 1848 with only Richards & Co. (linen) and Crombie (woollens) surviving. These have survived respectively at Broadford and Grandholm works, making world-wide reputations through quality products which compensate for peripheral location.

While textiles were expanding in the early 19th century, inshore fishing was by open boat and with the exception of salmon, supplied only the local market. There was a small fishmarket near the foot of the Shiprow. Aberdeen's fishing fleet in the 1860s consisted of around 120 open boats fishing for herring, and a further 112 engaged in inshore white fishing — with a total crewage of less than a thousand. Only from the 1870s did the introduction of the decked boat encourage a major investment in the industry — by which time Aberdeen had the important assets of railway links with the south, and the newly opened Albert Basin and associated site accommodation. In the 1880s, experimentation in steam-powered drifting and trawling proved successful, thus paving the way for the steam trawler. A new fish market was opened in the Albert Basin in 1889. Steam trawling was the catalyst for many subsidiary industries — supplying coal, ice and stores as well as shipbuilding and marine engineering, and by 1900, when textiles were at a low point, fishing had become the most important industry in the city — with some 25,000 out of a burgh population of 153,000 at least in part dependent on the trawling industry. At that time, over 200 trawlers were operating out of Aberdeen, most of them built in the city shipyards.

Like fishing, granite production was principally a creature of the later 19th century and the first third of the 20th century. The Aberdeen granite trade was characterised by three main features. The production of paving stones was already ongoing by the early 1800s, but was overlapped by the quarrying and cutting of large blocks for construction purposes — fuelled by the Victorian period of expansion of the city from the 1830s and the demand for materials for bridge and dock works throughout Britain and often beyond even to the southern hemisphere, while the manufacture of monumental granite stone took off in the 1840s, following MacDonald's pioneering activities in polishing carried out in his West North Street yard. Apart from the quarry-workers operating in a group of local quarries, several of which like Rubislaw are now abandoned and absorbed into the city boundaries, by the 1850s, the monumental side of the industry was employing over 2000 men, operating on steam powered machinery. Until the 1900s, almost all materials were derived from local quarries, although in the last decade of the 19th century, foreign imports doubled to 13,000 tons per year (by comparison with the 0.5 million tons produced locally in the area). The granite industry remained relatively buoyant until the First World War, following which the decline in terms of production and employment set in. The widespread association of Aberdeen with the traditional industries of textiles, fishing, granite and shipbuilding conceals other important 19th century employers — including food preserving and processing, paper and comb manufacture, and engineering.

The expansion of the city in the grand granite style of Victorian and Edwardian architecture epitomised by Union Street, Albyn Terrace and Queen's Road was based on the profits from traditional industries and on the service and professional job opportunities associated with the growth of Aberdeen as the regional centre for Grampian, a position which the town had consistently held since early medieval times. In their original form, these industries were based mainly on local products and local markets. As they grew, products like wool and granite were increasingly supplemented and replaced by imported raw materials — and the finished products increasingly sought external markets. Thus in the 20th century, many found themselves at a relative disadvantage compared with southern rivals whose transport costs were lower and whose locations were nearer the ultimate market.

In the 1950s and 1960s, the hinterland of Aberdeen was experiencing a slow but steady loss of population mainly by outmigration, while in the period 1961-71, the city population also fell. Then, as now, Aberdeen accounted for nearly half of the population of Grampian. The employment trend of the mid-sixties was a continuing contraction in Aberdeen's manufacturing base, and this contraction has accelerated in the period 1971-81, with some 7000 of the city's 20,000 manufacturing jobs shed.

Many of Aberdeen's best-known and long established firms trimmed their sails during the period including Wiggins Teape, Richards, SAI and Aberdeen University Press. This contraction and the effects of the national recession have been largely concealed and in part compensated for by Aberdeen's current position as the undisputed offshore oil and gas capital of Europe.

The first oil was brought onshore to Grampian in 1975 when the forward forecasts envisaged perhaps a maximum of 20 North Sea fields to be developed, possibly generating around 10,000 jobs peaking in 1981 (see Chapter 17). In fact, these forecasts have proved to be underestimates, and in 1985, Grampian had secured some 52,000 oil-related jobs based on 31 fields now in production with a further seven under development. Since 1980, when the oil-related jobs in Grampian totalled 33,000, the region has consistently accounted for around 70% of the Scottish total of such jobs. The effects of these opportunities on the city are clear to see. Since 1971, while the total Scottish population has fallen by around 50,000, Grampian has increased by 29,000. Gordon District (which includes a part of the north-west city suburban fringe and a part of its inner commuting belt) over the same period experienced an absolute rise in population of 14,000 (32% increase), with the growth mainly by immigration. There have been major new areas of private house construction notably in the Bridge of Don and Portlethen areas; the number of city hotel bedrooms doubled between 1970 and 1980, as did the number of restaurants. New office space has risen by around 6% per annum since 1979, much of it peripherally located in the expanding industrial estates at Dyce, Altens and Bridge of Don. The old Rubislaw granite quarry in the west end of Aberdeen, a hole from which it is claimed that much of Aberdeen came, is now appropriately ringed by oil company offices, administering an industry which directly or indirectly accounts for 28% of all jobs within Grampian. Aberdeen has geared itself up for its new opportunities by developing a much improved infrastructure — a £15m harbour improvement scheme allowing 24 hour access to eight oil supply bases, a new airport terminal to ease a tenfold increase in fixed wing passenger traffic between 1969 and 1980, and a heliport which is arguably the world's busiest. The arrival of oil and gas-related employment is doubly welcome in the face of decline in the traditional industries and the national recession. The city has thus weathered the national recession significantly better than most of its equivalents. Forward predictions based on likely offshore development activity have suggested that space may have to be found for a further 31,000 new houses in the Aberdeen area before the end of the present century. At the moment of writing, setting on one side the arguments about the accuracy of the predicted need, opinion is sharply divided on the merits of dispersal amongst existing settlements, as opposed to identifying a new town site, possibly in the Banchory-Devenick area. Wherever the required housing is located, there is a clear need for improved access from the commuting zone to the city, including a third crossing of the Don. The hydrocarbon fuelling of the Aberdeen economy has not extended beyond the city and its immediate commuting zone, with the exception of outliers at Peterhead and St. Fergus. The vast majority of Grampian continues to face a future with a slim base of primary and service activities. The traditional employers of fishing, agriculture, whisky distilling and food processing are extremely vulnerable to external influences such as EEC fishery and agricultural policies. The Regional Council have attempted to stimulate further economic activity in the rural areas through an advance factory programme which provides serviced industrial premises for letting. These have, however, tended to be established in the rather larger settlements such as Huntly and Elgin, although some smaller advance factories have been established at Dufftown, Insch and Ballater. Nonetheless, the continuing pattern of depopulation in the landward areas remains a subject of real concern for the future. Although the avowed regional planning strategy of the early seventies was to spread growth and employment investment throughout Grampian, the concentration of growth in the Aberdeen and Peterhead areas was perhaps inevitable in the face of the free market economy. In fact, it seems likely that only the immediate environs of Aberdeen, Elgin and Peterhead are likely to experience growth in population into the 1990s. Continued rural depopulation in Grampian seems inevitable in the face of diminishing opportunities in the traditional employers of agriculture, fishing, forestry and tourism.

Increasingly, the dominant urban market and employment node generated by Aberdeen is having an influence on its countryside within a belt around 60 km (37 miles) in width — well beyond the Aberdeen City District planning sphere of control and perhaps explaining the occasional conflict in development priorities emerging between Grampian Region and Aberdeen City District. Within this regional city hinterland, set within a predominance of farmland and woodland, there are nodes of economic and residential development — both old and new settlements. Within the commuting zone, there is a very wide choice of living environments — from Milltimber to the Forest of Birse. For this zone, the city provides work space, shopping space and social space, as well as appropriate facilities for its residents. The complex and busy flows of people and goods engendered by this population pattern involves radial movement towards Aberdeen along the main trunk roads, but also cross-city movements towards shopping supermarkets and industrial estates which are increasingly situated on the city edge. Such traffic movements are particularly difficult to solve satisfactorily in the case of Aberdeen which is located on the coast (and hence immediately loses a half of its potential expansion arc) while the remainder of its traffic flow is complicated by the twin crossings of the rivers Dee and Don. An improved transportation net appears to be a clear priority in the light of Aberdeen's emergence as the centre-point of a congested commuting pattern by private car.

With a population of over 0.5 million and a land area of 8800 km^2 (3400 $miles^2$), Grampian is the third largest of the nine Scottish regions in both size and population. The creation of the region from the old counties of Aberdeenshire, Banffshire, Kincardine and Moray in 1975 coincided with the first oil to be brought onshore from the North Sea. The decline in employment prospects in the traditional industries of agriculture, fishing, granite and shipbuilding has meant that the prosperity of the region is currently based increasingly on the oil and gas industry. Remarkable changes in the economic structure of the region have taken place over the last 15 years leading to an improved infrastructure in those areas directly affected by the oil-fuelled economy, but growth in employment opportunities has been strictly localised to the coastal seaboard, notably in the Aberdeen City and Peterhead areas. This growth has tended to mask considerable problems faced over the major part of the region which still await solution.

Part three

GENERAL

Chapter thirteen

AGRICULTURE

Dr. Graham Dalton

GENERAL DESCRIPTION

Agriculture contributes an estimated £350m towards the regional economy (Johns and Leat 1985) or 8% of the total compared with 4% for Scotland and 2% for the U.K. Its importance is augmented by both its downstream and upstream effects on suppliers and processors, some 22% of regional output being closely allied with agriculture. There are especially close linkages between livestock farmers and meat processors and slaughterers. Slightly more than half of regional agricultural output (56%) is from livestock although this proportion has been falling. The North East Survey (Catt and Rees 1969) showed that in 1966, 65% of agriculture's output was from livestock.

The main products of the region include finished cattle, pigs, sheep, dairy products and poultry. Barley is by far the most important crop although the area devoted to wheat, oilseed rape and peas has been increasing. Seed potatoes are an important export crop. The region exports some 60% of its total output mainly to England but in recent years an increasing surplus of grain has been exported out of the region's ports, mainly to Europe (Entwhistle and Crabtree 1985).

The region is traditionally farmed on a rotational basis with mixed farming the rule. The emphasis has shifted to more intensive grain production in response to market forces, new technology and support arrangements. Cattle are a capital and labour intensive enterprise and numbers have fallen in response to high real interest rates, a measurable shift in consumer preference against red meat (Revell 1983) and declining real prices. A most striking development has been the emergence of a sizeable cereal surplus for export.

The region's land is of variable quality, a good measure of productivity being the ratio of cash crops to total crops and grass as reported in the annual census. This is graphed on a parish basis in Figure 23. It

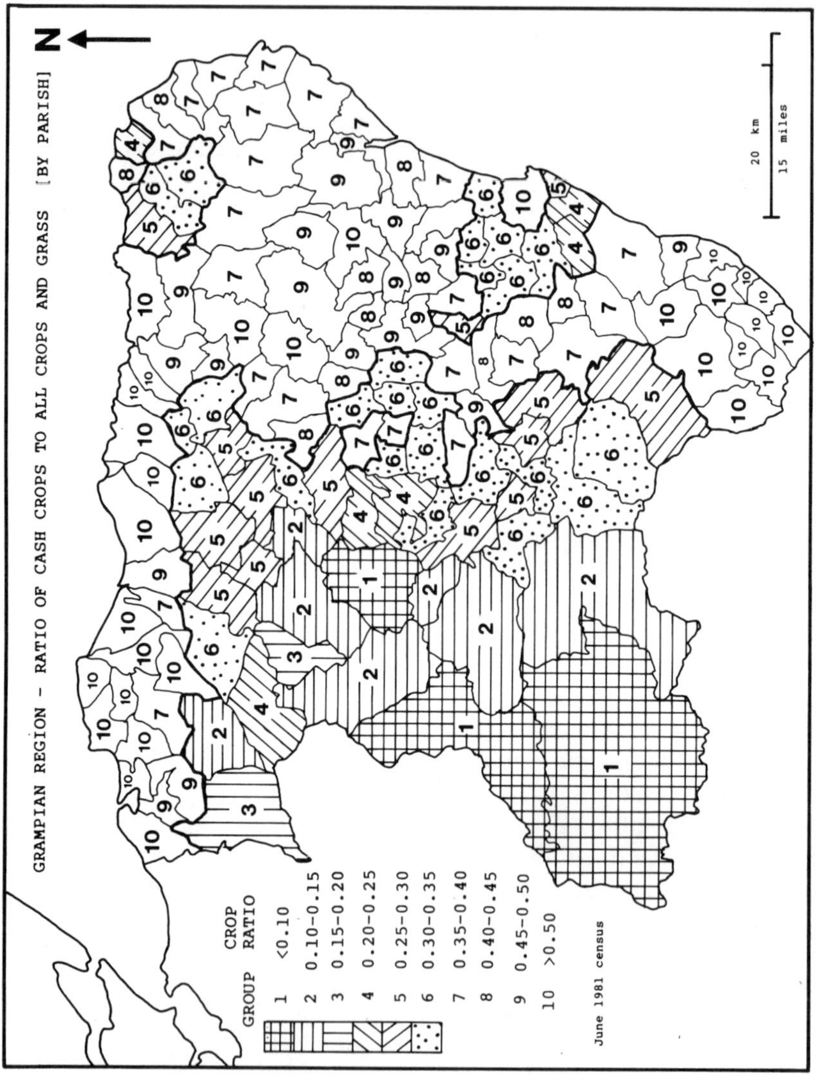

Figure 23 — Ratio of cash crops to all crops and grass, Grampian Region.

shows how the better land is confined to the coastal and central parts of the region except for the hinterland of Aberdeen and Fraserburgh. The solid line depicts a realistic boundary of physically disadvantaged parts of the region.

The farmed area has not changed significantly over time at almost 400,000 ha (988,000 acres) augmented by a further 200,000 ha (494,000 acres) of rough grazing. Each hectare of crops and grass produces on average sales of approximately £500. Cash crops and stock feed are grown on 190,000 ha (469,300 acres) so that almost half the cultivated area is ploughed each season, mostly for barley (136,000 ha; 335,920 acres).

Cattle are by far the major livestock enterprise, about 0.5 million animals of all types being kept (one beast per acre of grass). The dairy herd is small in numerical terms at 33,000 cows, a much larger beef breeding herd of 80,000 being found, for the most part in the uplands. Sheep numbers have been increasing with ewe numbers at around 0.25 million. Half of Scotland's pigs are to be found in the region. Currently the total pig population is around 200,000 or the output of some 20,000 sows, but numbers have been consistently falling.

Financial Trends And Structural Change

There are serious concerns in the industry at the present time over the adjustments necessary to cope with consistently falling real incomes and low returns on capital at a time of unprecedented high real interest rates as shown in Figures 24 and 25. Profitability sank to new lows in the very wet year of 1985 and has exacerbated the situation.

Part of the reason for this fall in incomes has been the fall in real prices for all of the main products of the region. Cereal prices kept up with inflation in the mid seventies on the back of the international grain price boom but have fallen by 24% in real terms between 1981 and 1986. Sheep prices have begun to move down after the peak year of 1984 while store cattle prices in 1985 were only 91% of 1981 levels with little technical progress or cheaper inputs to offset this.

The major adjustments made in the industry have been a reduction in the number of farmers and workers, an expansion in the size of farm and concentration on fewer enterprises. Currently there are some 6000 significant holdings in the region which support, given multiple holding operation, some 4791 farmers. This number has consistently fallen over the years, the North-east (including Nairn) supporting 15,578 holdings in 1950 (Catt and Rees 1969). The fall was particularly rapid in the 1970s but has slowed down recently. One of the reasons for this has been a stabilisation in the number of part-time farms which are growing in

Figure 24

NET FARM INCOME

N.F.I. (incl. BLSA*) PER FARM - UPLAND AND LOWLAND GRAMPIAN
1974/75 TO 1984/85 - thousands of pounds, 1985 prices

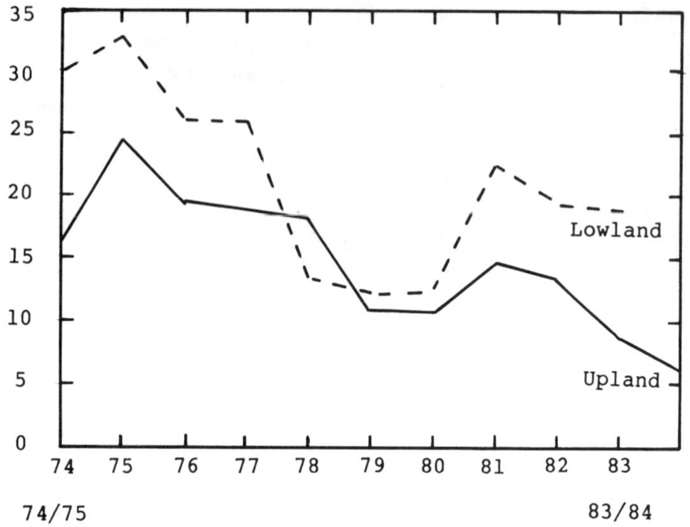

*BLSA = Breeding Livestock Appreciation

Figure 25

REAL RETURN ON TENANTS' CAPITAL

REAL RETURN ON TENANTS' CAPITAL PER FARM
UPLAND AND LOWLAND GRAMPIAN 1974/75 to 1983/84
PER CENT

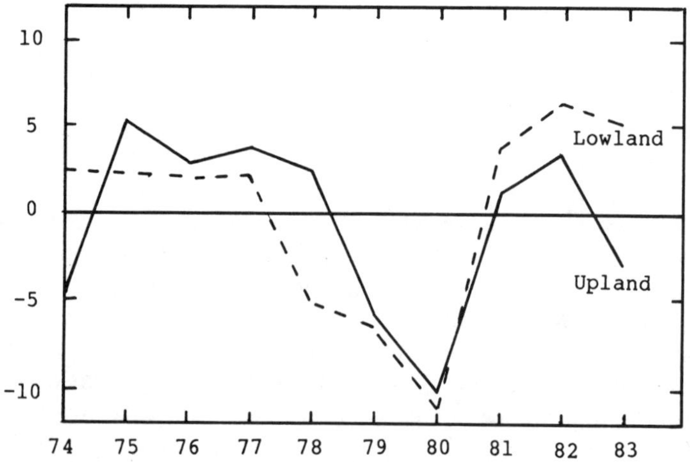

relative importance overall and absolutely in the uplands, as shown in Figures 26 and 27.

The profitability of farming is currently running around £100 per hectare so that to achieve a reasonable level of remuneration for a farm family something like 100 ha (247 acres) would be required to earn £10,000 per year. By comparison the average holding size is 62 ha (153 acres) of crops and grass or 83.5 ha (206 acres) per farmer. However, another pertinent phenomenon is the highly skewed distribution of farm size. Half the area of crops and grass is operated by 1117 units or 18% of the total. Forty-three per cent of farms (2724) control 80% of the cultivated area.

The number of hired agricultural workers who are mainly found on larger farms has fallen by 34% from 7723 in 1972 to 5097 in 1984. The rate of exodus is faster for women than for men, and for hired older workers than for younger people and members of the farm family. As with farms, so the relative importance of the part-time workforce has increased especially in the early 1970s and has since remained relatively stable. However, the number of part-time employees, at 931 in 1984, is small in relation to the total number of workers.

Modern farming involves close integration with the rest of the economy so that instead of a high degree of self-sufficiency and low cash requirements, farmers have increasingly to finance off-farm inputs. The demand for cash has also been increased through the growth in owner occupation to a current level in excess of 60% of the land. The acquisition of land and expansion by borrowing was an attractive proposition in the 1970s as inflation reached high levels, prices were well supported in an open-ended way and high rates of capital grants were available. Latterly, the scene has changed dramatically as real interest rates have reached high levels, land values have fallen by as much as 50% in 1985 and the downward pressure on profits has continued. Grant rates have also recently been cut to the levels shown in Table 7.

The average amount of tenant's capital used per hectare for a mixed farming operation is about £1,200 with more required on dairy farms and less on arable units. Total assets, including land, are about £2,000 per ha (Haughs 1985). An average farm in upland parts of the region would normally require £90,000 of tenant's capital, businesses here being smaller than in the lowlands where assets typically total £200,000.

Finance for farming, given the low returns on the main asset, land, is always difficult to service. This problem is compounded at a time of rapidly rising land values such as occurred during the 1970s and the need for individual businesses to grow to maintain incomes. Traditionally, the problem was eased by landownership and farming operations being

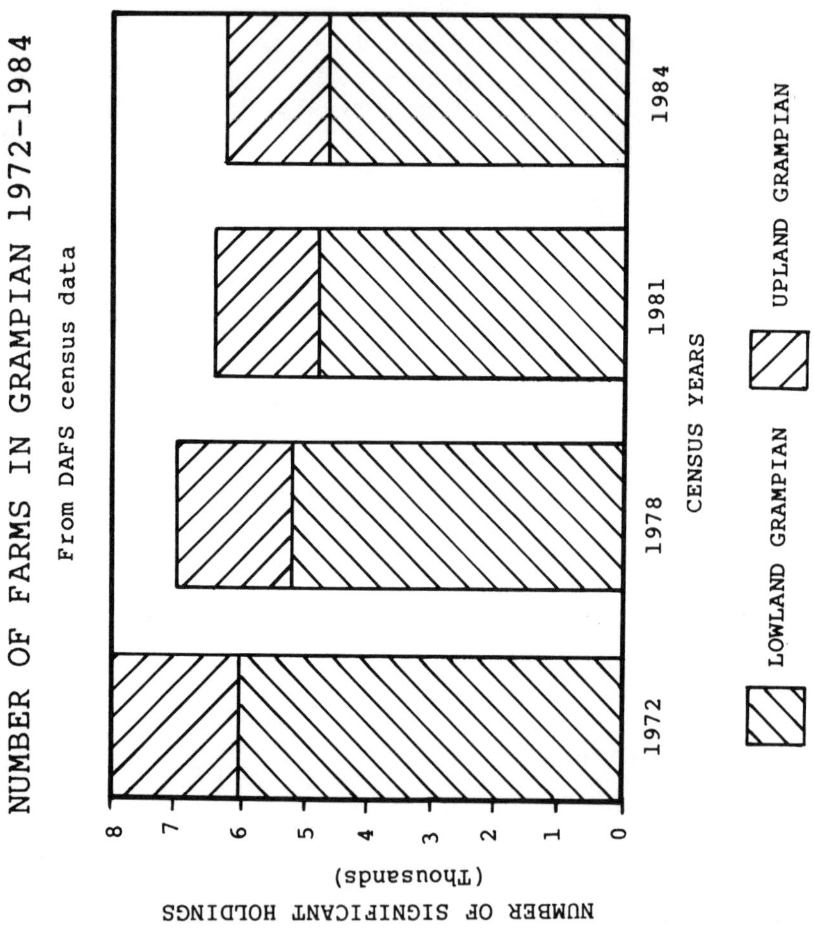
NUMBER OF FARMS IN GRAMPIAN 1972-1984
From DAFS census data
NUMBER OF SIGNIFICANT HOLDINGS
(Thousands)
0
1
2
3
4
5
6
7
8
1972
1978
1981
1984
CENSUS YEARS
LOWLAND GRAMPIAN
UPLAND GRAMPIAN

Figure 26

separate activities, but since the war taxation arrangements, inflation and security of tenure have all combined to stimulate owner occupation by both farmer tenants and landlords themselves.

New arrangements for the provision of finance are beginning to emerge. In the late 1970s financial institutions entered the land market using sale and leaseback arrangements. Essentially, existing landowners sold their farm to the institution, usually at a lower price than vacant possession value and then rented the same farm on a normal tenancy at a charge of 3½% - 5% on the capital value. The institutions have not been buying land in recent years.

Partnerships between landowners and farmers are beginning to replace traditional tenancies. The agreement normally lasts for 8 - 10 years with various arrangements for the provision of capital by both parties. The essential point of the agreement is that a tenancy is not created (NOSCA 1984).

In the current situation the average farm will not be generating sufficient profit to cover personal drawings and hence net worth will fall. Borrowings will increase or assets must be liquidated. It is therefore

TABLE 7

AGRICULTURAL IMPROVEMENT SCHEME GRANT RATES

	EEC	
	Non LFA	LFA
	%	%
Hedges, Dykes etc.	30	60
Handling and Storage of Waste	30	60
Shelter Belts	15	60
Hardwood Shelter Belts	30	60
Energy Saving Investments	15	30
Drainage and Water Supply	15	30
Roads	15	20
Buildings (Framework only), Yards	15	30
Fences, Pens, Dips, etc.	15	30
Bracken Control, Muirburn	15	30
Reseeding and Improving Grassland	—	30
Laying Down Permanent Grass on Cropping Land	15	30
Fish Farming Facilities	5	10
Tourism and Crafts Facilities	—	25
Arterial Drainage	—	—
Preparation of Improvement Plan	15	30

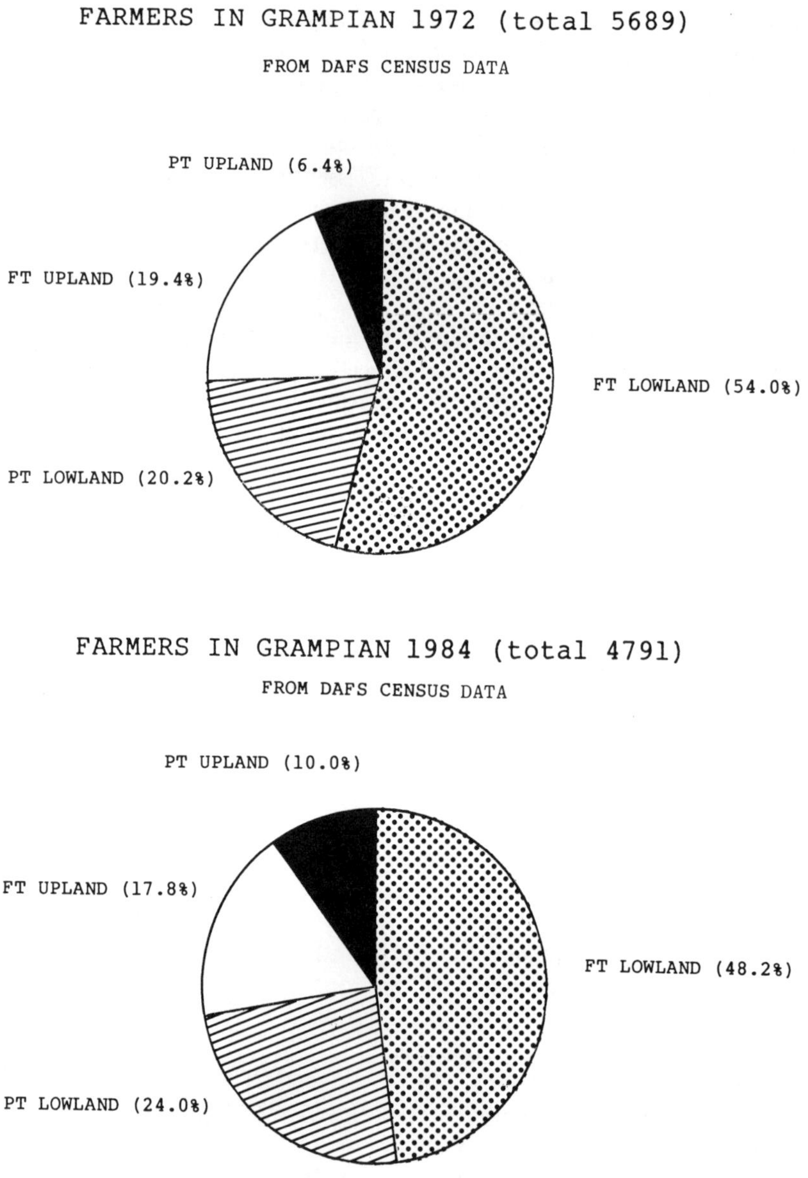

Figure 27 — Farmers in Grampian Region, 1972.

likely that further structural change must occur with fewer people deriving their livelihood, at least in full, from farming. The support of rural economic activity is one of the main reasons for Hill Livestock Compensatory Allowances being paid on breeding cows and ewes in less favoured areas. These headage payments in 1986 amount to £54.50 per suckler cow, £6.75 per hill ewe and £4.50 for an upland ewe on land classified as severely disadvantaged and at half these rates, £27.25 per cow, £2.25 per ewe, on disadvantaged land. Most of the farms within the solid line in Figure 23 will receive these subsidies. In addition, all owners of suckler cows receive a subsidy of £25 per suckler cow and all breeding ewes qualify irrespective of land type for the ewe premium of £7.32 in 1985/86. There are also preferential grant rates paid to farms in less favoured areas under the Agricultural Improvement Scheme (see Table 7) which has recently replaced the old Farm and Horticulture Development Scheme. The new Scheme is subject to an overall limit of £35,000 of expenditure per man employed and the grants rates are 60% less than the old rates except for the installation of hedges, shelter belts, dykes and the handling and storage of waste.

The reduction in grant rates, together with the removal of enhanced first year capital allowances and the low returns on capital employed in farming are bound to reduce capital inputs over time. Farms in financial difficulty are a more dramatic manifestation of the way this adjustment is taking place. The average farm is not overborrowed with three-quarters of assets being owned and most of the borrowings in the form of an overdraft. Leasing of machinery is currently a popular and cheap method of finance and there is a substantial amount of "mart credit" for cattle. Nevertheless, there is a marked skewness in the incidence of debt, about 15% of farms in the region owning less than half their assets, a level which makes their long term survival unlikely (Crabtree 1984). A common test for the viability of a farm business is that rent and interest charges should not exceed 15% of farm output. Rents in the region are around £50 per hectare with new entrants paying substantially more. If the average output is £500 per hectare, then there is little room for borrowing. An owner-occupier could sustain an interest charge of £75 per hectare or borrow, at current interest rates, £500 per hectare. An average tenant after paying his rent could only borrow £166 per hectare and even then might not have the collateral to obtain this size of loan.

The fall in land values in 1985 to say an average of £1,250 per hectare (local factors are most important) will have reduced the net worth of every owner occupier. There are grounds for thinking that prices will fall further as expectations for the industry are bleak and the skewed distribution of debt closes down overborrowed farm businesses thus increasing the supply of land on the market. At the same time, the confidence of potential buyers is low and collateral values are falling.

RECENT DEVELOPMENTS IN ENTERPRISES

CEREALS

The area of land producing cereals has grown to more than 160,000 ha (395,200 acres) an increase of 35,000 ha (86,450 acres) since 1972, at the expense of stockfeed, mainly swedes and grass (See Table 8).

TABLE 8

TRENDS IN GRAMPIAN CROPPING

	1972 ha	1976 ha	1981 ha	1984 ha
Wheat	5867	3460	6221	16479
Barley	97921	115697	131562	136084
Oats	30689	15534	12575	8230
Cereals	134477	134691	150368	160793
Potatoes	5924	5428	6912	7224
Stockfeed	22945	24185	18538	16525
Total Cropped Area	165402	166495	175349	190201
Grass	226808	223813	218306	203400

Note: 1 hectare = 2.47 acres

The region produces around 660,000 tonnes of barley from 136,000 ha (335,920 acres). Half of this production is surplus to regional requirements and 200,000 tonnes are exported annually through the region's ports, notably through Peterhead (Entwistle and Crabtree 1985). The grain is exported to a variety of destinations including the Baltic and other northern European ports for further transhipment. Unfortunately, the cheapest ports for handling purposes are not deep enough to cope with large vessels of more than 3,500 tonnes nor is there sufficient throughput to justify the loading facilities for vessels of 25,000 tonnes and over which could give a competitive edge in markets farther afield. This rise in barley production is primarily explained by rising yields at a rate of 2% or 3% per year especially since winter barley was introduced less than 10 years ago.

The wheat area and yields have grown rapidly especially in the last few years. Production is now well in excess of 100,000 tonnes. The region and Scotland as a whole are in deficit especially as wheat is now used by distillers (Entwistle and Crabtree 1985). There has also been a dramatic rise in oilseed rape production to reach 2300 ha (5683 acres) in 1984. Peas were grown on 1400 ha (3459 acres) in 1984 but the harvest experience in

1985 could well reduce this crop's prospects. Oats is still an important crop at 8230 ha (20,336 acres) in 1984 but it is later and lower yielding than barley so that a continued decline is to be expected from the days when it was the predominant cereal grown. New crops such as Triticale are to be found on sandy soils but as yet despite official exhortation and subsidies it is hard to see a viable alternative to established crops.

The rise in cereal yields can partly be explained by new varieties and the swing to winter cereals. However, improved husbandry techniques are also important with repeated sprayings of growth regulators to prevent lodging at high fertiliser levels and to control fungal attacks such as mildew. Tramlines at regular spaced intervals throughout the crop are now a common sign of precision in modern cereal growing.

The demand for cereal storage and grading facilities has risen as production has grown. Prices are supported on a seasonal scale by intervention purchases and as a consequence of rising surpluses, quality standards including the bushel weight are becoming more important. Centralised and group grain storage facilities have been built as a result of enhanced rates of grants for such facilities plus the substantial economies of scale that exist both for plant and specialist marketing services.

The importance of grain to the region means that local farmers have more than a passing interest in the means for resolving the EEC cereal surpluses. Even in upland areas, the land used for cereal production has expanded. A reduction in price would of course be attractive to the region's livestock producers but intensive enterprises such as pigs and poultry would presumably benefit most and hence be more able to compete in the overall meat market.

Other Crops

Some 70% of the region's potato area of 7224 ha (17,850 acres) is devoted to seed production. Somewhat surprisingly, due to the quota system operated by the Potato Marketing Board, the area has increased by a third over the last ten years. The crop is expensive to grow, especially if seed is in short supply and returns can fluctuate markedly between seasons. The most important policy change in recent years was the removal of trade restrictions on the importation of potatoes from the rest of the EEC. It is therefore highly unlikely that the boom years of 1976 and 1977 caused by the English drought will recur. Potato yields are increasing which reduces the area planted and hence the demand for seed. Seed potato exports to England and to North Africa face tough competition especially from Dutch and Ulster producers. The enterprise has become highly specialised with large insulated controlled environment stores, box storage and handling, stone separation and mechanical harvesting, although school children still gather much of the crop.

Swedes are a traditional form of stockfeed but a switch has occurred to silage over the years. The crop can produce very high yields of digestible dry matter but it is a risky crop being prone to drought at establishment and frost in the winter. Precision sowing, chemical weed control and mechanical harvesting have reduced labour requirements of the crop much of which is grazed in situ for the winter fattening of sheep.

Specialised crops of local importance grown in the region include hardy nursery stock, bulbs, carrots and soft fruit. There are some good examples of co-operative ventures for bulbs and strawberries (Warren and Daw 1982). The lateness of the soft fruit harvest has the advantage of extending the fresh fruit season for retail outlets.

BEEF

There has been a contraction in the region's beef breeding herd (see Table 9) which is a source of quality, i.e. beef type, animals.

TABLE 9

CHANGES IN LIVESTOCK NUMBERS — JUNE CENSUS

	1972	1976	1981	1984
Dairy Cattle	40012	41012	34759	33475
Beef Breeding Herd	98704	107227	89476	80819
Beef Cattle over 1 year	231360	258541	225657	225522
Cattle under 1 year	155648	160349	148453	151030
Total Cattle	538065	580861	510540	490846
Ewes	200559	196673	223330	250731
All Sheep	546308	535198	602518	658568
All Pigs	326881	282015	220676	191791
All Poultry	2375544	1900061	1639244	1521335

Conformation and yield of saleable meat are well established criteria for assessing quality and price premia. Ten years ago the region supported over 100,000 cows, the current herd being the same size as that in the mid 1960s. Over this same period the most marked technical change has been the change over to continental sires notably the Charolais and Simmental at the expense of the Angus and Hereford. The progeny are faster growing, have leaner carcasses and reach heavier weights.

The breeding herd is not large enough to sustain the beef production industry in Grampian so that there is a sizeable importation of calves and store animals, including an important trade with Orkney (20,000 cattle per year). Over 60% of the cattle slaughtered in the region each year (almost 200,000 steers and heifers and 13,000 bulls) are born elsewhere (Revell and Johns 1985). Up until the mid 1970s around 50,000 of imported cattle were forward stores of Irish cattle but latterly they have been replaced by suckled calves and light stores (50-60,000). More recently the number of imported young calves from as far away as Somerset has increased to 70,000 in 1981/82 (Sutherland 1984). These changes reduce the costs of importation and also mean that an increasing proportion of the liveweight slaughtered is produced locally.

The introduction of dairy quotas in 1984, which has reduced the national dairy herd and the swing towards the Holstein breed among dairy cattle (which has poor conformation), has serious implications for both the quantity and quality of imported calves. There are two further uncertainties in the beef trade: namely the proposed banning of growth promoters in 1987 which increase growth rates and carcass quality (leanness) and is probably worth about £30 per animal in extra profit. Moreover, doubts over future price support arrangements also exist. Currently, prices are supported by intervention buying for either whole or parts of carcasses of the highest quality animals, usually at the time of lowest prices (autumn). In addition, UK producers receive a variable premium on the difference between the UK market price and a seasonally varying target price subject to a maximum payment of 16.25 pence per kg deadweight (£30 to £50 per animal). To receive this subsidy animals must not be over fat and must be of a satisfactory conformation. Current proposals from the EEC are to remove this subsidy (despite the fact that it keeps market prices lower) and to substitute a small headage payment up to a maximum of 50 animals. Intervention buying would continue but could well be more selective.

The beef industry is a good example of producer co-operation. All livestock auction markets are operated by a farmers' co-operative, Aberdeen and Northern Marts. The decline in beef production and the development of more integrated forms of production are forcing the closure of small country markets.

The society made a loss in 1985, the first in its history, and is currently undergoing substantial rationalisation of its activities and facilities. Another farmers' co-operative, Buchan Meat, operates a slaughtering and meat processing plant. It has pioneered some interesting developments in integrating production with market requirements through formal links with a major supermarket and the suppliers and finishers of store stock (Graham 1982). It also operates a sizeable barley beef group.

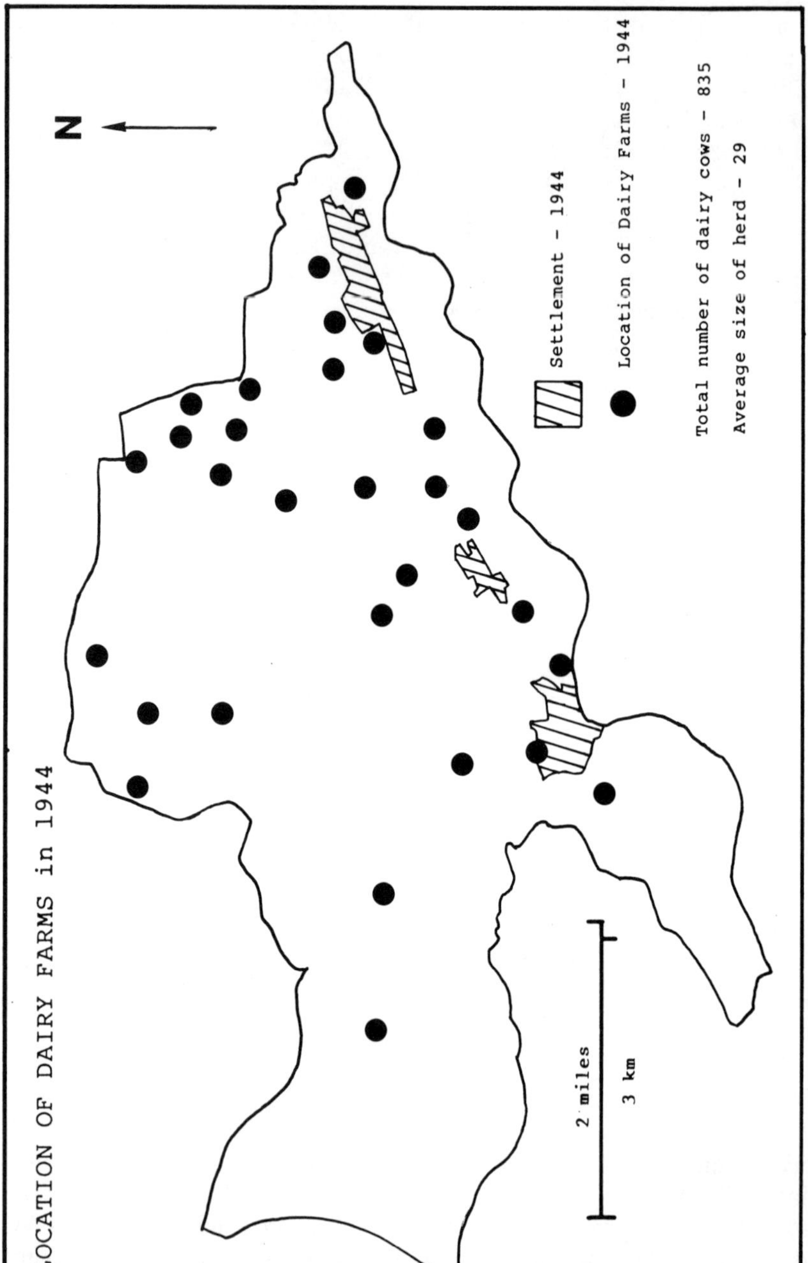

Figure 28 — Location of dairy farms in Peterculter parish 1944.

DAIRY

Dairying in the region is perhaps an extreme example of productivity, specialisation and concentration. The highest average herd size in the UK is to be found in the region with 212 registered producers keeping on average 120 cows. These cows yield on average 5150 litres (1133 gallons) per annum. Production in the Aberdeen Milk Board area has been fairly constant over the last decade at 120 million litres (26.4 million gallons) (MMB 1985). The average yield per cow 20 years ago was 3840 litres (845 gallons) and since then the number of cows kept has fallen from around 40,000 to 33,500 today.

The most spectacular change has been the fall in the registered number of producers from around 600 in the mid 1950s i.e. a reduction of 400 farms in 30 years. This is graphically demonstrated for a single parish (Peterculter) in Figures 28 and 29 (Adam 1985).

A crude estimate of the output per cow would be £1000 per annum. It follows that the total regional output from dairying would be approximately £33m or a tenth of the total, all from 212 businesses. Production is now pegged by quotas for the two Board areas; the Aberdeen Board and the North of Scotland Board which covers Moray.

SHEEP

There are 0.25 million breeding ewes in the region with slightly less than half of these in the upland area as defined in Figure 23. The expansion in sheep numbers is largely a result of the EEC sheepmeat price support regime which was introduced in October 1980. The rate of expansion has slowed but the growth of the national sheep flock maintains demand for breeding stock, a traditional product from the region. Greyface ewes for lowground fat lamb production are produced by crossing the Blackface ewe with a Leicester ram. Some low ground farmers act as a staging post in the provision of breeding stock by buying ewe lambs and selling them on as gimmers a year later.

Lambs are finished off summer grass, but also over the winter off swedes, lambs being imported from the north of Scotland for this purpose. An important trade is that from Shetland with 65,000 store lambs being shipped through Aberdeen each autumn.

Most of the lambs are sold through the live auction markets, mostly for export to the south and to France. The seasonal prices are supported by a variable premium scheme with its peak at Easter, its trough in August. The subsidy is based on the average UK price which tends to be lower in the summer months by as much as 15p per live kg or £3 per lamb in Scotland and the North-east (Rogie 1983).

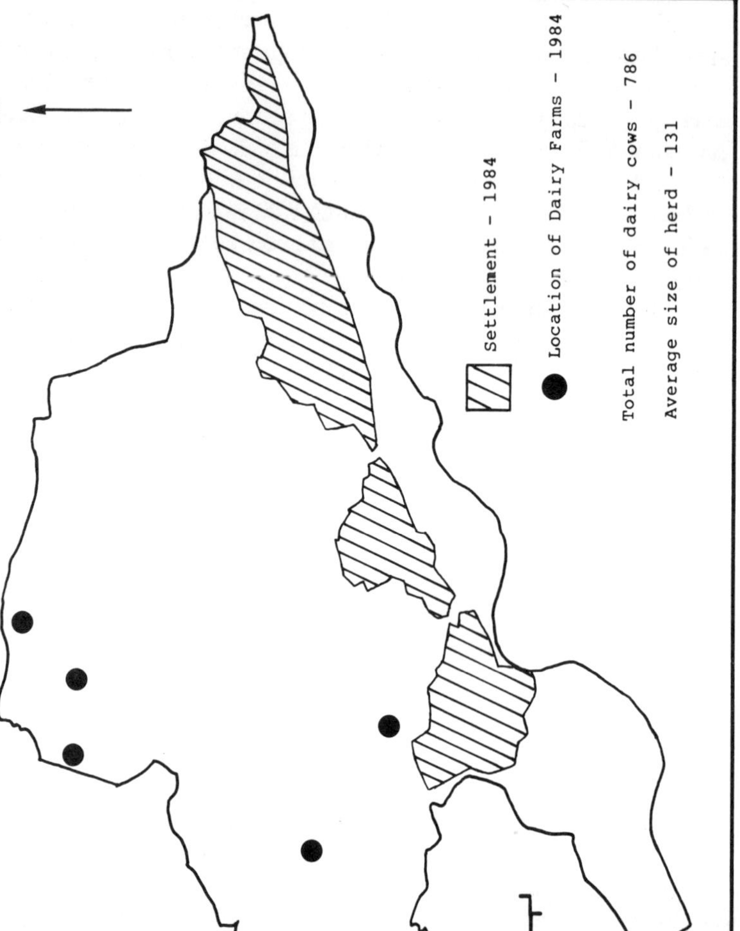

Figure 29 — Location of dairy farms in Peterculter parish 1984.

PIGS AND POULTRY

Pig production in Grampian went through a strong growth phase after 1950 right up until the early 1970s. The decline since 1973 can be explained by the fall in the price of pigs in relation to the feed price due to technological progress in terms of the number of pigs reared per sow per year and improvements in feed conversion efficiency (Fig 30). Grampian has, however, maintained its share of half the total of Scottish pigs but this represents only 2%-3% of the total for the UK. Currently there are around 20,000 breeding pigs in the region whereas in the peak year of 1973, 37,000 were kept which in turn was a 5-fold increase on the 1950 level.

Most of the pigs are kept in a few large units with only 449 holdings keeping pigs in 1982. The low pig population is attractive to pig breeding companies who require high health status and a number of companies multiply stock in the area. A feature of the industry is a highly successful marketing group, Grampian Pigs (Bisset 1982).

Poultry production has declined consistently since the immediate post-war years, with the importance of the region falling in relation to Scottish production. Approximately 1.5 million poultry were recorded in the June 1984 census compared with 4 million in 1950.

THE FUTURE

The trends towards ever larger and fewer farming businesses in Grampian as elsewhere are long established and there are few grounds for believing that they are about to change (Urquhart 1965; Naylor 1982; Adam 1985).

There have also been major shifts in product range, the swing towards cereals and oil seed and rape being especially marked. It is difficult to see the livestock industry being revived, except possibly for grain-fed animals if grain again becomes relatively cheap in the area. Sheep may continue to grow at the expense of suckler cows and fattening cattle.

The rate of labour exodus may slow due to the lack of alternative job opportunities within the region and part-time employment could well mean under employment for many in the future.

It is also highly likely that regional agricultural output could markedly decline, especially if prices for cereals are reduced in line with international levels or physical constraints to curb surpluses are imposed. In either event, less land in the region will be cash cropped although probably not on the better soils. Grazing animals will be kept more extensively and forestry with present tax arrangements will come down the hill especially if planning controls are relaxed.

Farms that do remain will continue to expand and will be able to

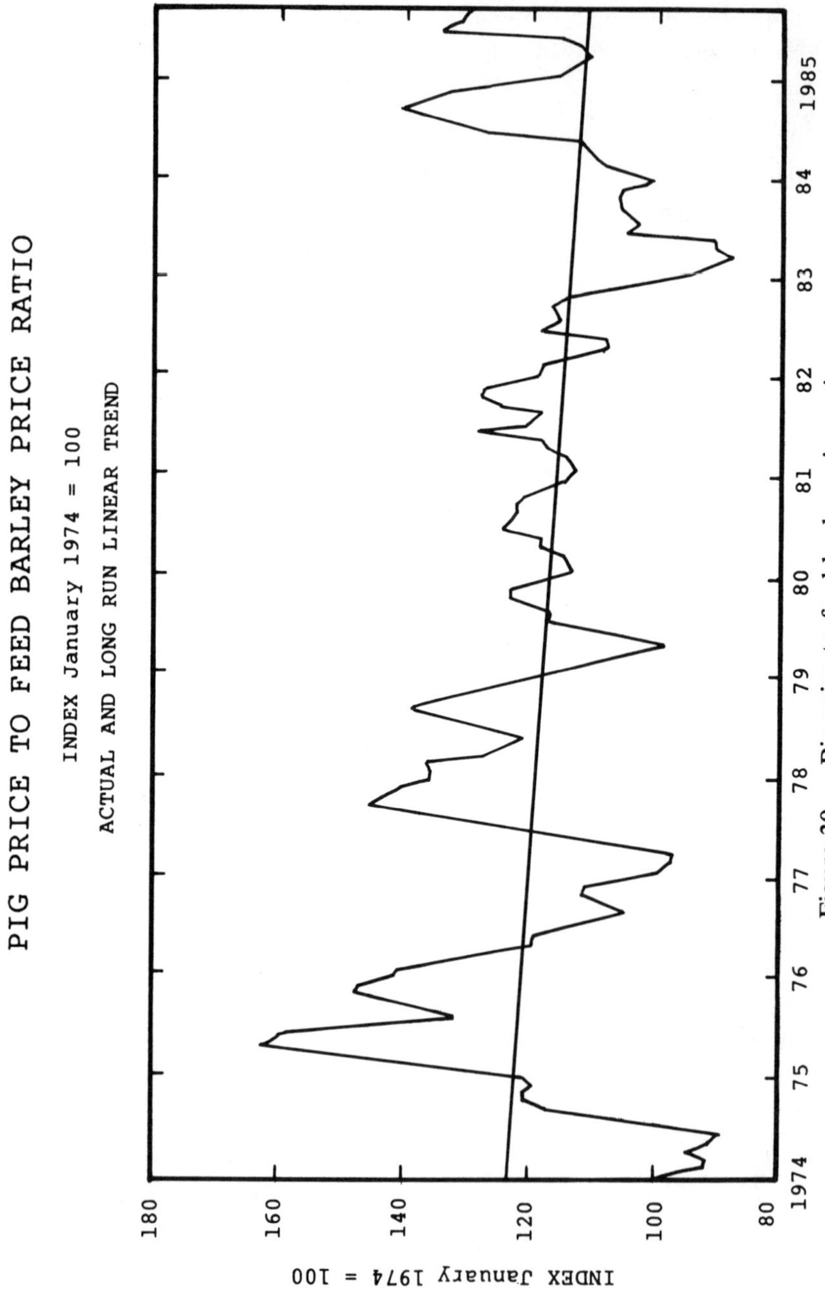

Figure 30 — Pig price to feed barley price ratio.

produce output at competitive levels of cost. It is to be expected that there will be a more rapid turnover of farmers than hitherto as those in financial difficulties are forced out of business.

Finally, developments in agricultural policy may arrest or compensate for the above changes. It is likely that highly discriminating support will be available on social or conservation grounds for farms in particularly poor or beautiful areas.

Chapter fourteen

FORESTRY

Mr Donald Cumming

INTRODUCTION

To many people the ever increasing extent of forests and woodlands on our landscape may appear a disturbing intrusion into our "Status Quo". It is true that in this crowded island where virtually every piece of land is put to some use, the introduction of forestry means that this is done at the expense of some other usage. In this region it is hill and upland farming, or sporting activities, particularly grouse, which suffer the losses. This section of the book seeks to demonstrate that forestry is not an intruder but a traditional and beneficial user of land, reflecting the economic changes which impinge on the country as a whole.

The increasing overproduction of grain, milk and meat within the EEC and the steps being contemplated to control these surpluses throw a great shadow over the marginal agricultural areas of the Grampian Region. One must consider forestry as a legitimate and useful alternative and this section seeks to show that we are repeating a historical past and that the forests and woodlands provide a wide range of benefits. These benefits include the provision of gainful employment, the production of a raw material for industry, the amelioration of the quality of life through landscaping, shelter, environmental habitats for wild life and the creation of a medium in which to enjoy leisure and recreation.

THE NATURAL FACTORS

An understanding of a land based resource requires some knowledge of the factors which nature has bestowed upon the area. The topography is dominated by the high Cairngorms whose maximum height of 4300 ft (1400 m) forms the western boundary of the region. Northwards, eastwards and southwards are undulating bare-topped ridges forming the catchment areas of the river valleys of the Findhorn, Spey, Deveron, Don, Dee and North Esk and flattening out into three plains of the Laigh of Moray in the north, the Buchan platform on the east and the Howe of the Mearns in the south. Altitude and steepness of slopes greatly determine the land usage. Arable agriculture seldom thrives above 1000 ft (300 m) elevation on steep slopes and in very wet areas.

The climate is primarily cold and dry. Rainfall on the Moray coast is one of the lowest recorded in Scotland, averaging 625 mm (25 in) and reaching 1500 mm (60 in) in the high Cairngorms. The bulk of the region lies in the 1020-1140 mm (40-45 in) rain zone. Rainfall distribution is uneven, having a January to June period much drier than the second half of the year. The length of the growing season, when temperatures are above 5.6°C (42°F) varies from some 200 days in Morayshire to 167 days in the west. A special climatic feature affecting growth of plants is that the dry cold spring means reduced evapotranspiration and therefore reduced stress on the plants. This makes it possible to grow barley and Sitka spruce with some success in the region. The main deficiencies of the climate are the cold, dry and windy spring and early autumn frosts which require care in the selection of adaptable varieties of trees.

The geology is dominated by the presence of large intrusions of granites predominantly in the southern third of the region but also occurring in the north-east and centre. The majority of the region is composed of mica-quartzite-felspathic schists of the Moine series in the north-west and of the Dalradian series in the east. Lastly, in the Laigh of Moray and in the Howe of the Mearns we find old and new red sandstone.

The soils derived from the granites and the schists tend to be acidic (low pH) and coarse grained which means there is a tendency for the development of leached ironpan and podsols. In contrast, the sandstones tend to produce more fertile agricultural soils. At high altitude with high precipitation, low temperatures and low evapotranspiration, peatlands develop. An examination of the soils occurring in the Forestry Commission areas of the region show the following soil groups being prevalent.

TABLE 10

PREVALENT SOIL GROUPS IN FORESTRY COMMISSION AREAS

Brown earths	13%
Podsols and ironpans	43%
Gleys and flushed peats	28%
Unflushed peats	6%
Others, mainly skeletal	10%
	100%

From Table 10 we see that forestry has adapted itself to using the less desirable soil types.

The vegetation of the higher ground, which in fact is the result of mans' activities, tends also to reflect geology and is of an acid tolerant type, characterised by the presence of heathers and heaths *Calluna vulgaris, Erica cinerea, E. tetralix* and *Vaccinium myrtillus* and of grasses and sedges like *Trichophorum caespitosum, Nardus stricta* and *Deschampsia flexuosa.*

Most grasses compete for water and nutrients with trees but an additional problem with the heathland vegetation is that it can so effectively deprive nitrogen from the spruces and firs that these important forest species can only grow and develop if the heathland vegetation is removed.

The combination of the factors described produce a relatively harsh environment for agriculture and for forestry. As far as the latter is concerned it reduces the range of tree species which can be grown and requires the employment of special ploughing and draining techniques to overcome the deficiencies of the soil. It also requires the removal of heath vegetation if spruce is to be grown.

The Human Factor

Climatic factors on a grand scale have caused major changes in forest types; during the "Atlantic" climatic period the tree level in Scotland was at 800 m (2500 ft) but during the current "Sub-Atlantic" climatic period it was reduced to about 700 m (2000 ft). It is man who has had the greatest influence on the forests in the short term.

During the early period of recorded history the majority of Scotland was tree covered, mainly with hardwoods, oak being on the fertile moist soils, ash and elm on sites with good natural drainage, birch and alder on less well drained sites and scrub oak with birch, juniper and holly on boulder clay. Scots pine was found mainly on sand and gravel deposits and at high elevations. The evolution of agriculture, particularly the introduction of enclosures, the requirements of the smelting of iron, copper, tin and glass, the demands of house and ship building and the introduction of sheep, all combined to accelerate the depletion of our forests and woodlands.

Early forest management and concern about future supplies began to emerge in pre-Reformation days in such ecclesiastical centres as Pluscarden, Kinloss, Urquhart, Deer and Fyvie but much of this work and knowledge was lost during the Reformation. In secular land ownership, forests as a habitat for deer called for some management and this led to the creation of royal forests such as Darnaway. In 1507 Alexander Elphinstone, Keeper of Kildrummy Castle, was granted a charter to manage the forests of Strathdon in order to maintain its deer hunting potential.

After about the year 1600 the commercial exploitation of Scots pine for export and building assumed significant proportions in areas north of the "Highland Fault". Loss of the tree growing stock and the realisation that financial gain was possible, provided a stimulus to tree planting. Archibald Grant in the period 1713 to 1778 established some 3000 ha (7200 acres) of forests at Monymusk. James Farquharson of Invercauld planted some 1½ million Scots pine and European larch in mixture and the 9th Earl of Moray — "The Tree Planter" — organised the planting of some 1800 ha (4450 acres) of Oak in the Darnaway forests. These exploits together with the development of techniques for rafting timber down the Spey, Findhorn and Dee and the building of sawmills and boat building yards, created a skilled labour force and greatly enhanced the economy of the region.

The year 1866 saw a turning point in these activities. In that year the last import duties on wood were removed and cheap and ample supplies flooded into the country from the Baltic, Scandinavia, Russia and Canada. Markets were lost, the home forestry trade went into decline and the incentive to plant gradually died away as far as timber production was concerned. During the period two other facets of forestry emerged. The first was the planting of trees for amenity, to beautify the "Policy" woods round large houses. Much of this was done through the use of introduced species such as Sitka spruce, Douglas fir, Lodgepole pine, Noble fir, the redwoods and Wellingtonias. Some species were selected because they were exotic and others because of their pleasing colouring and appearance. The important fact which emerged was that many of these trees grew extremely well and produced valuable timber and thus eventually became the nucleus for future commercial planting. The second was the planting of shelter belts and small woods for the protection of the light soils, as in the Laigh of Moray, or for homesteads and steadings on the Buchan platform.

The submarine blockades of World Wars I and II had dramatic effects on forestry. The first gave rise to the creation of the Forestry Commission in 1919, and the second to the inauguration of Dedication Schemes to encourage the active participation of the private sector in new planting. Together these measures led to a much higher rate of tree planting than before. The Forestry Commission pioneered the use of exotic species, worked out new techniques for planting sites previously deemed unplantable because of altitude or wetness, and undertook much research on diseases and pests. The Dedication Schemes provided the financial incentive and established standards which greatly encouraged

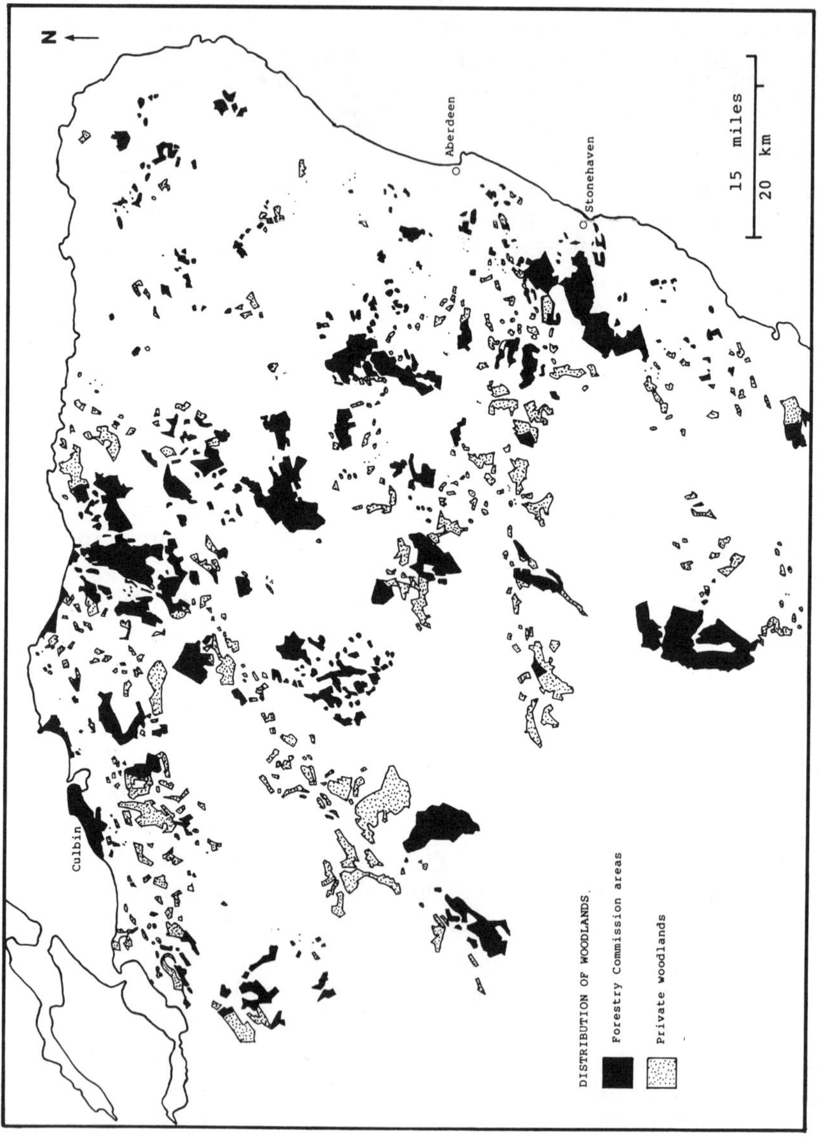

Figure 31 — Grampian forests.

landowners to resume the tree planting role which they had undertaken prior to 1866. Taxation measures aimed at encouraging investment in forestry gave rise to a new and enterprising breed of forest owners and the development of forest investment companies.

The combined effects of state and private planting, currently running at some 19,000 ha (46,900 acres) per annum for Scotland as a whole has resulted in increasing the forest cover of Scotland from 4% in 1919 to 11% in 1985.

THE RESOURCE

It is the objects of management which determine the way in which forests or woodlands are handled. To many people this objective is the production of wood for sawmills or pulp mills but this is far from the complete story. The range of objectives can be narrowed down for simplicity into three main types. First is the management to produce wood for use in sawmill, particle board factory, pulp mill or as fence and transmission posts or even as firewood. The second objective is for the conservation of wild life and the amelioration of the landscape. The third is that of providing a medium for relaxation and recreation. Skilled management can achieve more than one of these objectives on a particular unit of management. Examples of the three types occur in the region.

FORESTS AND WOODLANDS FOR PRODUCTION

An understanding of this subject requires an examination of statistics of the raw material in terms of quantity, size, species and age. Such data is available from *The Census of Woodlands and Non-Woodland Trees* prepared by the Forestry Commision in 1982 and relevant data for the Grampian Region has been abstracted.

The Forest Area: Convenience and lucidity calls for the use of tabulated information. Table 11 provides area information based on ownership and on management intensity.

TABLE 11 — *AREAS OF WOODLAND BY FOREST TYPE AND OWNERSHIP (All figures in hectares)*

FOREST TYPE	FORESTRY COMMISSION	PRIVATE	TOTAL
Mainly Conifer	58512	51186	109680
Mainly broadleaved	379	11580	11959
Total Productive	58891	63748	121639
Scrub	8	6094	6102
Cleared	467	2703	3170
Grand Total	59366	71545	130911

Table 11 shows that the region has more than 120,000 ha (290,000 acres) of managed productive woods which represent some 15% of the region's land area. Only Dumfries and Galloway amongst Scottish regions can exceed this percentage. Table 11 also reveals that 53% of the conifer woods are managed by the State and 47% are privately owned. In the case of broadleaved woods, the private sector controls 97% of them. The region has a well balanced ownership pattern i.e. 53% is state owned in contrast to 63% for Scotland as a whole.

Species Distribution: It is often imagined that forestry in the north is exclusively limited to Sitka spruce but Table 12 reveals the actual situation from which it will be seen that 90% of the managed woodlands are conifers.

TABLE 12 — *AREAS OF WOODLANDS BY PRINCIPAL SPECIES AND OWNERSHIP*

SPECIES	Forestry Commission	Private	TOTAL	%
Scots Pine	16389	27112	43501	40
Corsican pine	1342	32	1374	1
Lodgepole pine	11731	3774	15505	14
Sitka spruce	16413	7424	23837	22
Norway spruce	5013	4694	9707	9
European larch	944	3643	4587	4
Jap/Hybrid larch	4927	2366	7293	7
Douglas fir	1137	1144	2281	2
Other & mixed conifers	622	925	1547	1
Total Conifers	58518	51114	109632	100
Oak	17	2108	2125	17
Beech	110	1997	2107	17
Sycamore	19	1173	1192	10
Ash	18	237	255	2
Birch	127	3988	4115	34
Poplar	1	17	18	1
S. chestnut	-	2	2	1
Elm	1	316	317	3
Others and mixed	90	1786	1876	16
Total Broadleaved	373	11634	12007	100

A more detailed examination of the conifer species distribution reveals that the region differs considerably from the average in Scotland as a whole. The species distribution for Scotland is 35% pine, 45% spruce and 18% larch, whereas in this region it reads 55% pine, 31% spruce and 11% larch. The important part played by the pines, particularly Scots pine, should be noted.

The Age Class Distribution: The ideal forest should have approximately the same area for each of the age classes, which would mean a sustained level of output for industry. Like the rest of the United Kingdom such a situation is far from ideal due to the heavy fellings of World Wars I and II and to the severe wind blow of 1953. Table 13 highlights the imbalance, showing a preponderance of younger age classes.

TABLE 13 — *AREAS OF FORESTS BY PLANTING YEAR PERIODS (In hectares)*

PERIOD	CONIFERS	%	BROADLEAVED	%
Pre-1861	2375	2	1947	16
1861 — 1900	3190	3	2504	21
1901 — 1910	1522	1	599	5
1911 — 1920	1137	1	110	1
1921 — 1930	7689	7	697	6
1931 — 1940	8040	7	1508	12
1941 — 1950	13850	13	2197	18
1951 — 1960	31774	29	1177	10
1961 — 1970	26513	24	940	8
1971 — 1980	13542	13	301	3
TOTAL	109632	100	12007	100

Under the conifers, the preponderance of the younger age classes is obvious. In general terms only trees older than 25 years produce any income at all; one can therefore see that only 48% of the conifer forests currently produce income, but the potential from now on is set to increase very rapidly. The age class structure for the Grampian Region is much superior to that of Scotland as a whole where we find only about 20% is over 25 years of age. One of the main reasons for this is the high proportion of Scots pine which was planted prior to the 1950s.

Volume of Wood for Industry: The Census has established that the total growing stock standing in Grampian forests total 10.7 million m^3 (378 million ft^3) of Conifers plus 2 million m^3 (71 million ft^3) of broadleaves. Table 14 illustrates these volumes.

TABLE 14

STANDING VOLUMES OF TIMBER IN WOODLANDS

(by principal species and sizes in 1000's of m^3)

	SIZE CLASS (DIAM.)				
SPECIES	7-20 cm	21-30 cm	31-50 cm	over 50 cm	TOTAL
Pines	2492	1378	1493	543	5906
Spruces	1874	904	377	50	3205
Larches	561	380	247	4	1229
Douglas Fir	112	37	56	22	227
Others	36	26	28	38	128
Total Conifers	5075	2725	2201	694	10695
Broadleaves	316	300	565	871	2052
					12747

The total volume of trees standing in the Grampian Region represents some 22% of the conifer growing stock of Scotland and 15% of Scotland's broadleaves. The actual annual production of wood available for industry has been estimated as having the following volumes of logs suitable for sawing and logs to be used in the round.

TABLE 15

ANNUAL AVAILABLE TIMBER PRODUCTION

	ANNUAL AVAILABLE PRODUCTION IN 1000 m^3		
YEAR	Small Round Wood	Saw Logs	TOTAL
1985	170	186	356
1990	202	211	413
1995	246	269	515
2000	294	406	700

The data just presented shows that the Grampian Region has a substantial reserve of timber which has a wider species distribution and a greater proportion of large commercial conifers than Scotland as a whole. Such a forest structure has allowed the development of a considerable sawmilling industry, supporting some five large sawmills (employing 20 or more men each) and some five smaller mills on full-time production. Although there are no pulp mills in the region there are export outlets available to the market in Scandinavia through the ports of Buckie and Fraserburgh. The panel products industry (producing processed wood such as blockboard, particle board and fibre boards) though not currently existing within the region is located at Dalcross near Inverness and at Cowie near Stirling. These are sufficiently near to provide a market outlet for the region's produce.

A combination of climatic factors and history has led to the establishment of the most important tree nursery area in the United Kingdom within this and the northern half of the Tayside Region. There are five major forest tree nurseries in the area.

The full-time employment in forestry and wood processing is difficult to quantify accurately because of variations in intensity of work and cross boundary movement of workers. Table 16 will provide some indication of present levels.

TABLE 16

EMPLOYMENT IN FORESTRY AND WOOD PROCESSING

Tree Nurseries	120
Planting and tending trees	400
Felling and extraction contractors	150
Millers and processors	460*
Administrative	140
	1270

* This figure includes employees handling a proportion of imported timber.

FORESTS AS AMELIORATING THE QUALITY OF LIFE

This aspect of forest and woodland management is often taken for granted and it is the removal of trees which causes public concern. The amelioration of the environment in which we live takes many forms and most of these are represented in the region. In contrast to the important part played by the conifers in the preceding section we find under this heading that it is the broadleaved trees which play a major role.

Take, for instance, the Culbin and Roseisle forests along the northern edges of the Laigh of Moray. The primary objective of these Scots pine and Corsican pine forests is to stabilise the light easily blown sands of the coastal region which historically caused considerable damage to agriculture. Close by, in the spectacular gorges of the Findhorn river, it is the presence of mixed broadleaves such as Oak, Beech and Ash and conifer trees growing on the steep banks which prevents landslides and erosion and at the same time enhances the outstanding scenery. The patchwork of forest blocks, copses and belts in the braes of Glenlivet is the result of detailed consideration between the main upland users, as follows: arable agriculture 12%, stock rearing 43%, grouse 22% and forestry 23%. The forests provide shelter to homesteads, roads and stock, and so provide financial benefits to the farmer. In addition, these woodlands give variety to the scenery and landscape and also improve the habitat for wild life from roe deer to bark beetles and coal tits as well as for woodland plants and flowers.

"Royal Deeside" attracts many tourists and provides a desirable living environment to numerous families. Much of this attraction is due to well-sited woods and forests like the groups of larch at Invercauld, the splendid 300-year-old Caledonian pines of Ballochbuie near Balmoral and the similarly fine trees at Glentanar. Birch woodlands make their contribution west of Ballater by the Coil-a-Creich Inn and near Bridge of Canny. One cannot avoid a mention of Crathes Castle, noble enough by itself but greatly enhanced by a backdrop of magnificent Douglas firs and Redwoods and, until recently, the avenue of lime trees.

Some of the National Nature Reserves and Sites of Special Scientific Interest notified by the Nature Conservancy are linked to woodlands, as, for example, the Muir of Dinnet, the Morrone birkwood and the Dinnet oakwood. All such areas recognise the important part which trees play in our environment.

There are those who consider Buchan as bleak, dull and uninteresting and this is in no small way due to its location and topography but also because of the scarcity of trees on that landscape. Trees and woodlands add a vertical dimension to a landscape and this in turn modifies the condition for life by reducing wind speeds, depressing extremes in temperatures and sustaining the humidity. These factors, together with a wider range of plants, provide a protective environment and food material for a far wider range of plants and animals than either a pure conifer crop or a field of barley.

Forests and Woodlands for Recreation and Relaxation

With some 90% of our population being subjected to the stresses of modern life in urban surroundings but having reasonable leisure time and mobility it is understandable that there is a large and ever increasing demand for areas suitable for recreation and relaxation in the countryside. Woodlands and forests constitute a desirable medium for this because the trees offer protection against wind, noise and pollution; they offer a degree of privacy and also provide pleasant surroundings to the participant.

The range of activities which can be carried out is wide and varied. The simple forms of walking, trekking, wayfaring and orienteering, together with the more complex activities of pony trekking, bird watching, deer stalking with camera or gun, shooting, canoeing and motor rallying, can all be accommodated in forest areas if properly organised and segregated.

The Forestry Commission forests of the region can offer a wide range of facilities: 760 spaces in car parks, 8 picnic sites, 1 information centre, 83 km (52 miles) of forest walks, 18 km (11 miles) of bridle paths, 2 wayfaring courses and 51 trekking areas as well as nearly 200 shooting leases and 60 stalker/client deer hunting weeks.

The Forestry Commission work closely with the relevant governing bodies of the various sports and, as in the case of Bennachie forest, undertake to consult interested local pressure groups like the "Baillies of Bennachie".

The privately owned forests also cater for this demand: for example, the museum, guided tours and scenic walks which have been organised in the Darnaway forests.

The joint Countryside Commission and the estate ownership at Glentanar welcomes visitors to picnic sites, rural museum and numerous and interesting signposted walks. There are also those estates who judiciously manage their forest to enhance the value of the sporting aspects of management as, for example, at Dunecht.

CONCLUSIONS

Within the scope of this short article an attempt has been made to describe the benefits which efficient and far sighted forest management can bestow on the countryside. Under its varied ownership it not only provides an important and flexible raw material for a long established local industry, but it also provides a beneficial environment to humans, animals and plants in a rather harsh climatic zone. To further its development forestry needs your interest and your understanding.

Chapter fifteen

FISHING

Dr. James Coull

Introduction

Fishing has always been an important activity in the Grampian Region. Although the early record is inevitably scanty, it is known from archaeological evidence from prehistory, and documentary material testifies to its importance from medieval times onwards. It was for centuries important for both the salmon fisheries in the rivers and the white (or demersal) fisheries around the coast, while in the 19th century it became the main base for the herring fisheries not only of Britain but also of Europe. Available evidence suggests that the region was always the leading Scottish one in salmon fisheries, although for centuries it was less important than both the Forth and the Clyde for sea fishing. However, by the late 19th century it dominated all the fisheries of Scotland; and with the decline of the English trawling ports consequent on the delineation of the new 200-mile (320 km) fishing limits of the 1970s, the Grampian Region is now unchallenged as the main fishing region of Britain. At the ports of the region in 1983 the value of fish landed was £93 million — half of the Scottish total, and almost one third of the British; and this takes no account of the very considerable landings of the fleets of the region in other ports of Britain. Of the boats of 18 m (60 ft) or over which constitute the main part of the catching power, the region had registered in 1983 371 vessels out of a Scottish total of 527; and it has resident within it upwards of one-half of the fishermen of Scotland.

Salmon Fisheries

Much of the earlier activity was directed at the easier expedient of catching fish in the rivers rather than the sea; and while this included species like trout, pike and eels there is no question that the most important species was salmon (Coull 1967), which already in medieval times was caught for export as well as for local use. The region contains several of the biggest Scottish rivers, and the main objective was to catch the salmon at the river mouths in the summer part of the year as they entered the rivers on their spawning runs. The principal catching method was by net and coble in the estuaries, and also by cruives (weirs with gaps in them) beyond the tidal limits. While there was provision in the week-end closure for allowing salmon to get upstream, there was not infrequent friction between the upstream proprietors and those at the mouths over the numbers which reached the upper rivers — a thing not unknown to-day.

In the medieval period salmon fisheries were considered as a major national resource, and were given out by charter to the burghs and religious houses of the region for their operation. Thus the Priory of Urquhart had title to the fishings on the Spey, the burgh of Aberdeen to those of the Dee and Don; and those of the Dee were the most important of all Scottish rivers. After the Reformation the fishings passed into various lay hands, and in the modern period have mainly been operated by companies and lessees. From medieval times there have been conservation measures, including the setting up of a legally defined season, the prohibition of fishing for salmon on the open sea, and of taking out-of-season fish.

In former times, salmon were pickled in barrels for out of season use and there are on record complaints from some of the poorest people that they had too much salmon in their diet. There was also a considerable export to the continent, but from the late 18th century they were sent mainly to the home market (especially London) in a fresh state on ice by fast sailing vessel. For this purpose ice was collected in winter, or even imported from Norway, and stored in thick-walled window-less buildings. The value of the salmon increased, and few people in the region could afford it: it has remained one of the most valuable fish on the market. In the 19th century what has become the normal modern catching method began with the salmon being caught in "fixed engine" nets as they swim along the coast before entering the rivers.

Salmon fisheries have continued into the modern period although their relative importance has declined. Salmon is still a high value species, despite the strong growth of a rival source of supply from fish farming. However, there is concern now for the future of the salmon species over the whole North Atlantic. In its marine phase it oftens swims through several different zones of fisheries jurisdiction, and it is now fished by several nations along its migration routes which can extend over hundreds of miles. There is now a formidable challenge to the international community to formulate and enforce an adequate conservation regime for the salmon.

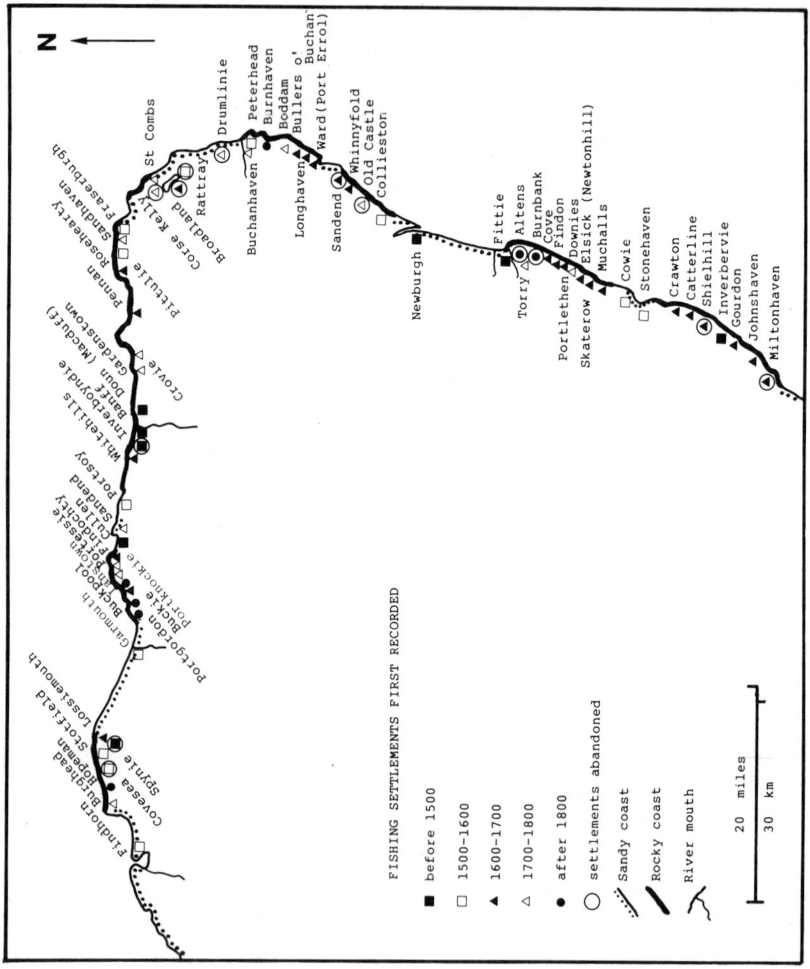

Figure 32 — Fishing settlements in Grampian Region: dates of origin.

Early Sea Fisheries

Before the modern period sea fisheries were very generally prosecuted from villages with landing beaches rather than towns with harbours, and the coast of the region has a frequency of fishing settlements with virtually no rivals in Britain (Coull 1969). There are 53 places actively or formerly involved in fishing, along with a dozen former fishing settlements which became deserted (Fig 32).

The earliest evidence of sea fishing is from the older coastal burghs of Aberdeen and Banff in medieval times. The record of origins of many of the fishing villages is scanty and incomplete, but several of them were certainly in existencc by 1600 along with a number of other burghs. There was a subsequent increase in both numbers and size of fishing settlements into the modern period, although the peak of activity in the great majority of the villages was around the third quarter of the 19th century, before fishing operations became concentrated at the main harbours. Most of the fishing villages started with small numbers of crofter-fishing families on coastal estates, but with expanding commercial opportunities they became involved in full-time fishing in the 19th century if not before. The siting of the fishing villages shows a marked preference for rock as opposed to sand coasts: these had coves and often shingle beaches where boats could be better brought ashore, and shingle beaches were also a real asset for spreading split salted fish to dry.

The work of fishing was generally done by lines by men for demersal (or white fish) species. The boats used were open and mainly propelled by oars, with the curved-stemmed "skaffie" being traditional on the Moray Firth coast, and the straight-stemmed "fifie" in the rest of the region. "Great-lines" were used from six-man boats for the spring fishery which concentrated on cod and for which the boats might go off 16 km (10 miles) or more; and "sma' lines", usually from four-man boats were used closer to the coast at other times of the year when the main catch was haddock and whiting.

Other members of the family were also much involved in the work. The women, helped by the children, collected mussels and other bait, and could have the daily task of baiting literally miles of line. The womenfolk also played an essential role in the disposal of the catch; they had the main burden of the gutting and cleaning of the fish, and of the salting and spreading on the beaches of the part of the catch which was cured; and a fish-wife might walk 32-48 km (20-30 miles) in a day in the hinterland of a village with her creel providing fish to the landward population and getting in return products like meal, butter and eggs.

The origins of many villages must have been associated with catering for local needs, but by the 18th century there were curers operating in some of them who were involved in a more organised trade, the main destination of which was the central belt of Scotland. Until the modern period the poorer classes saw very little meat in their diet, and there was a considerable sale for cured fish which was cheaper.

Apart from Whitehills and Gourdon, which have maintained active harbours, almost the only commercial fishery in the villages now is a restricted one for lobsters and crabs although a few of them are also bases for salmon fishing. Most of them have become dormitory settlements for fishing towns and other places.

The Rise of the Herring Fishery

During the 19th century there was a major new development which greatly changed life for most of the fisherfolk. This was the rise of the Scottish herring fishery to be a major one by any international standard in the 19th century (Gray 1978). Up to 1800 there was in the region a herring fishery only in the Buckie area in summer, while the main Scottish catches were taken in the Firths of Forth and Clyde and in the Minch. The Dutch, however, had shown for centuries that there was a great source of wealth in the herring fisheries off the Scottish east coast, although the Scots had neither the technique nor the organisation to make use of them. However, from the end of the 18th century the Scots effectively mastered the Dutch method of fishing by the drift net, while government promotion in the shape of incentive bounties and a system of quality inspection (enforced by the Crown brand on barrels of adequate standard) guaranteed the product for the market. From the early 19th century the summer herring fishery from mid July to mid September became a major activity along the coast of the region, and operations early began focussing on Fraserburgh and Peterhead as the ports adjacent to the greatest area of open sea. The Scots had an important advantage over the Dutch in that the herring could be caught close to the coast and cured ashore rather than on board: for much of the 19th century the big part of the catch was obtained within 24 km (15 miles) of the coast.

Previous to the 19th century there had been little use of boats of more than c. 7.5 m (25 ft) in length, but from the early days of the herring fishery sail boats of 9 m (30 ft) and over were used which had five-man crews and up to 20 nets; such boats needed harbours rather than open beaches, and it was at the few available harbours that herring curers concentrated on their operations. Success in the fishery led to reinvestment in bigger boats; in the later part of the century boats became part - and then fully decked, and by the 1890s the biggest boats were over 18 m (60 ft) in length, carried up to 70 nets and had crews of eight men. With these bigger boats the fishery not only extended considerably further offshore, but also into other seasons. In the earlier 19th century the fishermen simply reverted to lining for white fish outside the herring season, but investment in big boats from about mid century prompted them to fish for herring at other seasons, a practice which demanded mobility to other bases. It was possible to catch herring as early as May at the Hebrides or Shetland, at autumn at East Anglia, and even in winter in the Minch and elsewhere, and a characteristic annual pattern developed which was to encompass nearly all the coasts of the British Isles. The herring fishery was to reach its zenith with the advent of steam power at the close of the 19th century. At first small engines were installed and served for the heavy tasks of hoisting the sails and hauling the "bush" (main) ropes, but from 1900 bigger engines were used to propel the vessels: the steam drifter, three or four times the cost of the best sail boats quickly came to dominate the fishery. In the region were registered more than 80% of the Scottish fleet of these boats which was to total over 850 by 1914. The steam drifters had a crew of 10, carried up to 100 nets and could range over 160 km (100 miles) from land. With steam drifters and sail boats the annual herring cure in the region in the peak years of the early 20th century could touch 1 million barrels.

TRAWLING AT ABERDEEN

While Aberdeen did become a herring port, a major development of the last two decades of the 19th century was its emergence as the outstanding port in steam trawling for white fish. By this time there was a national distribution network for fresh white fish by the railway system. In its earlier phases this was supplied by English sailing trawlers, but the superiority of steam power for towing and hauling the heavy trawl gear was rapidly established from 1880 onwards. Steam trawling began in Aberdeen in 1882, and proved so profitable that there was a boom which resulted in over 200 trawlers, supplemented by numbers of steam longliners, working from the port by the time of World War I; and by that time annual landings exceeded 100,000 tons. In contrast to the family owned boats which dominated the herring fishery, the Aberdeen fleet developed on a basis of company ownership. Aberdeen became established as the main centre in Scotland for the processing and marketing of white fish, and so it has remained until the present time.

READJUSTMENTS OF THE INTER-WAR PERIOD

Most of the industries of Britain had great difficulties in the inter-war period, and the fisheries of North-east Scotland were no exception. There was a general problem of costs rising faster than fish prices, and this adversely affected both main sectors of the trawling at Aberdeen and the herring fishery at the other ports. In addition the north European markets on which the herring fisheries mainly depended were in a reduced and disorganised state: as a result of problems of balance of payments and runaway inflation in Germany, and with the aftermath of the revolution and civil war in Russia, herring fishermen and curers were left with excess capacity. The overall result was that the trawling sector stagnated and the herring fisheries contracted, while there was very little fleet replacement.

The main innovation of the inter-war period lay in the advent of the ground seine net for white fishing. The idea was taken up by some of the ports — especially Lossiemouth — which had formerly concentrated heavily on the herring fishery (Sutherland 1986). This technique employs a bag type of net like the trawl to catch white fish on the sea bed, but worked with ropes rather than steel warps; it could be operated more cheaply and with less engine power, and even at this difficult period white fish had a secure place on the home market. The method was originally borrowed from the Danes and pioneered from 1921; Lossiemouth was established as a seine net port by 1930 and the idea was later taken up around all the Scottish coast. Another development of the inter-war period was the increase in the use of motor power in the fishing fleet. This had begun with small vessels before World War I, but the ground seine gave it impetus for bigger vessels; however, the great part of the fishing fleet remained steam-powered till World War II.

DEVELOPMENTS SINCE 1945

In the period since World War II development has proceeded apace; and although the fishing has been prosperous overall it has had to meet a variety of problems.

Fleet modernisation has been helped by government grants and loans schemes, and latterly to some extent by EEC funds, so that a fleet of boats has been built up that can hold its own with any. Earlier post-war rebuilding was concentrated on wooden boats, mainly of the 18-24 m (60-80 ft) size and diesel powered, but within the last 20 years the leading sector of the fleet has become steel boats of 24 m (80 ft) or more (Plate 34). Engines have become more powerful and can be 800 h.p. or more, while auxiliary engines can be 150 h.p. — the same power as main engines of the early post-war period; and shelter decks are now the norm for safer and less arduous working. Rot-proof synthetic fibre nets have replaced the former manilla and cotton, and there has been a veritable revolution in other fishing equipment. Virtually all gear hauling is now mechanised with hydraulic winches; echosounders and sonar are regularly used in fish finding, radio transmitters are universal, while the Decca navigator which can pin-point position at sea is standard equipment. Icing of white fish at sea, and refrigerated sea water tanks for pelagic species, maintain the quality of catches till they reach market. While there has been a reduction in the size of the fleet, its catching power has certainly been enhanced.

There has also been improvement and change in fishing methods and diversification in the species caught. The drift-net fishery for herring continued to run down in the post-war period and was finally discontinued in the early 1970s. The drift-net was replaced by the more efficient methods of the pair trawl and (more particularly) the purse net, and mackerel as well as herring fishing has been conducted by these methods. The purse net, especially, shows the efficiency of modern methods: the net is up to the size of five or six football pitches, and is hauled by the power block: at times one haul of the net will yield several hundred tons of fish. For white fish, as well as the seine net the light trawl and pair trawl have come into use. Trawls have also been employed to catch a number of other species: these include nephrops (a type of shell fish), and various species used for reduction to meal and oil — sprats, Norway pout and sand eels.

A major readjustment has been the decline of the Aberdeen trawler fleet, especially since the early 1970s. The fleet had aged and was renewed with the help of a government grant and loan scheme in the years around 1960. A large sector of the fleet was of the middle water class, and concentrated much of its effort around the Faroe Islands — grounds which were largely closed off with the extension of national fishing limits to 200 miles (320 km). There are now only a handful of Aberdeen-registered trawlers remaining, and there has been a decline in landings too despite the very considerable expenditure in re-building the fish market and its quays. However, Aberdeen remains the main centre in Scotland for processing and marketing, although the merchants now buy most of their supplies elsewhere.

Meanwhile, Peterhead which until the early 1960s was largely bypassed for Aberdeen for white fish landings even by its own fleet, has risen to be the main white fish port in Western Europe. The discontinuation of Saturday sales at Aberdeen, together with increasing congestion there, saw the establishment of a large market at Peterhead; this has been accompanied by the substantial improvement of facilities, including the building of a large covered market. Peterhead is now the main landing port for a fleet of about 300 vessels, most of them registered in the North-East, and some from other parts of the Scottish coast. Fraserburgh also has retained a substantial market and lands pelagic as well as

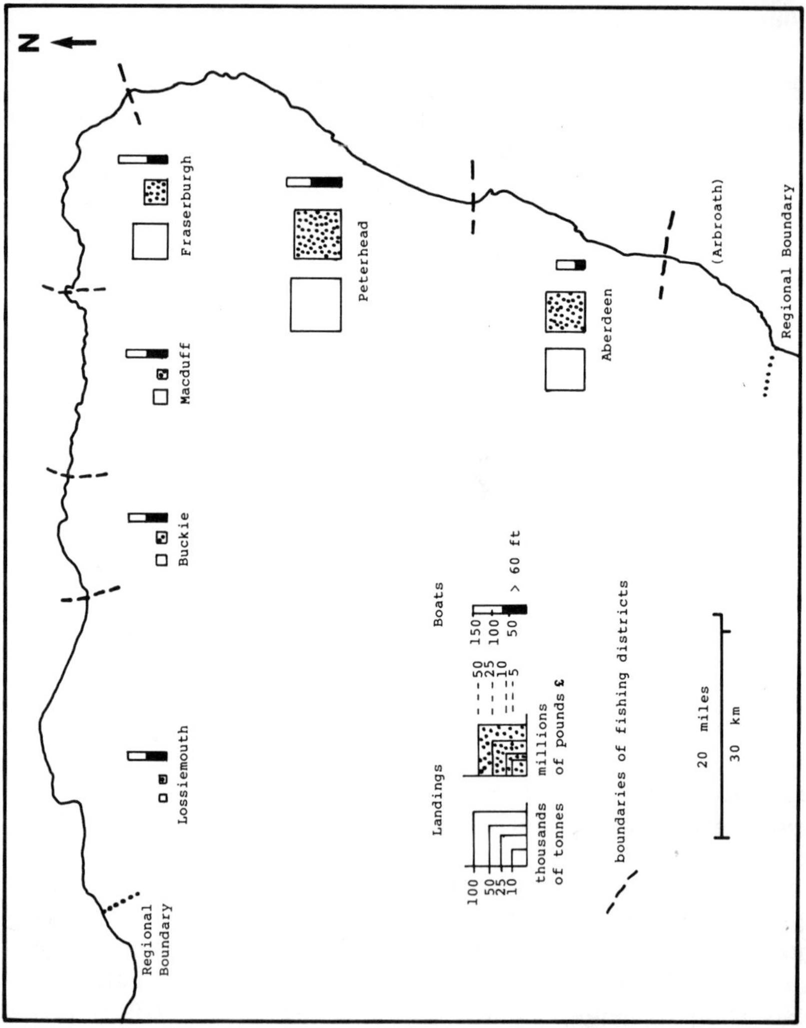

Figure 33 — Land and Fleets 1983, Grampian Region.

demersal species. Various other harbour improvements have been made in the region, and harbours now have quayside ice plants to provide the ice necessary for maintaining fish quality aboard.

Figure 33 shows that landings are concentrated at the three main ports of Aberdeen, Peterhead and Fraserburgh, while catching capacity is mainly spread in the districts between Peterhead and Lossiemouth. The relatively low value of landings at Fraserburgh is due to a higher proportion of pelagic species which fetch lower prices.

For over a century the landings made in the ports of the region have told only part of the story of its fishing. The bulk of the fish caught in the Minch and landed at ports like Kinlochbervie, Lochinver, Ullapool, Mallaig and Oban are caught by boats for which North-east ports are the home base. Much of the fish caught in Orkney and Shetland waters — and also off south-west Norway — are landed in the North-East; and the bulk of the mackerel catch at Cornwall is also taken by boats from Grampian Region.

Conservation and Policy Issues

In the modern period the drive towards over-fishing caused by improved fishing methods has created a need for greater conservation measures; and the restrictions embodied within these measures have been linked with considerable — and sometimes acrimonious — debate on the international plane. The fisheries of the region have inevitably been caught up in this situation.

Conservation measures until the early 1970s were enforced under the North-East Atlantic Convention, and operated mainly for demersal fisheries by stipulating minimum net mesh sizes and minimum landed sizes for different species. By that time it had become clear that such measures were not adequate in themselves, and that restrictions were also needed for the pelagic species of herring and mackerel, whose stocks had seriously deteriorated since the mid '60s with the onslaught of the purse-net. Since then the principle of annual TACs (total allowable catches) for important species has been accepted, and also the need for closed seasons and closed areas for pelagic species. In addition the principle of licensed entry to fisheries has been accepted, with the objective of promoting economic viability by preventing catches being spread over too many boats; inevitably this has meant a slow-down in fleet renewal.

Effective decisions and enforcement of conservation were much complicated by the concurrent debate on a fisheries policy for the EEC (Wise 1984). Here the main issues were the width of exclusive national zones, and the national quotas within the total TACs of the Community. On the former issue, there was an inevitable conflict between on the one hand the island nations of Britain and Ireland and the others; Britain especially wanted preferential rights extending out for as much as 80 km (50 miles) from the coast, but in the end had to settle for a general framework of national rights limited to 19 km (12 miles), although there was a special wider "box" agreed around Orkney and Shetland. Britain also has generally been awarded the biggest single share of species under quota arrangements. The different nations of the EEC have still administrative jurisdiction over their own quotas, and in Britain for the most important species of haddock, cod, herring and mackerel there are generally limitations set to the catch of individual vessels. One of the features of the modern period has been the formation of a considerable number of producers' organisations in which the fishing interests of the region are well represented. These play an essential part in the formulation of policy, and in the administration of conservation and other arrangements.

On the wider plane, the formulation of policy within the EEC was to an extent simplified after 1977 with the exclusion of a number of nations (especially the USSR) from fishing within the 200-mile (320 km) EEC fisheries limit. The EEC "pond" is not entirely exclusive, as there are "trade-off" arrangements with other nations, the main one being Norway's right to participate in the North Sea herring fishery in return for access to demersal stocks within the Norwegian limit. The fact that an EEC fishery policy has now become a reality after a long period of indecision is not, however, entirely the end of a chapter; with Spain now an EEC member, and the Spanish fishing fleet by far the biggest in Western Europe, the fishermen of the Grampian Region along with others are keeping a watchful eye on future adjustments.

Conclusion

The fisheries of the Grampian Region have been an important component of its life and economy in the past, and continue as such today. There has been a consistent theme of growth and adaptation, and now few regions anywhere can boast of such an up-to-date and proficient fleet. However, fishing even on the most modern boats continues to be work of discomfort and hardship. To the old problems of coping with sea and weather, and with fluctuations in fish stocks and markets, there are now added the man-made constraints of catch quotas and restrictions in access to resources. However, the indications are that the fishermen of the Grampian Region are still among the leaders in their profession.

Chapter sixteen

DISTILLING

Dr. Sheila Bain

THE HISTORY OF MALT WHISKY

The secrets of whisky manufacture probably came to Scotland from Ireland. It was first manufactured in the west and then found its way to the central Highlands. For centuries a spirit distilled from a fermented barley mash had been made all over the Highlands, where nature still supplies the essential ingredients for its distillation:

(1) home grown barley for the "malt";

(2) pure air of the mountains;

(3) unpolluted water of the hill burns;

(4) rich dark peat of the moors and perhaps

(5) the granite rocks from which the water springs.

There are still distillers who claim that the best malt whisky comes "off granite through peat". No two malt whiskies are, in fact, alike.

In the Highlands the distilleries were small and supplied mainly local needs. These needs could be considerable, even in the 18th and 19th centuries, for to the Highlander, whisky was a daily necessity. It stood on the breakfast table, or all day on the side table. It was drunk by all the household and pressed on every caller. It was and to a smaller extent remains the only drink at Highland weddings and the final door drink (deoch an dorus) to any parting guest. Even more so it was the drink de riguer at every funeral of rich and poor alike.

Aeneas McDonald, an excise man writing in 1736, said of whisky — "The ruddy complexion, nimbleness and strength of these people is not owing to water-drinking but to the aqua-vitae, a malt spirit which serves both for victual and drink". Because the Highlands were so isolated until after the 1745 Rising, the spirit made a late appearance in literature.

Burns, however, frequently sang the merits of whisky, and rated it far higher than brandy which he dismissed as "burning trash".

In Scottish historical records, whisky is mentioned at an early date. Before 1500 it had reached the royal table and as the records show it was appreciated by King James IV who fell at Flodden. It gave life and energy to the soldiers of Montrose, and in the 1745 Rising it sustained the Highlanders and consoled the Prince after Culloden. On the battlefield of Culloden, whisky was used for a sacred purpose, perhaps for the first time, when John Maitland, a Presbyter of the Episcopalian Church of Scotland, administered a Holy Eucharist to the mortally wounded Lord Strathallan with oatcake and whisky.

Culloden is an important date in the story of whisky. It ruined the Jacobite chiefs and exalted the Whigs who had supported the Hanoverians. The Highlands were opened up for trade and commerce for the first time, and whisky began to be transported and sold in large quantities south of the Highland area. After Culloden, the Highlands were invaded by excise men, known as gaugers, whose main task was to gauge the amount of spirits produced and impose a mass of crippling legislation including a rise of duty. The Highlanders then started a smuggling trade which expanded rapidly with a demand for Scotch Whisky in England, coupled with the imposition of an import duty of 9s. 6d. per gallon* (10p per litre) by the English Government. Illicit stills flourished, and at first the Government was powerless to suppress them. In 1814 all distillation in the Highlands in stills of less than 500 gallons (2300 litres) was prohibited, but at this time more than half the whisky sold came from illicit distilleries in the Highlands. These smugglers were instrumental in keeping alive the distillation of malt whisky.

By 1820 illicit distilling had become so widespread that in order to check this lawlessness and to restore the pre-eminence of Highland whisky, the Duke of Gordon raised the matter in the House of Lords. He suggested that the Government should sanction the manufacture of legal whisky of a quality equal to the illicit still product on a payment of reasonable duty and that he and other Highland landowners would then do their best to suppress smuggling.

The Act of 1823 sanctioned legal distilling on payment of a duty of 2s. 3d. per gallon (2p per litre) of proof spirit and on the purchase of a licence of £10 for all stills with a capacity of 40 gallons (184 litres) or more. This Act encouraged the manufacture of a good product and tended to favour the production of Highland malt whisky. Illicit distilling, however, carried on for a further 60 years and it may occur occasionally at the present time! Gradually, however, the English began to

* 1 gallon = 4.6 litres

28. The dramatically located Dunnottar Castle situated on an outcrop of conglomerate rock *(G. Stables)*

29. The farm of Carlincraig, Banffshire, in the 1920s. A ''start-an' -aa'' water wheel can be seen against the barn wall. Some of the roofs have straw and clay thatch *(Royal Museum of Scotland)*

30.
A turf gablet at Kinto
c. 1920
(Royal Museum of Scotland)

31.
Willie Ingram by the kitchen fire at Green-bogs, Grange, Keith. grating, made of piec of cartwheel rings, covers an ash pit. Th crook and the links h from a large iron swe
(A. Fenton)

32. The circular horse course at Mains of Newtongarry, Drumblade, Huntly *(A. Fenton)*

33. A ''strae-an' raip'' roof at Rora, Aberdeenshire *(A. Fenton)*

34. Steel built seine-netters at Peterhead. Boats of this type are now the leading sector in the catching of white fish *(J. Coull)*

35. Plan of the Newtown of Aberdeen, 1661 *(James Gordon of Rothiemay)*

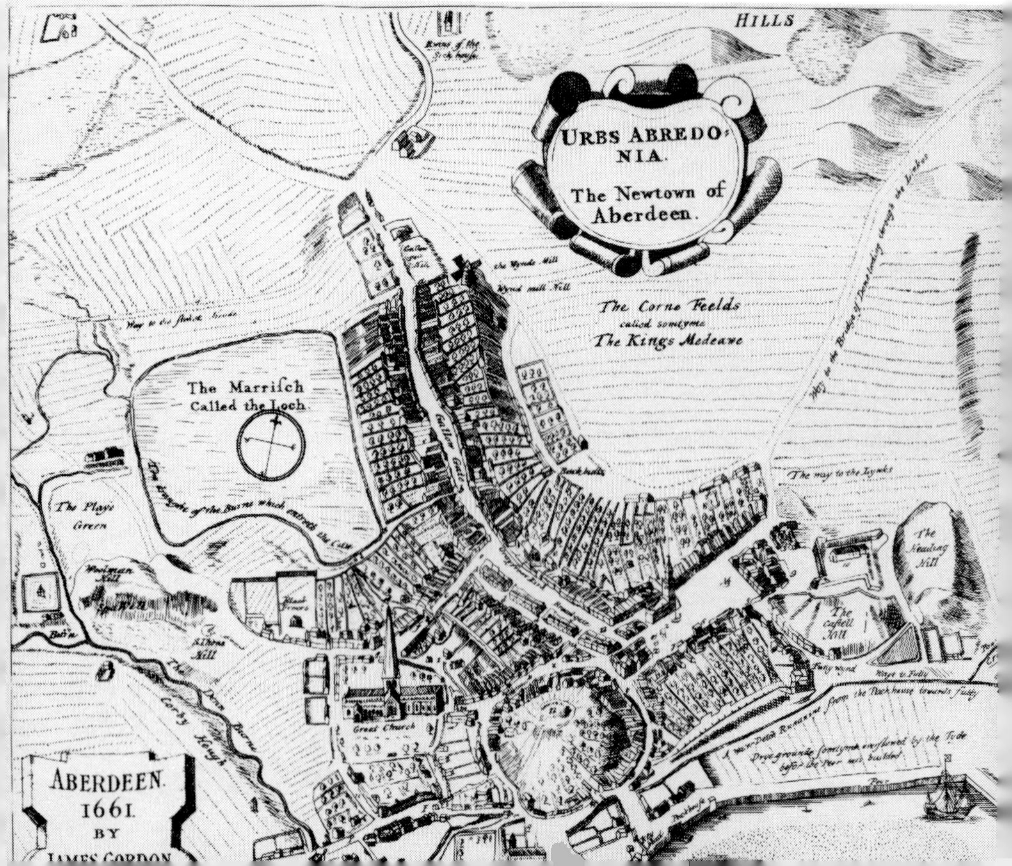

36. The fishing village of Crovie, Banffshire. Characteristically, the houses were placed close to the beach as most of the work such as baiting lines and gutting and cleaning fish was done in and around the houses *(J. Coull)*

37. Marischal College, University of Aberdeen *(J. S. Smith)*

38. St. Machar's Cathedral, Aberdeen. The impressive granite west front dates from the 14th century. The sandstone spires were added in the 16th century *(G. Stables)*

39. Oil service vessels in Aberdeen Harbour *(J. Livingstone)*

40. The St. Fergus gas terminal *(J. Livingstone)*

drink more and more whisky, and in order to meet the requirements of their taste, more blended whisky was produced, leading to a decrease in illicit distillation.

Up to 1850, whisky was still drunk mainly by the Scots and this is corroborated by the report on the drinking habits of Scotland, issued in 1842 by the Committee of the General Assembly of the Established Church of Scotland. In 1842, the population of England (15,000,000) consumed almost 8 million gallons (36.8 million litres) of spirit (brandy, rum and gin) or half a gallon per head of population; the population of Scotland (2,620,184) consumed 5.6 million gallons (25.8 million litres) of spirit (mostly whisky) or two gallons per head of population.

THE MANUFACTURE OF MALT WHISKY

The barley must be well-ripened, reasonably dry and above all, capable of fermentation. The general procedure is as follows (Fig 34).

Malting the barley: each grain of barley consists of a tiny barley plant enclosed in a skin which itself is packed in an outer skin or skins containing starch. Nature has provided the tiny barley plant with this storehouse of starch in order to supply it with food during the early stages of its life. It is the task of the distiller to deprive the plant of its food and to convert the starch into fermentable sugar. This malting process is performed by stimulating germination and then arresting it. The operation is a difficult one, for, if germination is allowed to proceed too far, much of the starch which the distiller requires for his malt would be consumed by the barley plant.

To start with, the barley is placed in large low tanks called "steeps". Water is poured on it and the barley is allowed to remain in the steep until moisture has penetrated every grain. Depending on the judgement of the maltman, this first part of the process takes from 40-60 hours. Then the barley is taken out and spread evenly over the floor of the long low-roofed malt-barns which are a feature of every Highland distillery. Here it begins to germinate and is continually turned over with large wooden shovels to maintain an even growth. In order to feed and satisfy the appetite of the growing plant, the grain, during germination, develops diastase, a compound which has the power of attacking moist starch and converting it to sugar. When restricted germination has reached this stage the process is stopped and the malt is then placed in a kiln, a chamber with a perforated wire floor below which a peat fire is burning. The smoke passes up to the malt, dries it slowly, and gives to it the peaty flavour which distinguishes most Highland whiskies.

The dried malt goes to the mill for bruising and thereafter proceeds

Figure 34 — Whisky making.

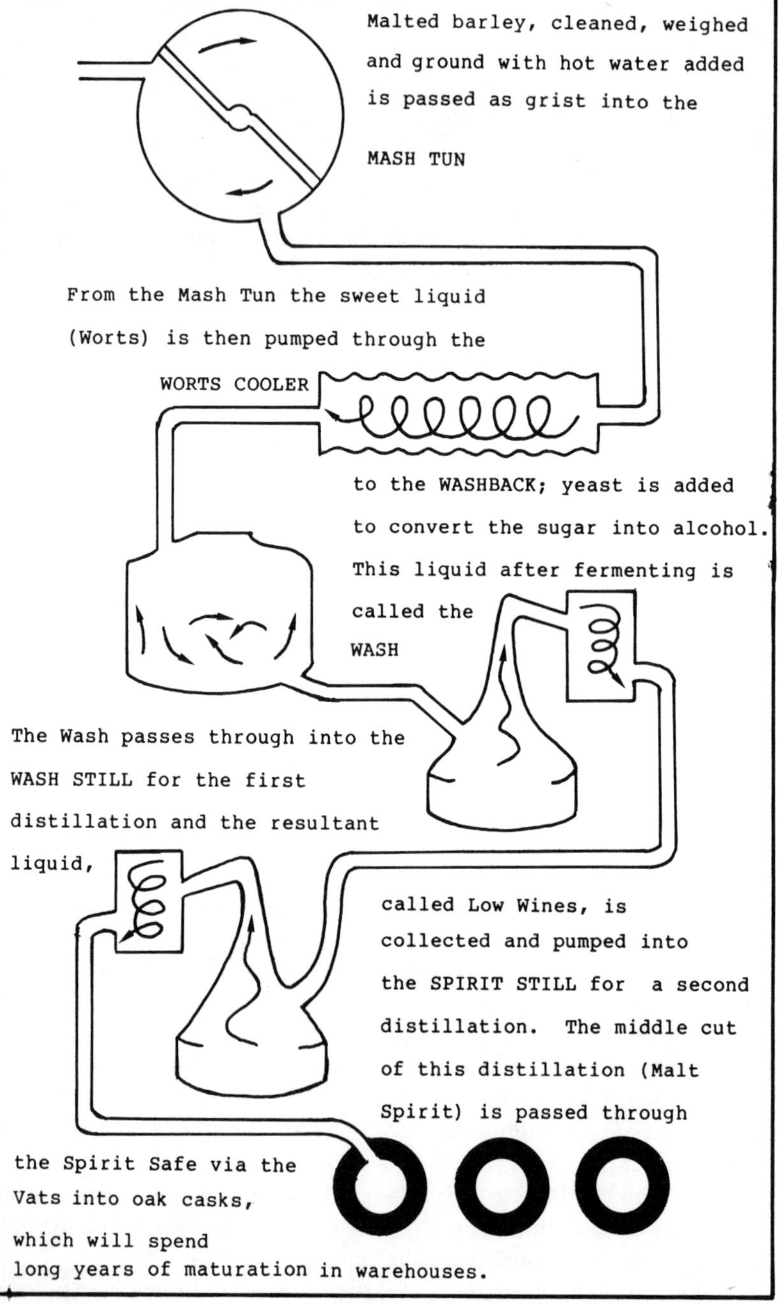

to the mash tun. Here it is mixed with hot water at a carefully regulated temperature and is stirred by machinery until the sugars in the malt are dissolved in the mash. The liquor thus obtained is strained off and produces a sweet, still non-alcoholic liquid which is called the "wort".

The following stage is that of "fermentation" when the brewer, an important man in every distillery, takes charge. The "wort" is passed into the fermenting vessels, huge round vats capable of holding anything from 2000-10,000 gallons (9200-46,000 litres) of liquid. In whisky, the fermenting agent is yeast, which, when added to the liquid in the vat, attacks the sugar and converts it into crude whisky. Other organisms such as bacteria play their part in giving a special flavour to the whisky, and some brewers are so fearful of any change affecting their product, that they will not allow even a cobweb to be swept away from the vat room.

The process of fermentation lasts from two to three days by which time a fully fermented liquid has been created. It contains crude whisky, yeast, and various by-products and also a quantity of unfermentable matter. The liquid thus produced has an alcoholic strength of only 10% or so and is now known as the "wash".

All is now ready for distillation, a process which for malt whisky requires the use of two stills. The "wash" is conducted into a large vessel, called the wash-charger which feeds the two stills known as the "wash-still" and the "spirit-still". The "wash-still" is like a huge copper kettle with a long spout turned down and extended through the wall of the still-room to the worm. This is a coiled copper pipe which lies in a large vessel of cold water. In the wash-still, the "wash" is heated to boiling point until the alcohol and other constituents of the malt rise in a vapour. This vapour then passes through the worm where it is cooled into liquid form.

The first distillate known technically as "low wines" is now ready for treatment in the spirit-still. Here the same process of vaporisation occurs, but is much more complicated for before distilling potable spirit from the spirit received, the still man has to eliminate and distill into another receiver the raw first runs and the undesirable last runs called respectively "foreshots" and "feints". This is the most delicate operation in the making of whisky and demands great skill on the part of the still man. He relies mainly on his experience and judgement, but has a further check in the hydrometers in the Distiller's Safe. This "Safe" is a brass case about the size of a large cabin trunk. The sides are made of glass behind which are the hydrometers. The pure malt whisky from the spirit-still is passed into this safe and here through the glass, the still man can test scientifically the strength and quality of his distillation. If

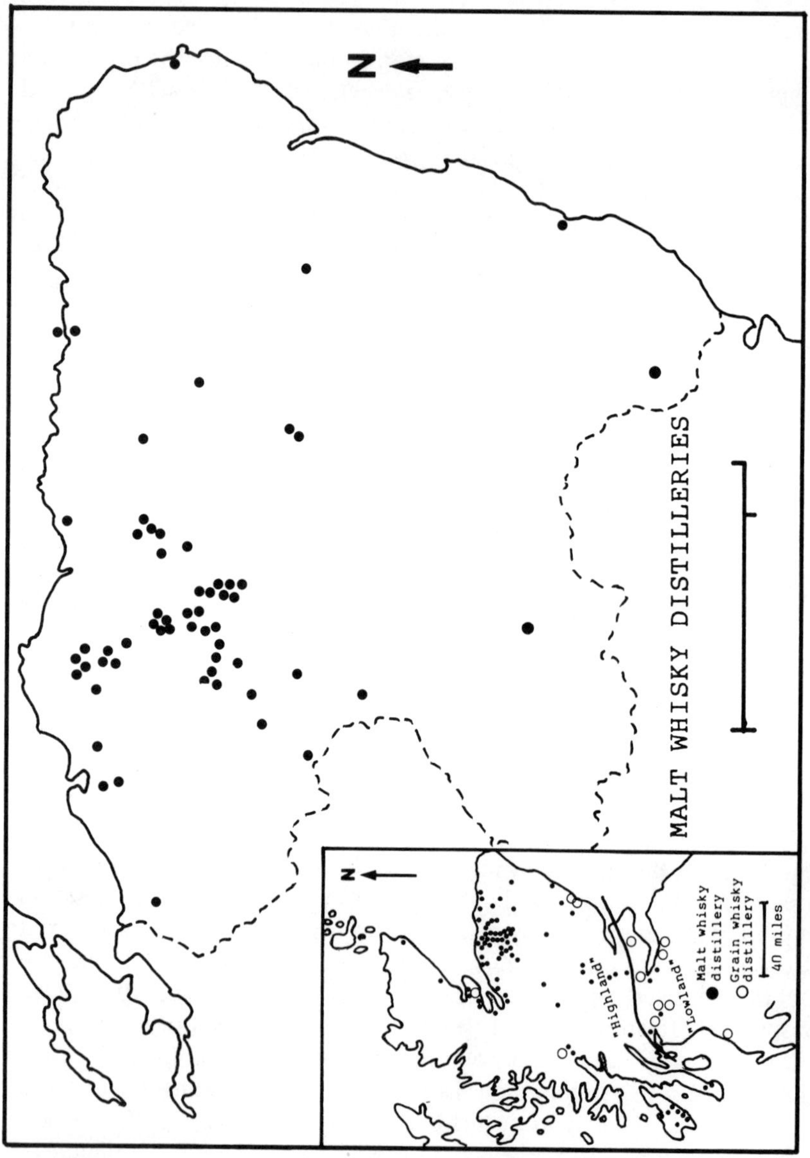

Figure 35 — Distribution of malt whisky distilleries.

he is satisfied with the result, he runs off the flow into the spirit receiver from which it is pumped to the store-room and filled into casks.

Malt whisky when it emerges from the spirit-still is as clear as gin and has to be matured in order to rid it of impurities and to improve its flavour. The choice of cask is all important and the best is an oak sherry cask. It was, in fact, the sherry in the wood which gave the malt whisky its rich amber colour, although nowadays a solution of caramel may be used to colour the whisky. Malt whisky is at its best between the ages of eight to 15 years.

Malt whisky is run into casks at 11.2° over proof and with increasing years loses some of its strength. When the time for bottling comes, the whisky is usually reduced to the customary standard of 30° under proof.

The Structure of the Industry

The structure of the Scotch whisky industry is both unusual and complex. The industry, on the basis of activity, can be divided into two main sectors, the distilling sector and the blending, bottling and marketing sectors. There also exists within Scotland a regional concentration of the various production activities. The major portion of malting and malt distilling is carried out in Grampian Region with a smaller proportion in Tayside and Highland Region, whilst the production of grain whisky, most blending and bottling, and a large proportion of the administration is carried out in the central belt of Scotland and even London. The whisky industry in Grampian Region represents under 10% of the total employment in the industry in Scotland. However, this is mainly a reflection of the difference in average employment size of production units rather than an indication of the significance of the malt distilling sector of the Grampian Region. Sixty of the 116 malt distilleries (open or temporarily closed) in Scotland are located in Grampian (Fig 35) and there is also a heavy concentration of both distilleries and other whisky related activities within Moray District.

In terms of ownership and control of the industry, the distinction between the two main arms of the industry has became blurred. There has been a considerable amount of both vertical and horizontal integration in the industry over the last 60 years, and now many distilleries are owned by blending and bottling companies which may also have acquired their own maltings and by-product plants.

Until recently the whisky industry in Scotland was dominated by some 15 major firms with approximately double that number of smaller independent companies. In 1985, The Guinness Company carried out a successful "take-over" of the well-known Bell's of Perth whisky company and in 1986 after a long "expensive" campaign between the Argyll

Company and the Guinness Company for the largest and most prestigious whisky company — Distillers — The Guinness Company again emerged as the victor.

Since 1980 many distilleries have been closed (whether temporarily or permanently is not yet certain) with many skilled men in the industry facing unemployment, a situation quite unknown except for the closures during the depression years of the 30s.

In recent years foreign companies, mainly Canadian, have also obtained ownership of malt distillers.

Malt distilling in Grampian also has a significant secondary impact on the economy through the development of new malting plants which have helped increase the market for locally grown barley and have benefited local transport industries.

By-product plants in Grampian Region, which number 15, represent an important element of the industry in the region. These plants use spent grain and effluents from the distilling process and convert them into high quality animal feedstuffs.

Cooperages and copper works are useful appendages to the whisky industry, together with the necessity for the existence of customs and excise officers at all distillers. Bonded warehouses also offer employment situations in the distillery areas.

The whisky industry also helps to boost the tourist trade, especially in those distilleries which offer facilities such as visitor centres and guided tours. The Whisky Trail is estimated to attract up to 60,000 visitors per year.

Problems Facing the Industry

Recent trends in the industry have seen a drop in production levels in distilling due to the combined effect of a declining export demand, a relatively stagnant home market and a build-up of stock in bond. The factors which have caused this combination of circumstances to arise are the trade barriers which allow overseas Governments to place restrictions of various kinds on imports of Scotch whisky; the export of bulk blended Scotch whisky which accounts for 21% of total exports and has remained relatively steady around this figure since the early 70s — this activity also deprives Scotland of the extra business and related employment in the bottling and packaging industries; and the steady increase in the United Kingdom of the excise duty which now represents 80% of the retail price.

Other problems of a more immediate kind which affect the whisky industry are the level of interest rates. The industry has a production cycle of approximately six years and so has a slow return on investment;

the strength of the pound in sterling, in relation to the currency of the importing country can greatly affect the demand for exports; the changes in drinking habits, from whisky to lighter spirits and wines also affects trade as does the volatile world economy.

Chapter seventeen

THE OIL INDUSTRY

Dr. Keith Chapman

INTRODUCTION

The development of the offshore oil and gas resources of the North Sea has had a major impact upon the national economy. The Grampian Region, and Aberdeen in particular, have played a decisive part in the exploitation of these resources. Some measure of the changes associated with these developments upon the economy and society of the region may be gained by reference to the principal conclusions of a study, published in 1969 just before the vanguard of seismic survey vessels and exploration teams first appeared in the harbours of the North-east, of the development potential of North-east Scotland (Gaskin 1969). Rarely can a predictive planning study have been so unfortunately timed as its assumptions and recommendations were overturned by the advent of the oil industry in the region. The study noted a slow decline in population, mainly as a result of outmigration, a rate of unemployment " . . . markedly above the national average" (p. 27) and a particular shortage of male job opportunities. Overall, its authors saw " . . . no evidence of a favourable trend down to the mid 1970s" (p. 67) and, with reference to the unemployment situation, they anticipated " . . . a worsening of the position" (p. 27). In fact within 2 years of publication of these predictions, the slow decline of population was reversed when the Grampian Region first showed a net gain on the balance of out- and in-migration in 1971 and the absolute increase in population has been one of the most rapid in the United Kingdom. Similarly, unemployment rates at the regional scale have consistently remained below the United Kingdom and Scottish levels. In mid 1985, for example, the Grampian rate of 7.8% compared favourably with United Kingdom and Scottish figures of 13.4 and 15.6% respectively (Grampian Regional Council, Autumn 1985). Thus the recent economic fortunes of the Grampian Region have proved to be very different from the expectations of the Gaskin report — a situation almost entirely due to the activities of the offshore oil and gas industry.

Aggregate indicators obscure the fact that the direct effects of the oil business upon the region have been very unevenly distributed, both in a social and geographical sense. The tangible effects of oil-related development are only apparent in Aberdeen, its immediate hinterland and a few other places such as Peterhead. Before reviewing these effects within Aberdeen itself and then the rest of the region, it is helpful to place them within the broader context of the development of North Sea oil and gas.

THE GROWTH OF THE NORTH SEA OIL AND GAS INDUSTRY

Whatever yardsticks are employed, the growth of the North Sea oil and gas industry has been impressive. Official estimates of oil reserves, which are notable for their caution, have steadily increased, whilst discoveries of natural gas in the northern North Sea are making major additions to the already substantial reserves contained in the earlier developed southern basin off the coast of England. Not only have discoveries been made, but they have also been rapidly developed. The United Kingdom became a net oil exporter in 1980; it ranked as the world's 5th largest oil producer by 1984 (Financial Times, 1986), and had a total of 31 fields in production by 1986.

These offshore achievements have necessarily generated substantial levels of economic activity onshore. Initially this activity was concentrated in East Anglia and especially Great Yarmouth as the southern North Sea attracted most commercial interest during the 1960s. This situation changed dramatically after the discovery of the first commercial oilfield in the United Kingdom sector in December 1969. The Montrose field lies approximately 225 km (140 miles) offshore due east of Aberdeen. Within 18 months, the giant Forties and Brent fields had also been found and, by emphasising the potential of northern waters, these discoveries accelerated the northward movement of the drilling rigs as the oil companies embarked on a search for oil in preference to the gas which had been the principal target in the south.

The most obvious indicator of the on-shore impact of these developments is provided by employment levels. In 1974, an estimated 13,500 were engaged in wholly North Sea oil-related work in Scotland; the corresponding figure for 1985 was 63,500 (Grampian Regional Council, Autumn 1985). These estimates take no account of indirect employment in, for example, engineering firms which sell part of their output to the oil industry. Although such an absolute growth in employment is impressive in the context of recent trends in the national labour market, even more significant from the point of view of Grampian Region has been its growing share of the total. The region accounted for 36% of the wholly oil-related jobs in Scotland in 1974. By 1985, the figure had risen to 82%, corresponding to 52,000 jobs, more than a quarter of total employment in Grampian Region (Grampian Regional Council, Autumn 1985).

The progressive concentration of employment in Grampian is related to the different locational requirements of the various phases or stages of activity associated with the exploitation of North Sea oil and gas. In general terms, a distinction may be made between exploration, development and production. These phases overlap and exploration continues in the mid 1980s, despite the fact that several older fields are in decline. Nevertheless, the relative significance of these activities in a major oil and gas province such as the North Sea changes through time as exploration is followed by the massive capital investments required to develop discoveries into producing fields which in turn must be managed and maintained throughout their operating lives. Proximity to offshore activity and the availability of harbour facilities are crucial in the exploration phase and bases have been established along the east coast from Leith in the south to Sandwick (Shetland) in the north. Quite different considerations have influenced the location of the fabrication yards involved in manufacturing the hardware associated with the development phase. These include the availability of deep, sheltered inshore water for the construction of concrete platforms, large, flat coastal sites for the fabrication of steel structures and associated concentrations of skilled, engineering labour. Most of these requirements are better met elsewhere in Scotland and much of the relatively short-term employment generated by the massive engineering projects of the development phase has been created outside the Grampian Region. However, Aberdeen has become the undisputed centre for the routine activities of the production phase. As service and administration functions replace the manufacturing jobs of the development phase, Aberdeen's overwhelming share of oil-related employment in Scotland will, if anything, increase.

Several factors have contributed to Aberdeen's emergence as the operational focus of the North Sea oil and gas industry. In the early stages, proximity to the fields, especially those discovered between 1959 and 1972, was important. However, several other localities with harbour facilities were equally well-placed including Dundee, Montrose and Peterhead. Of these alternatives, only Dundee was of similar size and it seems likely that the principal companies such as BP and Shell, which may be regarded as the decisive actors, quickly narrowed their options to a choice between Tayside and the "Granite City". As soon as it became apparent that North Sea oil had a long term future, these companies extended their concern beyond harbour facilities to include other aspects of infrastructure such as air services and road connections. It has been suggested that the appropriate agencies in Aberdeen were quicker to recognise the importance of improving these facilities than their counterparts in Dundee (Mackay and Moir 1980). Whatever considerations tipped the balance in Aberdeen's favour, the nature of the oil business is such that, once adopted by the major operators, its pre-eminence was assured. Despite its association with major multinational corporations, the exploration and production end of the oil industry is characterised by a fragmented commercial structure in which many activities are subcontracted to specialist firms. These supply materials, such as drilling muds and chemicals, and a wide range of services including offshore maintenance and inspection, catering and geological analyses. These firms depend for their survival upon contracts from the major oil companies and it is therefore important to be in the right place at the right time, which may be the bar of the Petroleum Club! This kind of business environment promotes geographical concentration and guarantees Aberdeen's position for as long as the industry continues to operate in the North Sea.

The Impact on Aberdeen

The initial impact of oil-related activity in Aberdeen was first apparent in the harbour area (Plate 39). Even before the oil industry arrived, both harbour and quay space were at a premium. The appearance of seismic survey vessels and supply boats added to the congestion and BP's decision to transfer its marine base to Dundee after less than 12 months of operating out of Aberdeen underlined the problem. A major improvement scheme was announced in October 1971, with the primary objective of making the originally non-tidal Upper and Victoria Docks open to the sea at all stages of the tide. This was essential to the harbour's role as a service base and was completed in 1976. Further capital expenditure has seen the construction of new roll-on/roll-off passenger and freight terminals which are able to provide a full 24-hour service.

Some measure of Aberdeen's importance as a service base is provided by the steady build-up of supply vessel movements which reached 4850 in 1984. This has taken place at the same time that the significance of the trawling fleet has declined. Although the supply boats were initially regarded as unwelcome intruders by fishing interests, the contraction of the trawling fleet has mainly been due to other factors. The entire character of the harbour has been transformed since 1970 and the scene once dominated by the characteristically neglected appearance of the trawlers is now associated with the less elegant, if generally better main-

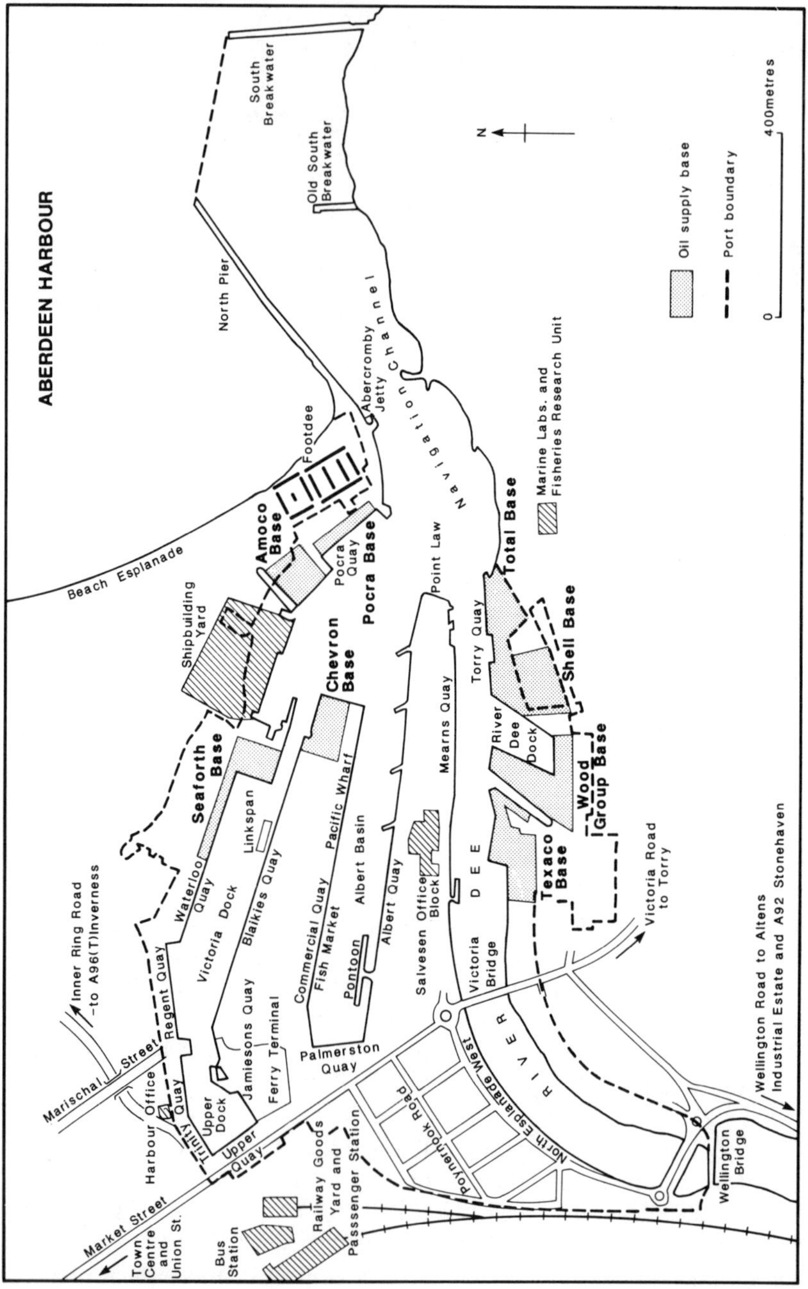

Figure 36 — Aberdeen harbour area.

tained, lines of the supply boats which transfer bulky items such as casing, drilling muds and chemicals to the rigs and platforms. These materials are assembled at the quayside at various bases which have all been established since 1970. The largest of these are located on the south bank of the Dee where considerable re-development has been required, notably in the controversial clearance of Old Torry, a 19th century fishing village, to make way for the Shell base.

The function of the supply boats in transporting materials is complemented by the role of the helicopters in transferring personnel. The airport on the north western edge of the city at Dyce is the largest commercial heliport in Europe, if not in the world. However, it is not only important as the focus for offshore helicopter operations, but also in providing the domestic and international links essential to Aberdeen's role as "the oil capital of Europe" — a role epitomised by the biennial Offshore Europe exhibition held in purpose-built facilities on a permanent site at Bridge of Don. The changes at the airport have been even more impressive than those at the harbour. Traffic increased from 150,000 passengers in 1970 to 1.75 million in 1984. This has been achieved by major investment in a completely new terminal and control tower. The existing terminal and related facilities, which are located on the opposite side of the airfield to the original buildings, provide an appropriately modern first impression to visitors arriving by air. This image is reinforced by the provision of associated facilities, such as the new access road from the A96 and the construction of hotel accommodation in close proximity to the airport.

Although over 40% of the oil-related jobs based in the Region actually involve working offshore (Grampian Regional Council, August 1985), the arrival of the oil industry has necessarily involved a significant expansion of onshore industrial facilities, mainly within Aberdeen. This has required a corresponding increase in the provision of land for industry and approximately 404.7 ha (1000 acres) have been developed on industrial estates within Grampian Region since 1975 (Grampian Regional Council, August 1985). This compares with a corresponding figure of 1295 ha (3200 acres) taken up by new housing. Before 1973, the annual rate of development on industrial estates within the region averaged 12 ha (30 acres). This increased to 30.3 ha (75 acres) in the next five years and reached a peak of 64.7 ha (160 acres) in 1980. Whereas some difficulty had been experienced in promoting the older industrial estates within Aberdeen before the arrival of the oil industry, resulting in very gradual rates of occupation, the situation has been transformed in recent years. The development of the East Tullos estate [60 ha; (148 acres)], for example, took at least 20 years to achieve; the much larger

Altens estate [121 ha; (300 acres)] seems likely to be fully occupied within 12 years.

The distribution of oil-related employment within Aberdeen has been strongly influenced by the policies of the local planning authorities. Most of this employment is concentrated in the various industrial estates around the periphery of the city, but the harbour area is also important. Despite their designation as "industrial" estates, most of the oil-related jobs on them do not involve manufacturing. It is difficult to obtain reliable figures, but probably little more than 20% of these jobs are actually engaged in manufacturing (mainly engineering). The remainder are associated either with office work or with the numerous "services" provided by specialist firms to the major operators. Most of these service firms are based in the industrial estates.

The geography of oil-related activities within Aberdeen has changed through time. The harbour was the initial focus, but it soon became apparent that pressure on space would be a serious obstacle to future development. Many of the early arrivals found suitable accommodation on the already established East and West Tullos estates which had previously been more than adequate to meet the anticipated demand for industrial land. Aberdeen's emergence as **the** centre for the North Sea oil industry caused the planning authorities to radically alter their forecasts of this demand and several major new areas were zoned for industrial development between 1971 and 1976. Many of these are near the airport at Dyce and a high proportion of the firms occupying these sites are engaged in oil business. The occupants of the Bridge of Don, Denmore and Murcar estates along the A92 on the northern edge of the city are more varied in character, but the large Altens estate to the south is heavily involved in oil-related activities.

Many oil-related jobs are office-based and the provision of suitable accommodation has had a notable impact on the urban fabric of the city. The growth of office employment relative to manufacturing jobs is a general characteristic of the modern economy. Some expansion of office accommodation in line with national trends may therefore have been expected in Aberdeen, especially in view of its traditional role as the principal administrative centre for North-east Scotland. However, the arrival of the oil industry has provided a major impetus to office development within the city. Thus of the stock of approximately 350,000 m^2 (3.77 million ft^2) of office floorspace in the Aberdeen area at the end of 1981, 200,000 m^2 (2.15 million ft^2) had been developed within the preceding 10 years, almost 60% of which was attributed to oil-related activity (Grampian Regional Council, Winter 1981-82). Overall, such activity accounted for one-third of total office accommodation at the beginning of the 1980s. The pace of office expansion has slackened in recent years and there is some evidence that speculative developers have been over-optimistic with the result that certain large properties, especially in the harbour area, have remained empty.

The pattern of oil-related office development has, to some extent, paralleled that of industrial development. At the beginning of the "oil boom", the major oil companies had to rent whatever was available, mainly in the city centre and near the harbour. Shell's first home was, for example, the former Corporation tram depot adjacent to the Victoria Bridge at the lower end of Market Street, a far cry from the massive purpose-built office complex the company now occupies at Tullos. Shell's experience is fairly typical of the principal exploration and production companies. As the offshore search proved successful, so these companies increased the level of the Aberdeen-based administrative and technical staff and took a more optimistic view of its permanency. Their growing commitment to the city has found physical expression in a series of large, new office-buildings. These have resulted in a significant decentralisation of office accommodation from the city centre, mainly because of the difficulty of finding suitable large sites in the inner area, but also because of restrictions imposed by the local planning authorities. Most of the major oil companies have established their offices on or near the industrial estates with, for example, Shell at Tullos, BP at Dyce and Occidental at Bridge of Don. The principal exception to the pattern is a substantial concentration of large new offices, developed and occupied by oil companies, close to the former granite quarry at Rubislaw in the west end of the city.

THE IMPACT ON THE REGION

More than 90% of the direct oil-related employment in Grampian Region is concentrated in the Aberdeen area. Most of the remainder is accounted for by Peterhead and the massive gas reception terminal 6 km (3.7 miles) to the north at St. Fergus. Peterhead was quickly identified by the oil industry as an attractive location because of its harbour. It does, in fact, have two harbours. The smaller, inner harbour, is usually crowded with fishing boats, whilst oil-related shipping is associated with Peterhead Bay. This is enclosed by two long breakwaters to form the Harbour of Refuge. It was eventually completed in 1956 having been constructed by labour from the adjacent prison and it comprises 1.6 km^2 (1 $mile^2$) of sheltered water. It is unique along the North-east coast in its ability to accommodate not only supply boats, but also the much larger drilling rigs and pipelaying barges. Two major bases have been established within the harbour, the biggest on reclaimed land at its southern edge. Despite earlier fears that these bases may prove to be short-lived (Chapman 1976), Peterhead has remained important as an offshore base and the number of supply boat movements is about 60% of the level out of Aberdeen. The Harbour of Refuge is, however, capable of receiving semi-submersible drilling rigs, something which is impossible in the more restricted spaces of Aberdeen harbour, and the maintenance and repair of such structures provides an important line of business for the Peterhead bases.

A number of sites on the edge of Peterhead have been suggested as possible locations for petrochemical developments (Grampian Regional Council/Banff and Buchan District Council 1980), following an earlier proposal by Shell to establish a natural gas separation and liquefaction plant, together with associated loading facilities in the harbour for the export of the products. Fears regarding the safety of refrigerated tanker operations out of a harbour surrounded by housing on its landward side eventually resulted in the abandonment of this scheme and, with it, the only realistic prospect of oil - and gas-processing activities within the region. Several industrial estates have been established around the town in much the same way as in Aberdeen. The Dales estate, in particular, is almost exclusively occupied by oil-related businesses, mainly engaged in service activities.

The St. Fergus gas terminal (Plate 40) provides the most spectacular visual evidence of the North Sea oil and gas industry in Grampian. It is located on a 200 ha (494 acres) site behind an impressive line of sand dunes. This facility receives gas from several offshore fields delivered by four pipelines and it represents a vital link in the chain connecting offshore platforms with gas consumers. The terminal removes water and other impurities before transferring gas of the appropriate specification into the onshore transmission system. The complex consists of three elements. Total Oil Marine (UK) Ltd. receives gas via two pipelines from the Frigg field, which straddles the boundary between the United Kingdom and Norwegian sectors, and from smaller fields along the way. Shell derives its supplies from a pipeline system which taps several fields (mainly Brent) in the East Shetlands Basin and another system which approaches the coast from the south east and originates at the Fulmar field. Most of the products from the Total and Shell facilities are transferred over the fence to British Gas to be compressed and fed into trunk pipelines heading for markets to the south. The volume of gas landed at St. Fergus makes it the most important terminal of this type in the United Kingdom and it is probable that further discoveries will justify the construction of at least one more offshore pipeline to the site.

Once established, initially to handle the first deliveries of gas from

Frigg in 1977, the terminal became the "natural" choice for all subsequent gas landfalls from the United Kingdom sector of the northern North Sea. However, the existing site was not the first choice. The original intention of the developers was to bring Frigg gas ashore 6 km (3.7 miles) to the north, passing the pipeline through the Loch of Strathbeg to a terminal to be built on a disused military airfield at Crimond. The Loch of Strathbeg is the largest coastal dune lake in Britain, an important staging post for wildfowl and a site of major scientific interest (Bourne *et al* 1973). In these circumstances, there was considerable opposition to the proposed development, resulting in its diversion to St. Fergus. This unusual success for the environmental lobby is interesting because it draws attention to a deliberately unobtrusive aspect of the St. Fergus project — the pipeline landfalls themselves. The establishment of a major gas reception terminal required a combination of a large, flat onshore site, a sandy coastline and a gradually sloping offshore approach. Coastal dune systems are notoriously sensitive to human intervention and considerable, largely successful, efforts have been directed towards minimising the damage resulting from pipetrenches not only through the St. Fergus dunes, but also those at Cruden Bay 20 km (12.4 miles) to the south, where oil from the Forties field is landed and pumped onwards to the Grangemouth refinery on the Firth of Forth. The precise locations of the landfalls are now difficult to find, a tribute to careful planning, construction and restoration (Ritchie 1980).

Apart from Peterhead and St. Fergus, the only other visual evidence of oil-related economic activity in Grampian Region beyond the immediate hinterland of Aberdeen is provided by various pipe-storage yards. Indeed, the more remote inland parts of the region continue to experience the kind of economic and social problems described in the Gaskin report. In some respects, these problems may have been exacerbated by the oil industry. The decline of traditional sources of employment has certainly been accelerated by upward pressure on wage rates created by increased competition for labour (McDowall and Begg 1981). It would, however, be perverse in the extreme to suggest that the region would be better off without oil. Nevertheless, the extent of Aberdeen's dependence upon this industry for its contemporary prosperity is a matter for some concern and it is, perhaps, appropriate to conclude with a brief assessment of the variables influencing future prospects.

THE FUTURE

External events in the world oil market have an important influence upon Aberdeen. The big oil price increases in 1973/74 and again in 1979 both had the effect of stimulating the development of the North Sea. By the same token, the collapse in the world oil price at the beginning of 1986 represents a threat to future development. Existing fields will continue to produce and companies will proceed with projects to which they are already financially committed. However, the economics of smaller fields and exploration prospects will be adversely affected by the instability of world oil prices. It is clearly in Aberdeen's long term interest that this uncertainty is resolved. The relevance of wider economic events is underlined by the fact that the majority of oil-related jobs in Grampian are provided by companies which have their headquarters in London, Houston and other world cities. In this respect, the region has less control over its own economic destiny than it did 20 years ago. Although there have been some notable exceptions, the involvement of essentially local enterprise in the oil business is limited (Hunt and Atkin 1979). This represents a continuing challenge to entrepreneurs and policy-makers in the region and the long term objective must be to create an indigenous expertise leading to the establishment of a manufacturing and, probably more important, a specialised service capability geared to international markets and not just the North Sea.

Chapter eighteen

TRADITIONAL BUILDINGS

Dr. Alexander Fenton

The lowland parts of Grampian Region are amongst the most densely settled and intensive farming areas in Scotland. This stage was not reached without a tremendous amount of hard work, trenching ground with spade and tramp-pick, draining of wet and boggy patches and channelling springs, raising and blasting yird-fast stones and gathering stones from the fields into heaps or building them into dykes. Amongst the great memorials to the sheer, dogged effort that went into land improvement are the "consumption" dykes at Kingswells, near Aberdeen, built from cleared stones in the late 1700s, broad enough to drive a horse and cart along, and stretching for up to half a mile. But apart from these spectacular examples, what really marks the landscape still is the pattern of stone dykes that bound innumerable fields, tons and tons of stone and mile after mile of dykes. They are, sadly, now falling into decay because dykers are scarce and costly, big machinery demands bigger fields, and stob-and-wire or electric fencing is easier to handle and maintain.

Agricultural improvements that began in the 1750s affected not only the fields, but the houses and steadings also. There was an immense amount of rebuilding. Mains farms on estates were often improved in advance of other farms, but the bulk of this activity lay in the late 18th and early 19th century for the more southerly and northerly parts of Grampian Region (Kincardine, Moray) and somewhat later, around 1860 - 1915, for the Banff and Buchan area. The building pattern is itself relatively recent, therefore, and this has consequences for the interpretation of what is meant by "traditional building", whether they are farmhouses or "crafties" and steadings, cottar houses and chaumers, smiddies and joiners' shops, meal mills and sawmills, or the like. A further factor is that farming is no more static than any other industry. As long as farmers depended on the horse as a source of power and for draught, and as long as the plough, carts and other equipment were on a scale that horses could handle, then buildings that had been put up new with their cart-sheds, threshing mill barns and grain lofts, stables and byres, neep-sheds and hay-lofts, could remain much as they had been. With the coming of technology, however, change became inevitable, and went far beyond the normal alterations due to wear and decay to which farms, like flesh, are heir.

First there was the threshing-mill that slowly replaced hand-threshing with the flail. On bigger farms, and then on smaller ones, the eident thump, thump, thump of the souple in the wee sma' 'oors was replaced by the clatter and dust of the threshing machines. At first they were driven by horse or water power. In the drier areas horse courses appeared alongside the barns, usually in the shape of open platforms round which one or more horses walked, harnessed to a pole that worked the gearing. When the present writer was at Turriff School, in the 1940s, he sometimes led a horse round such a course to drive "Wattie Black's mull" at Backhill of Hatton farm in Auchterless. This may have been one of the last to operate in the North-east, after a period of use of such mills that began in the 1780s or 90s. Most of the Grampian horse courses were not roofed over, as recorded in the manuscript diary of G. Grant, Glenfarclas, Blacksboat, Granton-on-Spey. The old horse course, clearly, was renewed in 1859:

3 Feb. 1859: Draving off the Stuf of the old Horse course.
15 Jan. 1867: Hade to cast our horse course of snow.

Very rarely, horse courses were covered, as in the still standing example, with its conical slated roof, at the back of the steading at Mains of Newtongarry, Drumblade, near Huntly (Plate 32). Where there was a good supply of water from a burn, mill-dams were constructed, with a sluice-gate or "cloosh" that turned on the water to drive the threshing mill wheel, which was often of the "start an' aa" type, with flat paddles (Plate 29).

Dams were prominent features in the layout of a steading, the haunts of water-hens, and places of great attraction to young boys, but with the coming of the tractor to the farms during the First World War, further change set in rapidly. Dams, and horse courses, began to be superseded by a simple wheel operated from the tractor by a pulley and belt. Pulley wheels marking the days of tractor-driven barn mills still protrude from many barn walls, though they themselves have long been idle as a result of the combine-harvester, which threshes as it cuts in the field.

However, that was not the end of the influence of the tractor on buildings. As they got bigger than the old "Fergie" and Fordson, they began to be used for bigger equipment which needed house room not usually available in the old steadings. When government regulations laid down a requirement for the fitting of safety-cabs, doors and cart-shed entrances proved to be too low. They had to be altered, or completely new sheds had to be erected. In some cases the old steading was completely swept away. This kind of process is now changing the character of steadings faster than anything else, and instead of steadings being dominated by a large dwelling house alongside (as on some of the larger farms), now the huge prefabricated sheds dominate the dwelling-houses.

We are now seeing the culmination of a long process. Ever since systematic improvements began, farms have been amalgamating with each other to make bigger units, and crofts have been getting swallowed up. In spite of this process of "engrossment", one of the characteristics of the area has been the mix of smaller and larger places, the one providing a reservoir of labour for the other. It is in the buildings of such smaller places that many traditional features could be seen even within the last 20 years, before the brush of modernisation started to sweep them cleanly away forever.

In earlier days, estate practices played a role in building construction, especially for the roof, since the roofing timbers were often supplied to smaller tenants. In the parish of Dallas, Moray, the laird supplied local planted fir in 1792[1], but it was up to the tenant to find the material for the walls and for covering the roof. In Kincardineshire in 1701, it seems that the tenants had the right to take roofing timbers with them when they moved, since estate regulations forbade any tenant, subtenant, cottar or grassman to do more than pull down enough of the house walls to free the timber to let it be taken away[2]. Another system was for the tenant to receive a certain quantity of timber by appreciation, on entry. He was then accountable for it, and if he made the roofing better, he was allowed, for example, by Lord Findlater in Banffshire, in 1763, to carry it away or agree with an incoming tenant[3].

In several cases, these timbers were of the type now described as "crucks", with couple legs built into the wall and extending well down towards the floor. The main couples, rising from the tops of the legs and joining at the roof ridge, were called **hoos**. To firm them up, there were two cross-pieces, a lower, full-width one called the **bauk** and a higher, shorter one, the **croon piece**[4]. Crucks were not unique to the North-east. They could be found all over Scotland, but in the North-east they were largely replaced, quite early on, by the ubiquitous A-frame couples.

Whether crucks or A-frame couples formed the base, there was a timber roof-ridge, usually a tree-trunk, along the top, spars called **pans** that linked the couples longways, and more slender **cabers** laid up-and-down. These formed a bed for divots cut with a flauchter-spade and laid to overlap like the scales of a fish and over this went the outer cover of thatch.

There were various forms of thatching. Heather was the best and longest lasting medium, but it was expensive and, outside the hill areas, the gathering of it required organisation. On the Monymusk estate in 1748, over 15 days were spent pulling heather(5). On 11 May 1859, John Grant of Glenfarclas was "Seeking Bell Innes to pull heather", and on 20 May he was "At Knockandoo at Bell Innes to pull heather". Later, on 1 June, he "engaged Georg Kanie to hether houses at 1/2 per foot"(6). By the 1790s heather thatching was being seen as an improved form of roofing in the lower lying airts. If well put on, it could last over 60 years.

An innovation of the 1780s was **stob-thatching**. By means of a **stob**, a fork with two short prongs and a hand grip, small bunches or **tippets** of straw were thrust into the underlying divots. A farm diary from Lewes, Fyvie, spoke of "tippeting" in the 1820s. Work was done in courses from eaves to ridge, each course being 61 - 91 cm (2 - 3 ft) wide, and consisting of rows of eight or more tippets. Stob thatch could make a nice, compact roof, replacing the older system, which was simply a thin coat of thatch laid over the divots, and fastened by straw ropes that crossed each other, network fashion. As was said in 1794: "Nothing can be a less sufficient roof than this. It is not one roof in a hundred that can keep out a violent rain even when new made. The wind breaks the ropes and blows away the thatch, so that it is in need of continual repair, and is never sufficient"(7). This is what is called a "strae-an'-rape" roof (Plate 33).

Another improved form of roofing, dating from soon before 1795, was clay-thatch. This became common from Sutherland and Caithness, through the North-east, into Fife and across to Ayrshire. As the thatch — of straw, bent grass, rushes, heather, reeds or even broom — was laid on course by course, a fairly liquid clay mixture was used to impregnate it. The ridge was finished off with a good layer of much more solid clay. When dry, this made a fine, firm roof, that needed no ropes, and was more or less watertight. That the technique was good is shown by the fact that it lasted till the 1970s in the area of Urquhart in Moray, carried out by skilled thatchers like Sandy Mackenzie from the Muir of Urquhart, and Mr Brockie of Cranloch, and in the New Pitsligo area by men like James Strachan. Such men were the last "clay-thackers" in Scotland, but there were also countless folk who, in the usual Johnnie Aa-thing way, simply did it themselves when necessary. The story is told in the Diary of George Gall, Oldtown Atherb. On 15 August 1868, he was mending holes in the barn roof with straw and clay. On 9 October, he was "mixing clay as the man Dicky is come to mend up some holes in the roof of the Henhouse, taking up two loads of sand to make the clay freer". Next day he was carrying clay for the henhouse, and cutting straw for mixing in it.

Slate roofs were coming into fashion by the late 1750s[8], but at first only on the dwelling houses of the bigger farms. Outhouses and the roofs of smaller farm-houses continued to be thatched for a long time, as well as houses in some of the villages:

Byth for the biggins
Wi' the strae-thackit riggins.

Along the coasts, in the fishing villages, a good deal of roofing tiles could be seen, from tile-works like the one at Blackpots, Whitehills, unfortunately demolished within the last few years after something like a century and a half of life.

Substantial buildings that were slated early on had walls of stone and lime. Lesser places, however, continued to be built with walls of turf, pure clay, or stone mortared with clay or earth. In the hillier areas, there were examples of wattle walls, as on a large barn erected in the 1790s in Moray. The open-work wattle let in a good breeze to keep fresh the crops stored inside[9]. In crofters' houses in the same districts, there could also be found a technique of walling with alternating courses of turf and stone. The turf no doubt helped to grip rounded stones that were not easy to build into walls on their own[10]. In the lower-lying parts alongside, walls were often of turf alone, though by 1810 or so these were becoming scarce. The older ones were said to have had no windows, or just a small opening that could be shut by a board on hinges, like a door. They could have one room only, with a box bed in it, or later on two or three rooms with a window in each. The turf could even be daubed with clay plaster, or whitewashed, to make all look trig[11]. Bits of turf building survived into fairly recent times, since turf was often used to complete the upper triangle of a gable. There is a photograph of this at the Townhead, Kintore in the 1920s (Plate 30) and in 1962 a turf gable built in herring-bone fashion could still be seen at Gartly, Aberdeenshire.

A walling medium that has a long tradition behind it is "mud" or clay. Mud houses are mentioned in Forres in 1586[12] and a number survived till recent times, in Garmouth, and in parts of Banff and Buchan. The clay was well mixed with heather or straw, or small stones, to give it more endurance, and footings of stone were needed to keep the damp away. Clay could make a strong, enduring and well-insulated wall. There was also a special form of it, known as "clay and bool" or

"Auchenhalrig work", in which stones and clay were laid in alternating courses. This characterised Moray and Nairn, with outliers into Banffshire[13].

The daytime focal point in all houses of traditional character is the kitchen fireplace, the kitchen functioning also as living room, and often sleeping-place, with a wooden box-bed or "bun'-in" ("bound" or built-in) bed at the back of it. In earlier days the peat-burning fire was at floor level, against a wall, and the smoke was carried out through a "hingin'-lum", a canopy set against the wall. This was the forerunner of the built chimney in the thickness of the gable or internal partition wall. In front of the fire there could be a pit in the floor, covered with a grating, into which ashes were swept, tea-leaves emptied, etc., and from which the contents were taken from time to time to manure the fields. Examples of such pits have been noted in recent years at the croft of Hardbedlam, New Deer, and at the farm of Greenbogs, near Keith (Plate 31). At Blindburn Croft, Bennachie, ashes were said to have been cleared every three weeks in the 1920s[14].

Inside the "hingin' lum" was a **rantle-tree**, a bar of wood or iron from which the crook and links hung. The use of a **swey,** hinged to swing out so that heavy pots of boiling liquids could be more easily lifted off the crook, goes with the coal-burning grate which began to appear from the 1790s, as at Forglen in Banffshire[15].

The characteristic 19th century form of the North-east "hingin' lum" was that of an inverted wooden funnel above a fairly narrow fireplace space, sometimes with a press at each side, or a press at one side and a peat-neuk at the other. The common arrangement of kitchen fireplaces with protruding stone cheeks, even when the chimney is in the thickness of the wall, seems to be a continuation of the "hingin'-lum" principle. The example at Greenbog, Grange, Banffshire was built about 1880-90. Tradition dies hard.

On bigger farms, the fireplaces were much bigger, taking up a good deal of the width of the gable. Such big hearths, with lums almost big enough to sit under, were to be found in the more northerly and higher lying parts of the district, especially where there was plenty of timber for firing. A barrow-load of peats could also be stacked handily in a corner of it.

On the outside, the chimneys of "hingin'-lums" can be spotted by the fact that they protrude a little way in from the gable (Plate 33). Survivors of recent days have been of wood or tin, but earlier on they were beautifully thatched and roped around. The thatching of the roof and of the lum were things in which craftsmen could take great pride. According

to George Gall's **Diary**, both joiner and farmer were involved at Oldtown, Atherb:
1868 7 October "The Wright was up working the most of the day, mending the Lums".
10 October "Making rapes for the purpose of winning the Lum and platting it".
And then on 12 December, he was "Teeming the ash hole before the Fire".

The elements of traditional buildings discussed here are integral parts of the structure. The form and layout of the whole have to be considered also.

In the second half of the 18th century, improved farm-houses were beginning to be built by lairds like Lord Findlater, between Cullen and Banff. His were of two storeys, with a steading on three sides of a square(17), but the most common form of farmhouse, on the general run of farms, was of 1½ storeys. Uppermill of Pitglassie, Auchterless, is an example of a two-storey farmhouse, and Logie Newton in the same parish has 2½ storeys, looking curiously massive in its surroundings. On this scale, farmhouses do not form part of the steading, but stand nearby. On smaller places, however, integration with the steading was and remained much closer. Small places with the barn, byre and house joined together in line reflect a widespread pre-improvement layout, though with improved buildings.

The major general change was from one-storey to 1½ storey houses. Extra accommodation was provided by the two rooms and a landing above, and on the ground floor, the two or three rooms and a closet or later a milkhouse, remained much as before. A major difference, however, was that whereas earlier buildings had, as often as not, belonged to the tenant (except for the roof timbers), new ones were owned by the estate, and rents were paid. It is, however, a point of great interest that the new tradition of estate building did not squeeze out traditional features like forms of layout and roofing, the kind of kitchen fireplace, internal room divisions formed by wooden box beds, presses, partitions and doors, and so on, for a long time. In spite of the spread of slated roofs, walls of stone and clay mortar, and chimneys in the thickness of the gable wall (at first sometimes "ben the hoose" only), several of the older features have remained to be recorded within the last two decades. Nevertheless, the rate of change in the late 1700s and early 1800s was quite phenomenal, as is sharply shown by comparison of parish accounts in the **Old Statistical Account** of the 1790s with those in the **Second Statistical Account** of the 1840s. Few farming areas have ever experienced such intensive changes, and it is probably the characteristic mix of large farms, medium-sized and small farms and crofts, each in a great degree depending on the other, that has allowed traditional elements to survive so long, since in the very democratic nature of North-east farming, there was no special pressure to clear away outmoded features just for the sake of prestige.

References

1. *Old (First) Statistical Account,* IV (1792), 107.
2. *Court Book of the Barony of Urie,* ed. by D. G. Barron, 1892 (Scottish History Society), 113.
3. Seafield Papers, Box 38, Bundle 1 (Scottish Record Office).
4. *An Echo of the Olden Time from the North of Scotland,* by Rev. Walter Gregor, 1874 (John Menzies & Co., Edinburgh and Glasgow; David Scott, Peterhead), 14.
5. *Life and Labour on an Aberdeenshire Estate 1735 - 1750,* ed. by H. Hamilton, 1946 (Third Spalding Club, Aberdeen), 75 - 76.
6. *MS Diary,* by J. Grant (private possession of G. Grant, Glenfarclas).
7. *General View of the Agriculture of the County of Aberdeen,* by J. Anderson, 1794, Edinburgh, 96 - 99.
8. *General View of the Agriculture of the County of Banff,* by J. Donaldson, 1794, Edinburgh, 22 - 23.
9. *A Survey of the Province of Moray,* by J. Grant and W. Leslie, 1798, Aberdeen, 238.
10. Alternating Stone and Turf — An Obsolete Building Practice, by A. Fenton. In *Folk Life* 6 (1968), 94 - 103.
11. *General View of the Agriculture of Nairn and Moray,* by W. Leslie, 1811, London, 58 - 59, 67.
12. *Annals of the Royal Burgh of Forres,* ed. by R. Douglas, 1934, Elgin, 450.
13. Clay Building and Clay Thatch in Scotland, by A. Fenton. In *Ulster Folklife* 15/16 (1970), 28 - 51; *Clay Building in North East Scotland,* by B. Walker, 1977 (Scottish Vernacular Buildings Working Group, Dundee and Edinburgh).
14. Agriculture in Aberdeenshire in the Sixties. In the *Deeside Field,* 1927, 29ff.
15. *Old Statistical Account* XIV (1795) 545.
16. *General View of the Agriculture of Banff,* by D. Souter, 1812, Edinburgh, 89, 90.
17. *General View of the Agriculture of the County of Banff,* by J. Donaldson, 1794, Edinburgh, 21 - 23.

Chapter nineteen

SETTLEMENTS AND COMMUNICATIONS

Dr. John S. Smith

Grampian experienced a period of agricultural and fishing-inspired colonisation in the historical period. Its settlement pattern reflects resource distribution and laird initiative. The rich agricultural bases of the Garioch, the Laich of Moray and the Howe of the Mearns nourished old established royal burghs, although some of the best ground was only successfully taken into agriculture in the late 18th and early 19th centuries following sustained drainage works such as those around the former Loch of Spynie in lowland Moray. Contrasting with these rich meat and meal girnals, the dispersed smallholdings won their ground by pushing up onto stony hills and into lowland peat mosses as in Buchan and on the Aultmore. Amalgamation of holdings and a retreat from the high tide mark of agricultural endeavour has brought depopulation to these marginal areas, both in lowland and upland situations. However, in general, the royal burghs have consistently strengthened their position in the hierarchy of settlement, notably Aberdeen and Elgin (Plates 43 and 48).

The main centres in the Grampian settlement hierarchy originated as royal burghs with commercial privileges. Their monopoly of trade held back the upstart baronial burghs like Fraserburgh and Peterhead which were founded several hundred years later. The old established centres — Inverurie, Kintore, Banff, Cullen (Plate 47), Elgin, Forres (Plate 49) and Inverbervie — all competed with the highest order royal burgh of Aberdeen which had the advantages of size and a coastal location backed by an environmentally-favoured lowland with agricultural potential and marketable products. The gaps in the settlement net contained kirktons and milltons forming very small population clusters grouped around what were historically considered to be essential rural services. These were subsequently to decay in favour of new nucleations (hamlets) springing up at road junctions or around railway stations — of which the shift in centre of gravity from Bridge of Alford to Alford in middle Donside is the classic example. Another surge of settlement foundation took place in Grampian in the 18th and early 19th century under the aegis of landowners who sought to accommodate the surplus of agricultural population released by estate improvements by introducing rural domestic trades and marketing/servicing facilities — sometimes entirely new village creations as at New Pitsligo and Laurencekirk, elsewhere grafted onto small existing nuclei originally associated with castle and church foundations as at Huntly and Keith. In the latter case, two neighbouring landowners were involved, with New Keith founded in 1750 by the Earl of Findlater while Fife Keith was subsequently developed by the 4th Earl of Fife. Such planned villages are generally laid out in distinctive grid patterns, usually with a prominent central market place. The grid plan helped to maximise housing densities perhaps with the aim of conserving land, and the buildings sat directly onto the street to prevent untidiness. Long tenements — in the case of Fife Keith, feus of between 0.8 and 2.4 hectares (2 and 6 acres) — stretched behind, permitting a kitchen garden and a cow. Such a facility was perhaps useful insurance against a failure to attract or sustain rural industries, and indeed the New Statistical Account of 1840 noted that "the whole village of Fife Keith from a commercial point of view has been a complete failure, for except for a few merchants' shops and some three or four tradesmen, the population may be said to depend entirely on their crofts of land". At the time of feuing, each planned village had its own particular building regulations and many had stated criteria for selection of applicants attracted by newspaper advertisements. Some villages such as New Pitsligo were founded on wilderness sites, although these offered the twin advantages of ready access to peat and building stone. Some were planned with an eye to spatial location in relation to existing centres, eg. Tomintoul, while others — probably the majority — were established much at the personal whim of the landowner, thus resulting in an uneven distribution. While some of the earlier villages were seen as a means of eradicating Jacobite sympathies (in upland Banffshire and Aberdeenshire), the main raison d'etre envisaged was the weaving industry. The choice of a name like New Leeds and the size of the churches built in some planned villages is a fair reflection of the landowner's original aspirations. Occasionally, as at Ballater and Cruden Bay, recreation was a prime motive, while Maud and Craigellachie related to the development of the railway network. On the coast long established fisher settlements had developed from the 16th century onwards, often on exposed or cliff-girt sites with no opportunities for harbour development. These were based on inshore fishing from open boats, with the products marketed in the inland centres. Larger fisher settlements on less physically restricted sites like Fraserburgh, Macduff and Lossiemouth-Branderburgh were quickly to achieve burgh status, and to join a remarkable string of fishing settlements clinging to the rocky sections of the coasts of Moray, Banffshire, Aberdeenshire and Kincardine, and augmenting the older burghal establishments like Cullen, Portsoy, Banff and Inverbervie. Remarkable efforts were made to develop harbours in the 19th century as at Lossiemouth-Branderburgh, both for Elgin's sea-borne trade and for commercial fishing. There were great swings in the fortunes of coastal settlements. Kingston-on-Spey in the 18th and 19th century was a successful shipbuilding centre, launching around seven hundred schooners, the largest being the *Lord Macduff* of around 800 tons. The schooners operated on the Australian and China runs at a time when Kingston could boast seven shipbuilding yards. The village took its name via the origins of two Yorkshiremen who in the 1780s purchased the right to fell timber in the Strathspey woodlands of the Duke of Gordon, and floated the raw material down the Spey to its mouth. The overall pattern of nucleated settlement in Grampian is thus an amalgam of historical individualistic decision-taking superimposed over an older pattern of nuclei related to mills, churches and castles. Many villages have lost their original raison d'etre, with, for example, fishing settlements turning increasingly to tourism and retirement, while even those who retain their complement of fishermen, like Portknockie (Plate 47), have their boats operating from the larger centres like Peterhead or even, in the season, Kinlochbervie in north-west Sutherland. The "suit-case fishermen" commute at weekends to their homes on the Moray and Banffshire coasts by minibus. The present pattern of landings is dominated by Peterhead (around £40m) and Aberdeen (£23m) per year, with Buckie, Macduff and occasionally, Whitehills, coming a long way behind in fish landings. Fishing activities have become increasingly concentrated in the present century.

The majority of the settlement types sketched out above predate the development of a reasonable road network in Grampian. The 18th century road net depended very much on the investment in time and money supplied by landowners, particularly in building bridges. Where they did not supply the money, landowners supplied the necessary initiative, as with the Earl of Kintore for the first bridge across the Don at Inverurie. The Old Statistical Accounts written around the end of the 18th century frequently note the exertions of "gentlemen" in raising money for road construction. Under the prevailing system of the times, road construction and maintenance was the duty of the Commissioners of Supply within each county, deriving their muscle from the 1669 Act of the Scottish Parliament which entitled the levy of "highway money" from landowners, and legally required tenants and cottars to work without payment for up to six days per year on the roads. Not surprisingly, the success of this mechanism was locally variable, but generally quite inadequate, and was perhaps best summed up by the Alford minister who wrote in the 1790s that "where the statute labour is performed in work by country people, it is found inadequate to the support of the roads". However, where those liable to statute labour could be persuaded (or indeed found it feasible) to commute their labour into cash, some professional road construction could be attempted. The improvement of the notorious Tyrebagger hill leading from Blackburn to Aberdeen was one example of early professional road construction. Nonetheless, 18th century Grampian roads were generally very poor and scarcely fit for wheeled traffic, but rather carried pack horses or even sledges. Only in 1795, when planned villages were already in some cases a generation old, did Parliament provide the necessary machinery to enable the setting up of Turnpike Trusts, squarely putting the responsibility for organisation of road construction and the planning of alignments into the hands of the wealthy land-owning classes in the countryside, and those in the burghs whose estate exceeded £400 Scots. All such men of means were entitled to become Turnpike Trustees, with the right to appoint surveyors, to locate tollgates, and fix the toll payments. These trustees appear to have been extremely effective as within a decade, several hundred miles of turnpikes had been completed in Aberdeenshire, focussing on Aberdeen as the prime trading and market centre. By 1840, over 30 trusts had been formed in Aberdeenshire alone, albeit generally failing to break even financially. Only the Inverurie turnpike and the Bridge of Dee toll were able to wash their face financially and pay off their subscribers through revenue, but the difficulties of concentrating marketable products and distributing imported lime, coal and slate were greatly eased. By the 1860s, the railway network was fast extending throughout Grampian, and capturing much of the turnpike traffic even in remote rural areas. In 1865 the Aberdeenshire Road Act dissolved the Turnpike Trusts, replacing them with a body of trustees financed out of the rates, and in 1866, the toll gates were finally removed. While improved roads and eventual rail links clearly benefited existing settlements, eg. Maud for rail shipment of cattle, the overall settlement pattern was already firmly established in its essentials before major improvements in communication.

In the period 1801 to 1961, while the total population of Grampian doubled, the number living in and immediately around the prime regional centres of Aberdeen and Elgin rose by a factor of six during the same period. This process was principally achieved by a population redistribution. Settlements of burghal status (small towns) held twice as many people in 1961 as they did in 1801, but the rural parishes generally display a marked and accelerating decline in population numbers following a peak in the early 19th century. For rural parishes, the decline is least marked in Lower Moray and in the Aberdeen area. A marked feature of the post-1961 period has been an increasing concentration of Grampian's population in the Elgin-Forres corridor and along the Aberdeen-Peterhead seaboard, with spokes of comparable concentration in lower Deeside and lower Donside. A significant part of this growth has resulted from in-migration rather than the preceding pattern of population regrouping. Over the same period (1961-1981), the larger settlements outwith these areas have maintained their population size much better than the small villages and hamlets.

The Grampian Regional Structure Plan (1983) provides a useful summary of population changes within the countryside over the period 1961 to 1981. A pattern of decline in population numbers is typical of the two decades, but with the rates of decline decreasing latterly. However, within this generalisation, there are considerable variations in the trends, notably between settlements and countryside areas. Almost without exception, countryside areas irrespective of location, continued the post-war decline in population numbers between 1961 and 1981. The rural areas of Deeside, West Gordon, Banff, Buchan and Moray all experienced 20% declines, yet for the small settlements within these rural areas, there were increases of over 15% in Banff and Buchan, Moray and Deeside over the same period. In Moray and Lower Deeside, these increases are in part a result of planning decisions on new housing locations and investment in advance factories. The demand for new housing in satellite settlements within easy commuting reach of the prime growth area of Aberdeen relates to the opportunities for jobs created by North Sea Oil and Gas, and the city's role as the prime sea-base for exploration and development. Overall, the total population living in the countryside areas has slightly increased (c. 4%), mainly in the last decade, and this growth is localised to those areas within convenient commuting distance of the largest settlements. Thus the major centres of the Aberdeen area, Elgin-Forres and Peterhead-Fraserburgh dominate the population geography of Grampian settlement, and this picture is likely to strengthen in the 21st century.

The decline in countryside population numbers is closely related to the fortunes of Grampian's agricultural economy and related services. Economists at the North of Scotland College of Agriculture in Aberdeen have estimated that farmers have generally been suffering from falling incomes since the late 1970s, with the result that many are carrying severe bank overdrafts in the face of declining land market values (see Chapter 13). A recent study concluded that about 20% of all Grampian's farms are currently facing severe financial problems. The drive to overcome these problems by increasing agricultural output and re-investing profits which was the traditional response to such situations appears to be largely ruled out by a Common Agricultural Policy squeeze on agricultural supports, aiming eventually at tailoring overall EEC production to demand. Thus for many there is little option but to sell out, a procedure which results in continuing depopulation and the creation of larger farms through amalgamation. Between 1972 and 1981, the total number of farm enterprises in Grampian fell by 18%. Reduced numbers of stock, particularly cattle, have been responsible for the recent closures of marts at Keith and Alford, and this is just one symptom of changes in agricultural production having effects on related services.

Within this pattern of countryside contraction in population, a few settlements have grown remarkably over the last two decades, notably in Buchan and East Gordon. The overall trends for Buchan in the period 1921 - 1981 are illustrated in Table 17.

TABLE 17 *BUCHAN — POPULATION 1921 - 1981*

1921	54,051	
1931	50,475	minus 8.1%
1951	50,081	minus 0.8%
1961	47,327	minus 5.5%
1971	46,400	minus 1.9%
1981	54,180	plus 16.8%

Increasingly, over the last two decades, population growth has centred on Peterhead whose traditional fishing, light engineering and food processing base was diversified in the seventies by oil supply bases and constructional activities associated with the St. Fergus Gas Terminal and the Boddam Power Station, resulting in an 18% increase in its population between 1971 and 1981. The inland Buchan villages have experienced varying fortunes as measured by population trends. In the pre-oil period, point investment was favoured as a planning tool in rural situations, and Mintlaw was chosen as the best "point d'appui" in Central Buchan, principally because of its central location for accessibility, superior existing water and sewage infrastructure, and the surrounding land not being of the highest agricultural capability. Point investment policy was chosen as a deliberate alternative to dispersal of investment in

Buchan. The investment began in the early 1970s with a programme of council house building and the construction of an Academy around the old village nucleus which had surrendered its original raison d'etre of market centre to neighbouring Maud and Turriff, and was primarily peopled by a retired population. Mintlaw's population growth since 1971 by comparison with other Buchan villages is given in the following table.

TABLE 18 *SETTLEMENT POPULATION COMPARISONS*
1971 - 1981

Settlement	Population		Percentage increase (+), decrease (-)
	1971	1981	
Mintlaw	657	2300	+260
Maud	634	700	+10
New Deer	601	620	+3
New Pitsligo	1125	1080	- 4
Strichen	962	900	- 6

In the period 1975 to 1981, Mintlaw's housing stock increased by just under 500 units. A new primary school and Academy were completed in 1978 and 1981 respectively. These new and enlarged educational facilities have drawn off Senior Secondary pupils from Peterhead Academy, but at the same time led to the closure of Junior Secondary Schools at Strichen, New Deer and New Pitsligo — an inevitable result of point investment of resources in a rural setting. Many of the incoming population were associated with the constructional activities then ongoing at Boddam Power Station and at the British Gas Corporation Gas Terminal at St. Fergus. Several of the Council House streets at Mintlaw became locally known as "Little Glasgow". As houses were vacated with the ending of the constructional boom, they were taken over by people transferring from the smaller outlying Buchan settlements like Maud and New Deer, encouraged by the superior standard of housing in Mintlaw and nearness to higher educational facilities. Although the growth in Mintlaw's population has led to the traditional merchants' shops becoming branches of Spar and Mace, the range in commercial facilities remains similar to the pre-growth period. It has nonetheless drawn population from surrounding settlements and has thus made them less viable as local service centres. The result of this experience appears to favour a planning strategy of spread of investment in resources as opposed to point investment as more appropriate to a rural environment, assuming the aim of the exercise is to conserve the quality of village life by maintaining a viable size of population and range of services.

All the smaller settlements in Grampian have been affected by changes in the distribution of retail services. There is an increasing trend towards the centralisation of shopping facilities. There are major gains for both customer and entrepreneur in seeking economies of scale, and socio-economic changes, notably the above-average rates of household car ownership in Grampian (over 90% in 1985) mean that consumer behaviour favours shopping in the larger settlements, usually on a weekly basis. The superstore now stocks a very wide range of goods, some of which would form the mainstay of a specialist shop. Depopulation from the smaller settlements and from the surrounding countryside places increasing pressure on the village shop, whether specialised or general merchant. The large retail organisations with co-operative marketing facilities — such as Spar, Tesco and Mace — establish themselves in the larger settlements, and their success is compounded by the car mobility of the majority of the rural population; yet, it makes life difficult for the older age groups who depend on the local shop or travelling van. Rural depopulation means the increasing absence of local services including resident doctor, local primary school, post office and bus service, even a local filling station. A recent survey revealed that over 50% of the parishes in Grampian did not have a local doctor and around 25% no petrol outlet. On the positive side, the rural electrification programme is virtually completed, with Cabrach, Corgarff and Glenbuchat connected up in the early 1980s.

The railway network has greatly contracted from its peak in the late 19th century, although it still retains advantages for moving bulk commodities. The Dufftown to Keith and Burghead branch lines remain open for freight associated with the distilling industry. Nonetheless, the 580 route kilometres (360 miles) of the Grampian rail net of the 1950s, is currently reduced to around 130 kilometres (80 miles). This reduction not only reflects the implementation of the proposals of the 1963 Beeching Report, but also the demise of coal and livestock traffic, while the once lucrative fish-transit has been captured by road haulage. By the time containerisation was implemented, only the main Aberdeen-Inverness line and its southern extension remained open, and thus the potential freight traffic which the Peterhead line might have captured, remains merely a gleam in the railway buff's eye. On the positive side, the railway links to the south from Aberdeen have been improved both with local services aimed at the commuter market and long distance travel to London, the latter to compete with the shuttle. London services currently stand at seven trains per day on weekdays, and five daily high speed trains have cut the journey time to below seven hours. Line speeds and frequency have been improved on the Aberdeen-Inverness line. For local commuter traffic, both Dyce Station (1984) and Portlethen Station (1985) have been re-opened and studies are ongoing to assess the feasibility of re-opening other stations in the Aberdeen area. At present there are no plans to continue rail electrification north of Edinburgh, but the main line south of Aberdeen has been improved to permit the carriage of standard containers, while a facility for container carriages on the Inverness line within the normal passenger run has also been recently introduced.

Grampian's ports and small harbours exhibit the same symptoms of the "big is beautiful" characteristic of shopping and educational facilities. In terms of cargo and range of port facilities, Aberdeen remains the premier port of Grampian, although its fish landings have been eclipsed by rival Peterhead — a result of the problems inherent in existing dock labour legislation. Aberdeen's vociferous opposition to the current proposals for harbour expansion plans at Peterhead which include improved fish landing facilities tends to suggest that this pattern will continue. On the other hand, the Aberdeen Harbour Authorities have reacted positively to the challenge set by North Sea Oil by completing a £15m tidal improvement scheme (basically removing the dockgates and making the port a 24 hour operating system irrespective of tide), and by finding space for seven oil supply bases. In 1985, fish landings represented less than 2% of the total weight of goods passing through the harbour, while offshore installation traffic accounted for 43%. Much of the commercial cargo was also oil-related. The growth of vessels of the oil supply type rose from 259 movements in 1969 to over 4000 in 1978. The corresponding number in the year ending 1985 was 5333. Aberdeen harbour is the main sea-base in Europe for offshore exploration and production activity. The Harbour Board has recently reconstructed Pocra Quay as a further support base for bunkering and bulk drilling fluids. A new fish quay and market was opened by H.M. the Queen in 1982. Rival port Peterhead, in addition to its fish landings which are handled by casual labour, includes in Peterhead Bay Harbour a pair of oil supply bases and successfully developed rig servicing in competition with Invergordon and Bressay Sound, Lerwick, all three making use of deepwater at the quayside. Grampian Region Roads Department is responsible for the management of a total of 13 small harbours around the North-east coastline, including Buckie, Stonehaven and Macduff. Despite efforts to increase business in these smaller harbours, the coastal trade is generally on the decline, as are shore-based activities connected with the sea. Boating associated with inshore recreational activities has been notably developed at Burghead and Findhorn. At Burghead and Buckie, the combination of Scandinavian shortfall in pulp timber feed and the closure of the Corpach pulpmill has led to a welcome export trade in shipment of forest thinnings. Fraserburgh remains an important harbour for both fish and general cargo, and has recently received a grant of £1m from the EEC for a new slip and dredging programme.

A feature of the '70s and '80s has been the growth and diversification of traffic at Aberdeen Airport, Dyce, notably in the helicopter traffic serving the North Sea. The last 10 years has witnessed expansion and re-modelling of the airport with new helicopter facilities, terminal buildings and new taxiways. At Aberdeen Airport air transport movements rose from 6000 in 1970 to over 35,000 in 1975 (40% of these helicopter movements) to reach 80,000 in 1983 (58% helicopter movements). Growth in helicopter traffic at Aberdeen since 1980 has reflected new technology with the Chinook being capable of flying direct from Dyce to platforms in the East Shetland Basin, thus cutting out Sumburgh, Shetland. A smaller heliport is operated at Longside near Peterhead. Aberdeen Airport is currently the busiest heliport in the world.

The settlement geography of Grampian has been increasingly dominated by job opportunities generated within Aberdeen City District. Since 1975, the built-up area has increased by some 15%, much of the land being used for construction of around 14,000 new houses, although over 300 hectares (740 acres) of land has been developed for "industrial estates." The development axis of the city, previously east-west, has been re-aligned north-south, with major expansion north of the Don and south of the Dee along the coast. The green belt has been breached for housing, but there has also been much inner city re-development of gap sites for housing. Planning inquiries occur frequently in relation to the more contentious planning issues. Growth has been largely peripheral and in outlying satellites like Ellon and Inverurie. Estimates published by Grampian's Department of Physical Planning suggest that daily and periodic commuting (including offshore workers journeying to Dyce heliport) rose by around 60% between 1981 and 1984. This has resulted in major increases in traffic flows into Aberdeen, particularly on the A92 (Stonehaven-Aberdeen), the A96 (Inverurie-Aberdeen) and the A92 (Ellon-Aberdeen) corridors. The peak congestion occurs at the bridging points of Dee and Don. Traffic growth has been spawned both by the growth in City District population and by an increased car ownership, reflecting the increased levels of prosperity. The growth of car-owning households in the "suburbs" of North Kincardine and East Gordon has been almost three times the national rate of growth between 1971 and 1981. Major road improvements within the district include the Skene road near Westhill, the continuing work on the Inner Relief Road, and the Don crossing at Persley. A new bridge — the Queen Elizabeth bridge — was opened across the Dee near Craiginches in 1985. However, much work remains to be done, notably on the old east-west artery of the North Deeside Road, to take commuting traffic flows into the 21st century. The heavily-used Stonehaven road has now been dual-carriaged and a flyover provided for Portlethen. At the time of writing, the current economic assumptions on which future demands for housing and industrial land are based, are increasingly subject to criticism, both in terms of specific locations and on their validity as forward predictions. The recent slump in oil prices (April, 1986) appears to be already hitting hard at the sharp end of the oil industry — notably affecting drilling contractors and suppliers, service and supply vessel companies and hardware manufacturers. Smaller companies seem likely to be absorbed into larger ones if the present low price of oil continues, and already predictions for job-shedding in Grampian are running at between 7000 and 12,000. On the other hand the scale of job reduction may be considerably less if companies divert their resources into gas projects and if the Government is willing to maintain the momentum of exploration and production activity by cutting its oil tax take. For a number of North Sea oilfields, profits only begin at an oil price of 15 dollars a barrel, and although shut-down is apparently technically difficult, continued low oil prices are sure to break the continuity of exploration and production development and servicing which has been a feature of Grampian's participation in the North Sea industry since the mid 70s. Thus the future prosperity of Aberdeen City District is closely tied to the fortunes of the oil and gas industry.

Over greater Grampian the small settlements and countryside areas are currently experiencing a period of social and economic decline — a situation which led to the Gaskin Survey of pre-oil days. Although this economic survey into North-east development potential eventually produced NESDA — the North East of Scotland Development Agency — with a remit to promote rural development in sparsely populated areas, the task of so-doing has proved extremely difficult, particularly in a period of time when the immediate demands and benefits of oil-related development seemed to open up a lengthy period of prosperity for Grampian. In fact, the rural hinterland has experienced only minimal benefit from oil-related growth, and there is still a need for policy to counteract decline of population numbers and services even in lowland rural areas. Villages are increasingly dominated numerically by the retired age groups, and their status as shopping, social and educational nodes continually eroded. Even the rural industry of distilling in Speyside is suffering from years of overproduction and changing tastes amongst the consumers. Thus the flood of initiative and enthusiasm for planned village foundations in the past and their inertia has created major problems for planning strategies in the second half of the 20th century. For upland Grampian, it has been frequently argued that the area exhibits similar problems to its neighbours in the Highland Region who enjoy a range of assistance from both the Highlands and Islands Development Board as well as regional and social fund assistance from the European Community. Grampian Regional Council has very recently approached the Secretary of State for Scotland with the proposal that, in view of Grampian's loss of Assisted Area Status, H.I.D.B.'s boundaries be extended to embrace the upland areas of Moray, Gordon and Kincardine/Deeside. The removal of Assisted Area Status in August 1982 automatically removed eligibility for automatic regional assistance and for most European Community grants. Inclusion within H.I.D.B. boundaries is under active consideration at the time of writing.

In conclusion, the major feature of settlement and communication infrastructure in Grampian of the 1980s is an increasing imbalance between the Aberdeen area with its marked growth, and the major part of the remainder which is experiencing contraction of opportunity and depopulation. The settlement hierarchy has been inherited from a period when settlement location was an individual decision. Since then, many settlements have lost their original raison d'etre, and their catchments have experienced accelerated job-shedding in the primary sectors of farming and fishing in a situation where there are few alternative job opportunities. Under the current difficult economic circumstances rural unemployment has risen sharply and it is difficult to see how vigorous rural and village communities can be retained in the remoter areas; sadly, the pattern of decline seems likely to continue.

Chapter twenty

MOUNTAINEERING COUNTRY

Mr William Brooker

Although there are 277 "Munros" or Scottish mountains of 915m (3000 ft) or more, Grampian Region includes in entirety only 17 of them, sharing another 16 with Tayside and Highland (Fig 37). Nevertheless over 20% of the total area of Grampian lies at over 400m (1310 ft) and might reasonably be described as hill country. Additionally, of the total of 142 km^2 (55 $miles^2$) of high ground over 900m (2950 ft) around the regional boundary, no less than 109 km^2 (42 $miles^2$) lies within Grampian. This includes the huge expanse of Beinn a'Bhuird (Plate 4) and Ben Avon (Plate 6) the largest continuous area of high plateau in the country. Geological and glacial factors have combined to fashion most of the high mountain country of Grampian in this form, with an arctic climate and tundra type vegetation. Other sizeable plateau massifs largely within the region are Cairngorm — Ben Macdui, Glas Maol — Lochnagar, Braeriach — Cairntoul (Plate 3) and Monadh Mor — Ben Bhrotain. As indicated in Chapter One, most of the main hill masses are of intrusive igneous rocks. Associated features of their summit areas are the granite tors, a relict of the preglacial landscape and particularly prominent on Ben Avon, Beinn Mheadhoin and outlying hills such as Ben Rinnes, Bennachie and Clachnaben.

The obstacles the Grampian hills present to the cross country traveller are those of distance, altitude and weather rather than of terrain, and a number of traditional hill crossing routes pass through them to connect the river valleys of Spey, Don, Dee, Tay and the lowlands of the North-east and Strathmore. Since the gaining of the tops presents no difficulties and the hillways were in frequent use by cattle drovers, whisky smugglers and other travellers, there is little doubt that the mountain summits would all have been visited in early times without being recorded. Aside from references to the delights of the summer

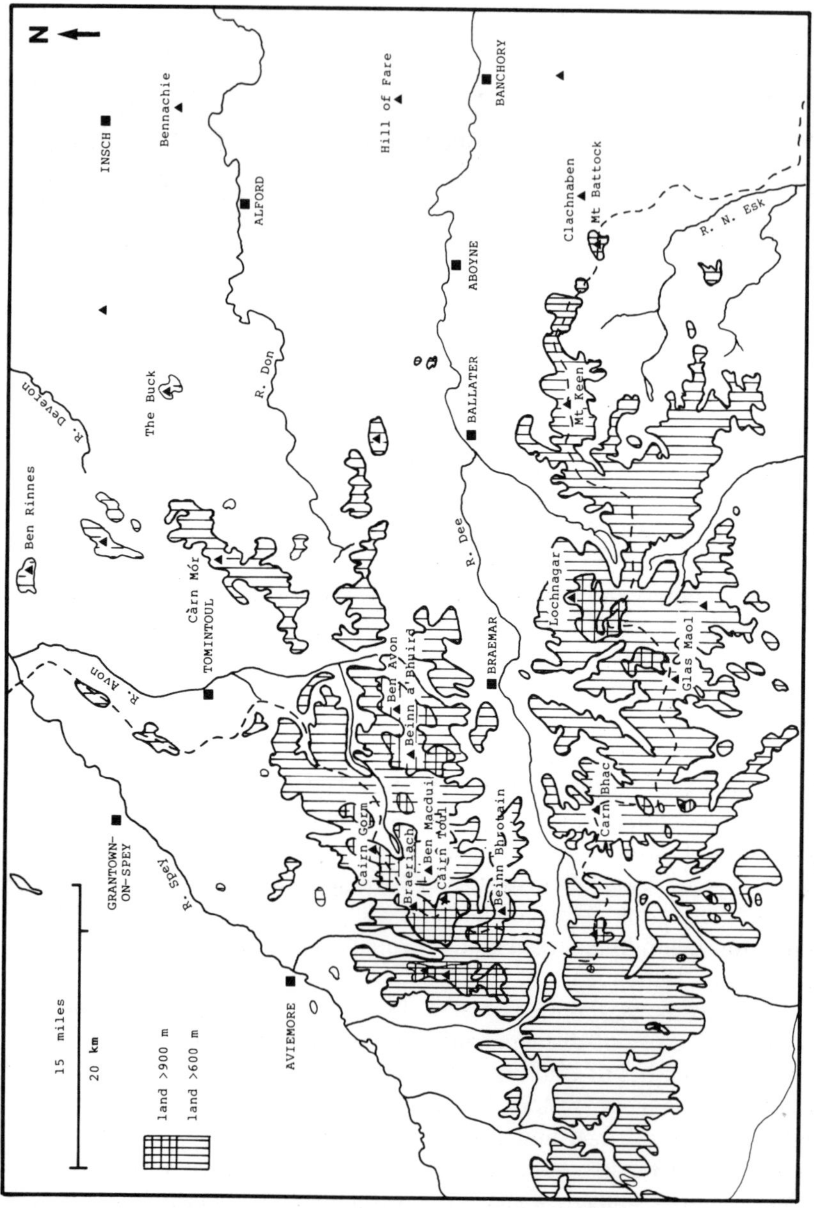

Figure 37 — Topography of Grampian Region.

shielings in Gaelic poetry, mountain scenery inspired distaste rather than approval among writers until well into the 18th century. John Taylor, "The Water Poet", climbed Mount Keen in 1618 but this was in transit over the Mounth road from Glen Mark rather than a recreational excursion. Writings such as those of Scott were to transform the perception of mountain country from oppressive gloom to exaggerated awe. Characteristic of this was the description by Sir Thomas Dick Lauder in 1829 of Loch Avon as a place where the cliffs of Ben Macdui "overhang its southern extremity in frightful masses", and where "for several of the winter months the sun never shines on the surface". However, the feelings generated by Highland mountain scenery were by now memorable and even inspirational. In 1803 Lord Byron climbed Lochnagar as a 15-year-old lad and the poem he later wrote, 'Lochin y Gair' (he was clearly no Gaelic scholar) was to make this one of the most famous of all Scottish mountains. Queen Victoria was also much impressed by Lochnagar, perhaps because it was on her own estate. Most Aberdonians ascend it at some time in their lives and it holds a special place in the hearts of natives of the North-east. This was well-expressed by J. C. Milne in his poem 'The Patriot'.

Fecht for Britain? Hoot awa!
For Bonnie Scotland? Imph, man, na!
For Lochnagar? Wi' clook and claw!

— from 'Poems', Aberdeen University Press (1976).

although he may not have meant it quite literally.

The use of traditional routeways through the hills for droving and other purposes declined in the second half of the 19th century. At the same time many landowners were becoming involved in the development of their estates for deer stalking and grouse shooting and some saw the limitation of public access and even the closure of a number of the old routes as desirable. By this time the exploration of the hills by town dwellers and other visitors for recreational and scientific reasons was under way. Conflict was inevitable and often reached the law courts where disputes between landowners and those maintaining their right of passage were usually resolved in favour of the latter. The publication of the first Ordnance Survey One Inch maps in the 1870s contributed to the increase in numbers going to the hills and the 1880s saw a spate of claims by the Scottish Rights of Way Society which only abated when the Local Government (Scotland) Act of 1894 made the maintenance of Rights of Way a Local Government responsibility.

In 1889 the Cairngorm Club was formed, based in Aberdeen, to be followed, a few months later, by the Scottish Mountaineering Club. Both of these clubs were involved with mountaineering and with the exploration and cataloguing of the Scottish mountains. They were the first such organisations to be established in the British Isles, apart from the Alpine Club. The Cairngorm Club has a particular interest in the Eastern Grampians and with nearly 400 members is the largest of the hundred clubs in membership of the Mountaineering Council of Scotland today. However, it is now only one of a dozen or so clubs in the Grampian Region with similar interests.

Although there is no accurate way of measuring the number of people engaged in hillwalking and mountaineering, indicators such as the sales of equipment, accident reports and simple observation suggest a dramatic increase over the last twenty years. This increase is related to a general rise of participation in informal recreation which has become more apparent with the greater mobility afforded by the growth in private car ownership. A recent survey of the Scottish adult population revealed that 36% had participated in long walks of a mile or more during the previous year. While only a proportion of these would have been classed as hill walking, there is no doubt that this is no longer the pursuit of a small minority but a significant area of recreation. Mountain recreation can take different forms and people who enter through one activity often extend into others; thus someone who takes up the growth sport of skiing may continue involvement with the mountains by summer hillwalking. A number of other obvious factors has played a part in the growing recreational use of Grampian hill country. These include the publicity given by the media to mountain sports and to scenic areas like the Cairngorms, the growth in population in Grampian Region itself (by 14% from 1971 to 1984), the development of outdoor education and the establishment of outdoor centres by a variety of organisations.

HILLWALKING

Hillwalking is by far the most widespread form of mountain recreation both geographically and in terms of participation. By its nature it can take place anywhere that is hill country but inevitably some areas attract more people than others. As an activity it is not sharply defined but involves those whose primary interest may be in climbing, ski touring, natural history, geology, and so on. The popularity of different locations depends not only upon their character and attractiveness but also upon ease of access. Obviously the higher summits over 915 m (3000 ft) are the main attraction. Those easily accessible with the aid of chairlifts, namely Cairngorm and The Cairnwell, will be reached by thousands who are not hillwalking in the usual sense. However, the high level access afforded by the Cairngorm ski road has made hills which were once relatively remote such as Ben Macdui, Beinn Mheadhoin and even Braeriach, easily attainable by day visitors. Similarly, the A93 which reaches 665 m (2180 ft) at the Cairnwell pass encourages exploration of the high level walking readily available among the hills on either side so that summits like Carn Aosda and Carn a'Gheoidh to the west and Glas Maol, Cairn of Claise and Carn an Tuirc to the east rank among the most frequently ascended in the region. The Lecht road which reaches almost as great an altitude does not appear to have generated nearly as much hillwalking activity, probably because the hills are more subdued and the summits fall well below the magic 915 m (3000 ft).

Lesser hills also attract large numbers of visitors where a location advantage or some other quality or characteristic makes them attractive. Morrone has an easy access track from Braemar and is a splendid viewpoint. Clachnaben has a huge granite tor which makes it such a recognisable landmark; Ben Rinnes, The Bin of Cullen and Bennachie (Plate 5) all tower prominently above their neighbouring lowlands. Relatively few people visit Oxen Craig, the true summit of Bennachie, most going to the more spectacular Mither Tap, 2 km (1.2 miles) distant and 10 m (33 ft) lower, but forming a pointed top with its rocky tor and-prehistoric hill fort.

The Grampian hill country is not rugged and even in its most mountainous parts lacks the pointed summits and sharp edged ridges to be found in the West and North-west Highlands. This is largely due to their glacial history, but this same history has left a rich legacy of splendid corries and associated features. It is from within these corries that the scenic qualities of the higher hills are usually best appreciated. Other features much enjoyed by hillwalkers are the forests encountered on some of the approaches. Extensive native pinewoods clothe the lower slopes in Glen Tanar, Glen Quoich and Glen Derry while smaller pockets of residual pine and birch are to be found in many other places. Sadly the survival of most of these delightful embellishments to the mountain landscape is threatened with overgrazing by sheep or deer.

Since all the summits can be gained without difficulty Grampian hillwalking need not involve any climbing techniques — at least in summer. In winter conditions, however, snow and ice may require the effective use of an ice-axe and sometimes crampons to maintain safety, and hillwalkers devoid of basic mountaineering skills are well advised to restrict their activities to lower levels.

Rock Climbing

Rock climbing in some areas of Britain has developed as a specialised sport which can be conducted on outcrops and artificial climbing walls. However, apart from the seacliffs and a few small outcrops, rock climbing venues in Grampian require some hillwalking to reach and the activity is still largely practised within the broader framework of mountaineering. It is appropriate here to make further mention of the North-east sea cliffs. These offer the rock climber a surprising variety of rock types from sandstone to gneiss but the most popular are intruded granites and their associated metamorphic zones. These have produced bold cliff outcrops of sound climbing rock which exceed 30 m (100 ft) height in many places. All told there are some 400 separate named climbs between Aberdeen and Newtonhill, and another 300 between Cruden Bay and Peterhead. Other less important locations occur along the Moray Firth coast as far as the sandstones of Hopeman.

All the rock girt corries offer worthwhile rock climbing in some form and without exception these are formed on granite intrusions. As described in Chapter One, the granites are all of similar age and type, just over 400 million years old, coarse in grain and pink in colour. Occasional injected dykes of finer grain (aplite), coarser grain (pegmatite) or veins of white quartz provide variety. On Lochnagar and the neighbouring basin of the Dubh Loch the granite is less homogeneous and usually somewhat smaller in grain than elsewhere. Although the underlying rock is pink these cliffs are predominantly grey in appearance due to their coating of algae and lichen. Granite crags are prone to be vegetated with the nature and quantity of vegetation being strongly influenced not only by the rock chemistry but also by altitude and aspect. The higher the altitude and the sunnier the aspect, the less vegetation there tends to be. Although blaeberry usually dominates, the more north-facing a crag the grassier it becomes and the sunnier its aspect the more heather and crowberry it will carry. Early climbing explorations focussed on gullies and other major lines of weakness with the result that these granite corries gained an unattractive reputation for vegetation and friable rock, both of which abound in such places. Since the 1950s, however, climbing developments have moved on to the buttresses, ridges and open faces which afford excellent sport. The cliffs which offer the best known and most notable rock climbing are those around Loch Avon, particularly the face of the Shelter Stone Crag and at the Dubh Loch where the extremely steep Creag an Dubh Loch extends for 1 km (0.6 mile). Both of these cliffs. reach or exceed 250 m (820 ft). All the other rocky corries offer climbing, often of high quality and sometimes amid dramatic rock architecture like that composing the Mitre Ridge (Plate 7) in the Garbh Choire of Beinn a' Bhuird. The first climbers' guide book to the Cairngorms was published in 1962 and the latest edition contains 500 climbs, on cliffs located mainly in Grampian Region.

Ice Climbing

Ice climbing is an aspect of mountaineering in which Scottish climbing has been prominent, even in international terms. This activity is obviously associated with the high corries where suitable conditions occur. An important factor is accessibility and climbing in the more remote locations is constrained by winter daylight hours and by the time it may take to reach the cliffs. The building of the Cairngorm ski road has made for easy access to the northern corries of the Cairngorms and the Loch Avon basin so that these areas now see much winter climbing. However, Lochnagar remains the best known venue. Like Ben Nevis and Creag Meagaidh it is noted for its snow and ice conditions and when these are good it is not unusual on a fine weekend to see fifty or more climbers simultaneously engaged on the ascents of the gullies and buttresses in its great NE corrie.

Ski Touring

Ski touring takes two main forms, Alpine and Nordic, depending on the equipment used. Alpine style touring uses skis and boots similar to those for downhill skiing. Uphill progress is effected with special bindings which allow the heel of the boot to lift and by attaching "skins" with a strong one way pile to the sole of the ski. This equipment is both heavy and expensive but allows good control on steep or difficult descents. It is often termed "ski mountaineering" and is especially appropriate to the terrain of the Alps or Western Highlands.

Nordic style touring uses longer and narrower skis with soft flexible boots attached to the ski only at the toe. Ascent is usually assisted by sticky waxes or by a fish scale or similar pattern embossed on the ski sole. Such skis are difficult to control on steep or icy slopes but are very light and well suited to the undulating hill areas of Scandinavia or the Eastern Highlands. It is often termed "cross country" skiing or "langlauf" in competitive events.

Both these touring methods are to be seen in the Grampian winter landscape, with Nordic equipment becoming particularly popular for the exploration of glens and forest tracks when snow cover may make ordinary walking difficult. Whichever equipment is used, the ascent of hills in the high mountain country is a more serious matter, requiring not only competence on skis but a level of navigation and mountain skill as high or higher than that demanded by hillwalking in winter conditions.

Downhill Skiing

The premier ski development in Scotland, that at Cairngorm, lies just inside Highland Region, but two of the other three commercial ski centres are within Grampian. Table 19 makes a simple comparison between

TABLE 19

SKI DEVELOPMENTS — COMPARATIVE TABLE

Ski Centre	Tows	Chairlifts	Max height differential	Total Uplift Capability (000s)	Cars	Coaches	Persons	Cafeteria Seating
LECHT	8	—	185m (600 ft)	420 p-m/hr	500	20	2650	250
GLENSHEE	17	2	410m (1350 ft)	1860 p-m/hr	1200	80	7800	180
CAIRNGORM	11	4	560m (1835 ft)	2290 p-m/hr	1200	50	6450	500

Uplift capability is expressed in person-metres/hour obtained by multiplying the capacity of each lift in persons/hour by its vertical height gain in metres.

these centres. Much the larger of the Grampian developments is operated by the Glenshee Chairlift Company and is known as "Glenshee" although it does not lie in Glen Shee itself but at the Cairnwell, and is located entirely on the Grampian side of the watershed. First established in 1962, it rivals Cairngorm in popularity and although the maximum height of its ski runs is lower and its snow season is usually shorter it suffers less from complete or partial closure due to problems of access or severe weather conditions. Permanent ski facilities at the Lecht were not built until the early 1980s and are on a much smaller scale than the others. As such they are less attractive to experienced skiers but have become very popular for beginners and family groups. An unexpected feature of the Lecht has been its good snow record in years when snow has been very late in arrival at Cairngorm. Snow conditions at Scottish ski centres are notoriously unpredictable: at Glenshee in 1980, a very good year, there were 95,000 ticket sales; in 1981, a very bad year, this figure fell to 27,000. Both of the Grampian ski developments enjoy the advantage of being located on 'A' class public roads and the convenient access this entails. Both these roads used to be closed by snow for prolonged periods during the winter months but because of the skiing much effort is now expended by the local authorities to keep them open. Even so there have been occasions when severe blizzards have resulted in skiers being trapped overnight in the car parks by drifting snow.

Because of commercial and other forms of promotion there has been a considerable growth in demand for downhill ski facilities. This has led to serious congestion at all the ski resorts at weekends and holiday times when conditions are suitable. Ski developments have a pronounced environmental impact and proposals for expansion sometimes encounter opposition from conservationist and other interests. However, long ski lift queues, overcrowded cafeterias and inadequate toilet facilities at these busy times do not seem to deter people and it appears that the availability of car parking is the only effective limit on numbers.

Accidents

By their very nature mountainous areas contain potential hazards and however much attention is given to mountain safety it seems inevitable that some accidents will occur. Figure 38 illustrates the growth of recorded mountain accidents between 1966 and 1985. It reflects the increase in numbers involved in mountain recreation but under-represents this increase because significant improvements in equipment and in the awareness of mountain safety factors took place during this period. On occasion the mountain rescue services are called out simply because people are overdue or lost and eventually return or are located without

Figure 38

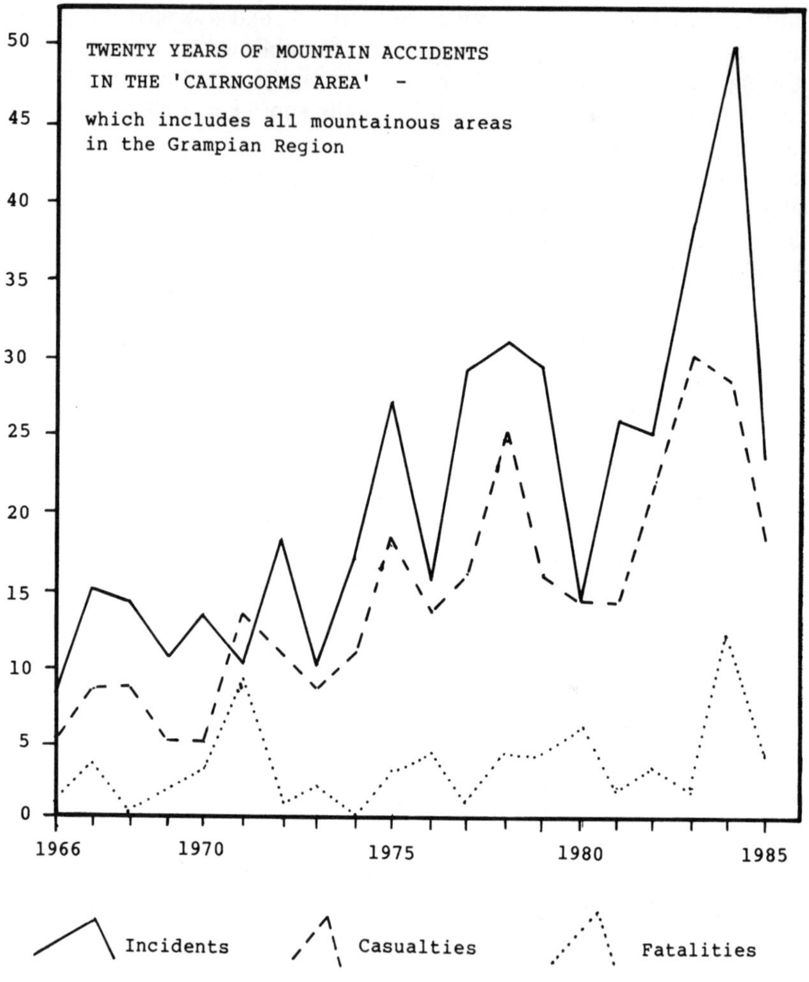

Casualties: all cases of rescue and evacuation as a result of injury, exposure, illness or being cragfast

Incidents: all occasions where Mountain Rescue services are called out

further mishap. Such incidents are particularly common in these hills where visitors unfamiliar with the area are liable to underestimate the scale of the landscape and the severity of the weather they may encounter. It is easier to go astray in the Cairngorms than in the more rugged parts of the Scottish Highlands and competent application of map and compass is vital. The principal mountain rescue teams located within the region are the Aberdeen MRT, the Braemar MRT and the RAF Kinloss MRT. However, rescue groups from Highland Region such as the Cairngorm MRT and the Glenmore Lodge MRT are frequently involved, particularly since more visitors enter the Cairngorms from Speyside than Deeside.

Conflicts of Interest

As Figures 39 and 40 indicate, the hill country of Grampian which nurtures this growing recreational activity also includes three national nature reserves and a dozen sites of special scientific interest. Additionally, much of it is used as deer forest or grouse moor. It is inevitable therefore that conflicts of interest occur. Hillwalkers may disturb deer or grouse and thus interfere with planned stalking or shooting. In order to improve access for their management and practice, sporting estates have made many miles of roughly bulldozed tracks which have marked visual effects on the landscape, and as a result of opposition these are now theoretically subject to some planning control. Commercial pressures on estates are increasing and the need to satisfy them may lead to the felling of mature timber valued for its amenity, or to the planting of stands of conifers which may interfere with existing Rights of Way. The rating system takes no account of the fluctuations of income which sporting estates may experience through natural cycles in the grouse population upon which they depend and makes no recognition of the considerable benefit which the community derives from informal recreational use of privately owned hill land. There is an urgent need for landowners, conservationists, commercial developers and recreational users to avoid precipitate and unilateral actions which may cause unnecessary conflict and to consult and co-operate with each other if the full potential of the wonderful hill country of Grampian Region is to be realised.

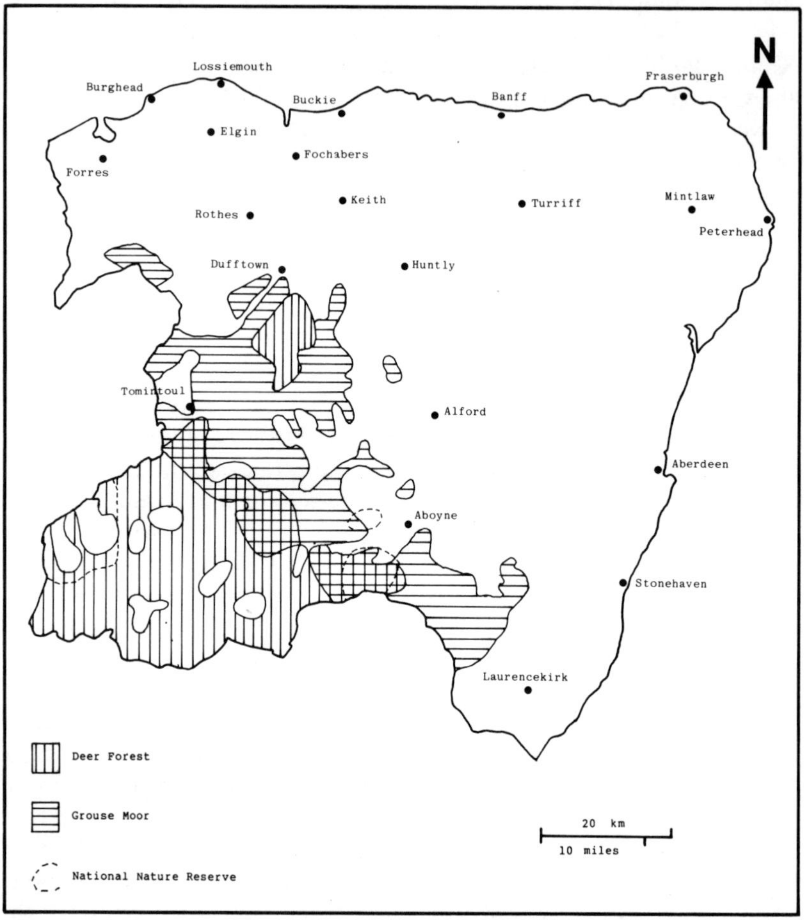

Figure 39 — Distribution of grouse and deer forests.

TABLE 20

THE "MUNRO" SUMMITS OVER 915 m (3000 ft)

Name of Mountain	Altitude metres(feet)	Nearest public road access: approximate distance kilometres	Nearest public road access: height to be ascended metres	Regional location of summit area
Ben Avon	1171(3842)	17.5	870	Grampian
Beinn a'Bhúird	1196(3924)	14	870	Grampian
Beinn Bhreac	931(3054)	10	570	Grampian
Beinn a'Chaorainn	1082(3550)	15	730	Grampian
Ben Macdui	1309(4295)	8	700	Grampian
Cairngorm	1245(4085)	3	610	Highland/Grampian
Beinn Mheadhoin	1182(3878)	8.5	980	Grampian
Bynack More	1090(3576)	6	790	Highland/Grampian
Cairn a'Mhaim	1037(3402)	11.5	700	Grampian
Derry Cairngorm	1155(3790)	11	830	Grampian
Braeriach	1296(4252)	10.5	840	Highland/Grampian
Cairn Toul	1293(4242)	17	1040	Grampian
Devil's Point	1004(3294)	15.5	700	Grampian
Monadh Mor	1113(3652)	11	950	Highland/Grampian
Beinn Bhrotain	1157(3796)	14	1130	Grampian
Carn an Fhidleir	994(3261)	18.5	630	Highland/Tayside/ Grampian
An Sgarsoch	1006(3300)	17.5	640	Tayside/Grampian
Carn Bhac	946(3104)	12	600	Tayside/Grampian
Beinn Iutharn Mhor	1045(3428)	13	700	Tayside/Grampian
An Socach	944(3097)	6.5	560	Grampian
Carn a'Gheoidh	975(3199)	4	320	Tayside/Grampian
Carn Aosda	917(3008)	1.5	260	Grampian
The Cairnwell	933(3061)	0.6	270	Tayside/Grampian
Glas Maol	1068(3504)	3.5	440	Tayside/Grampian
Cairn of Claise	1064(3491)	4	560	Grampian/Tayside
Carn an Tuirc	1019(3343)	3	510	Grampian
Tolmount	958(3143)	6	500	Grampian/Tayside
Carn an t-Sagairt Mor	1047(3435)	9	680	Grampian
"White Mounth"	1118(3668)	11	790	Grampian
Lochnagar	1155(3789)	9	800	Grampian
Cairn Bannoch	1012(3320)	11.5	610	Grampian/Tayside
Broad Cairn	998(3274)	10	600	Grampian/Tayside
Mount Keen	939(3081)	9	680	Grampian/Tayside

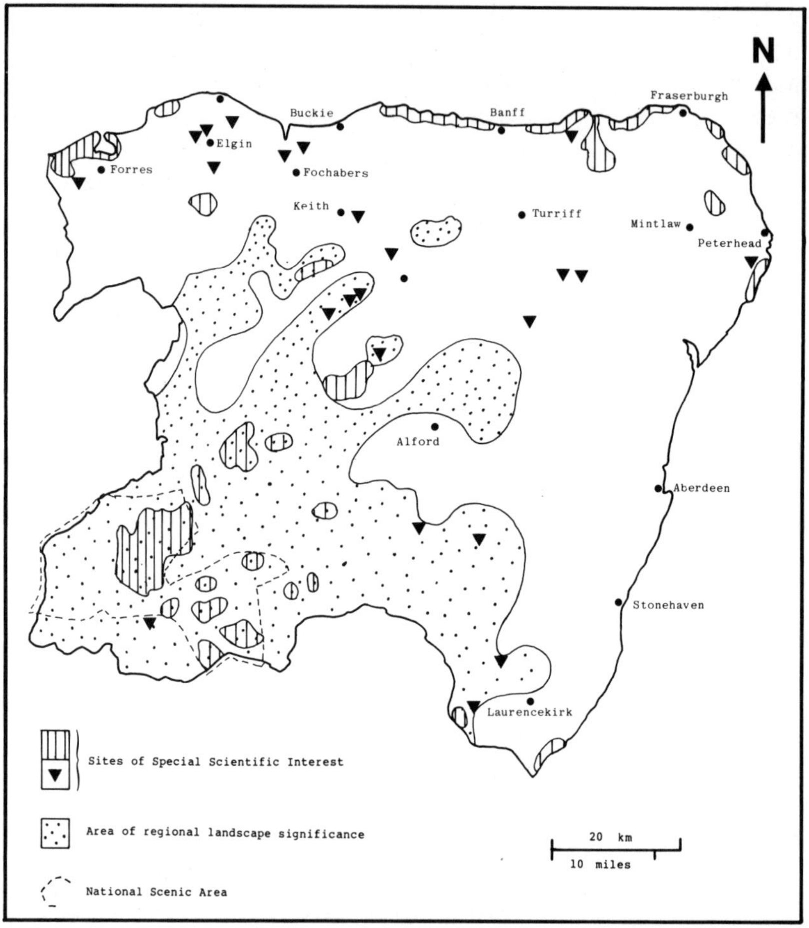

Figure 40 — National Nature Reserves and Sites of Special Scientific Interest.

Chapter twenty-one

PLACE NAMES

Mr Donald Macaulay

Any comprehensive study of the place names of the Grampian Region would require not a chapter in a book, or even one book, but several books, as the excellent studies by Adam Watson and Elizabeth Allan, The *Place Names of Upper Deeside* or W. M. Alexander's *The Place-names of Aberdeenshire* clearly show. All we can do here, then, is to give a sample of the toponymy and try to give some idea of its nature and of what it adds to our knowledge of the area. Covering as it does almost the whole of the North-east of Scotland one would not expect homogeneity or an even distribution of the name types throughout the region, and indeed we do not get that. The terrain differs from the coastal plains to the inland straths, from the low-lying foothills to the highest peaks in Scotland and this brings with it implications not only of different distributions of descriptive naming elements but also of patterns of migration and vestiges of those people who settled the area in the past.

Historically, the North-east has seen settlement by three language groups, the Picts, the Gaels (the original Scots: *Scotti* being the Latin name for the inhabitants of Ireland) and the 'Inglis' whose descendants now speak (modern) Scots and English. As far as place names are concerned these groups are linguistically defined, for in naming we can only distinguish them from each other in terms of the toponyms they applied to their environments in their own tongues.

It is not always easy to reconstruct names from languages which have now disappeared or even from earlier forms of languages which are still extant but have undergone considerable historical change. It is particularly difficult when a name as we now possess it has passed from the speakers of the original tongue to the speakers of a second or even a third (or fourth) language, as is the case with many of the names in Grampian Region. Each successive group, as it were, chews the name up and spits it out in a different form. It is therefore particularly important to have access to early sources giving early versions of names, such as the Episcopal Register of Moray (RM), published for the Spalding Club in 1837, which has material dating to the early 13th century; or the collection of *Antiquities of Aberdeen and Banff* published for the Spalding Club in four volumes 1847 - 1869 and containing material going back to the 12th century, or to the more generally applicable *Register of the Great Seal* (RMS), for example.

The Picts are the first historical people we recognise in the area. Our evidence about their language is not extensive, but it points to the fact that at least one of the tongues spoken among them was a Celtic tongue akin to Welsh, i.e. a British rather than a Gaelic type of Celtic language. There appears to have been another tongue spoken among them but we are unable to decipher it, and of course any name elements in such a tongue would be unintelligible to us. This plurality of tongues is probably reflected in the names that we find in the map constructed by Ptolemy, the earliest geographer to leave us cartographic evidence of Scotland. Some of the tribal names, for example, the *Vacomagi* who occupied the Moray plain, are probably Celtic but the major tribe, the *Taezali*, which occupied the Buchan promontory do not have a name of Celtic origin.

Pictish-Celtic names are well established throughout the region in early settlement areas, with a special concentration on Donside. The most distinctive of those are the set of names beginning with the element *pit/pet(t)* meaning 'portion of land'. Well known examples are *Pitmedden* (AB) 'middle portion' and *Pittodrie* (AB) probably 'portion of the dunghill'! The connection with the Picts is established both by the coincidence of distribution with Pictish material culture artefacts, for example their decorated stones, and by association in early texts.

An interesting case of the latter is to be found in notes written in the manuscript *Book of Deer* dating from around 1130 - 1140. These notes are interesting for several reasons. They represent the earliest manuscript containing Gaelic surviving from a local Scottish source. The occasion of their writing would appear to be incursions upon the lands of the Abbey of Deer by the new aristocracy of Anglo-Norman origin being settled by the family of Malcolm Canmore to extend their control of the kingdom and introducing new feudal and ecclesiastical structures. The notes tell of the founding of the abbey by Columba and Drostan and detail the grants of land made to him by 'Bede the Pict who was the *mormaer* (the chief administrator) of Buchan' and other local leaders. Bede, for example gave the ground between '*Cloc in Tiprat*' and '*Cloc Pette Mic Gartnait*" i.e. the 'Wellstone' and the 'Stone of the Son of Gartnat's Portion'. Others gave '*Pett in Mulenn*', the 'Mill Portion' and '*Pett Mic*

Gobroig', 'The son of Gobhrog's Portion' and *'Pett Malduib'*, 'Maldubh's Portion' to the foundation.

One of the pleasures (and frustrations) of early documents is that they sometimes give explanations of names. In the notes on Deer we are told that the name 'Deer' originated from the fact that when it was time for Columba to part from Drostan who was to take charge of the new foundation Drostan shed tears, *'déara'* in Gaelic, and Columba decided that the foundation should be 'called "Déar" henceforth'!

One of the interesting features of the *pit* names is that the second element in the name is almost always of Gaelic origin, for example the two Aberdeen names cited above and the following:-

(MY) — Moray; (BB) — Banff and Buchan; (GN) — Gordon; (AB) — Aberdeen; (KD) — Kincardine and Deeside:

Pittensier (MY)	*peit nan saor*	'the artificer's portion'
Pitgaveny (MY)	*peit gamhna*	'the heifer's portion'
Pitglassie (MY)	*peit glasaich*	'the grassland portion'
Pitcaple (GN)	*peit capaill*	'the horse portion'
Pitmuck (BB)	*peit muic*	'the pig portion'
Pitmurchie (GN)	*peit Mhurchaidh*	'Murdoch's portion'
Pitcullen (BB)	*peit cuileann*	'holly portion'
Pitcows (KD)	*peit coll*	'hazel portion'
Pitcowden (BB)	*peit calltainn*	'hazelwood portion'
Pitfodels (AB)	*peit fodail*	'portion of the sub-division'

(The final 's' in these examples is an English plural ending).

According to W. J. Watson in his *History of the Celtic Placenames of Scotland* there are 119 *pit* names in the area covered by the Grampian Region.

Another Celtic element associated with Pictish and Welsh rather than Gaelic is *aber*. There are fewer of these in our area but *Aberchirder* (GN), *Aberlour* (MY) and, of course, *Aberdeen*, are well known examples. *Aber* means 'confluence', *Aberchirder, aber-chiar-dobhar*, means the 'confluence of the dark water', *Aberlour* means the confluence of the *labhar* or 'loud' water, and *Aberdeen* (see below) means the 'confluence of the Don' — where the river Don joins the sea. Its Gaelic equivalent is *inver*, as in *Inverurie* (see below).

The element *-mond* that we get in names such as *Crimmond* (BB) and *Garmond* (BB) and many others is also of the same origin and was borrowed into Gaelic as *monadh*. Originally it meant 'mountain' (with which term it is cognate) and generally it means 'upland territory'.

The other most important element of this origin is *carden* meaning 'copse'. This is found in such names as *Urquhart* (MY) from *ar-charden* 'on the copse'; *Kincardine* (KN), (MY), (GN) from *ceann* + *carden* 'head of copse'.

Most of the names in the area are of Gaelic or English origin. The picture we get of the names is (as indicated above and as we would expect from our historical knowledge) of a Gaelic population superimposed on another Celtic one (and perhaps non-Celtic one), this other Celtic one speaking a different, British, branch of the language. On top of that comes a superimposed English-speaking layer. Almost all of our names are now interpreted through this English layer. It is therefore not very easy to determine, for example, the exact chronology of settlement. This is made more difficult by the fact that many early documents were written in Latin, the *lingua franca* of the mediaeval world. As far as the Gaelic names are concerned the early documents indicate that their scribes had little knowledge of the writing conventions of the Gaelic language, and this reinforces our evidence that for example the Anglo-Normans brought in their own clerks and clerics as they settled the area. Probably the most striking feature of the nomenclature from the settlement point of view is that it quite clearly shows that the displacement of Gaelic population took place earliest on the fertile coastal plains and proceeded gradually to the inland and upland areas. Gaelic names in the latter areas are very clearly formed and even have reasonably correct written representation on the Ordnance Survey maps. In the former areas, however, they are often disguised and sometimes even totally obscured. We know of the survival of the Gaelic language until recently in Braemar and upland Banffshire. The names indicate very generally the stages to its extinction. A good deal of historical research would have to be done, however, to clarify the details of its displacement and to get us a coherent picture of the development of settlement in the region. Place name evidence would be a prime datum in any such study.

Another of the interesting features of the toponymy of the region, especially as it has a very extensive coastline, is the complete absence of Norse settlement names so common in other parts of Scotland, from Beauly to the north and on the west coast and Hebrides for example. This indicates the power of the Pictish kingdom and later of the combined Picts and Scots, particularly the strength of their sea defences at the time of the Norse raids and during their period of settlement.

English and Scots names are, as one would expect, often self-evident in their meaning: *Milton, Hatton, Newton, Kirkton, Midton, Ladysford, Lairds Seat, Red Muir, Whiterashes, Newbiggings,* and so on. Some names can however, be deceptive *Dunottar* (KD), for example, has, contrary to local belief, nothing to do with otters: it derives from *dùn fhother*, 'fort of the (terraced) slopes' (it appears in the Pictish Chronicle as 'opidum Fother', 'Fother fort'); and *Rosehearty* has to do with neither hearts nor roses, deriving from *Ros Abhartaigh*, 'Abhartaigh's Point' (it appears as *Rossawarty* in RMS in 1508); Abhartach is a Gaelic personal name.

There are also names which combine English and Gaelic elements (we have seen Pictish and Gaelic in the *pit* names above). Many English names with *hill* are of this kind in our area, for example, *Lurg Hill* (MY), 'shank hill', *lurg* being Gaelic for 'shank', *Wishach Hill* (GN), 'ashwood hill' *uinnseach* being Gaelic for 'ash' (adjective), and, an example where the two parts are translation equivalents *Knock Hill, cnoc* being one of the Gaelic words for 'hill'. (c.f. *Knox* (KD), which is *cnoc* with the English plural 's'.)

It should not be forgotten, also, that even where the names have an obvious derivation they may still have a fascinating history. When we ask ourselves why such and such a place has its particular name the answer often involves the most interesting information about the history of the locality and its people. *Fraserburgh* (BB), for example, seems transparent enough and indeed it is: the 'burgh' called after 'Fraser'. But why was it called after 'Fraser' and to whom does 'Fraser' refer? In fact *Fraserburgh* was so named at the end of the 16th century (1601 is the earliest example of the actual form 'Fraserburgh' but we have, in Latin, the 'harbour and burgh of Fraser' ten years earlier) after Sir Alexander Fraser of Phillorth. When discovering this we find out that it existed as a free burgh of barony since 2 November 1546 and that its name at that time was *Faithlie*. Moreover, it is referred to locally and by the many fishermen who have frequented it as *The Broch*. This reflects its Gaelic name *A' Bhruaich*, though which came first 'broch' or 'bruaich' (which means 'bank' (of river or shore)) as a name for the place seems impossible to determine. This aspect of place name study is of prime interest when looking at town or city names, an area of the subject that is often unjustly neglected. (See the section on *Aberdeen* below.)

MORAY DISTRICT

Moray, Gaelic *Moireabh* is an ancient name, deriving apparently from Celtic *mori-treb* and meaning 'sea settlement'.

Some of the parish names are of interest.

Aberlour (RM Aberlower). The first element, as we said above, is *aber* meaning 'confluence' and the second one probably means 'loud': G(aelic *labhar,* W(elsh) *llafar,* is a common element in stream and river names.

Alves. This probably derives from *all-mhagh-fhas* meaning 'rock plain settlement' but the evidence is not entirely clear.

Birnie (RM Brenach), is probably from Gaelic *braonach*, 'a moist place' (with the common 'r' metathesis of early Scots).

Cullen (RM Inverculan). The RM form would indicate a confluence name as *inbhir* has that meaning in Gaelic (the equivalent of British *aber*). The name probably derives from *inbhir-cuileann* meaning 'confluence of the holly'.

Dallas. This belongs to an interesting class of names ending *-as/-es/-is* in our area. The most likely derivation of this element is G. *fos/fas* or British *gwas* meaning 'settlement' (see *Alves* above).

Dallas is probably *dol-fhas* 'meadow settlement', *dol* being the British term for 'meadow' borrowed into Gaelic especially in place names.

Drainie. This represents a form of G. *draighneach*, 'thorny place'.

Edinkillie (RM Edin Kelye) is from *aodann-coille* 'woody (hill) face'.

Elgin. In Gaelic *Eilginn*, this name probably derives, like *Banff (Banbha)* and *Earn* (*Eirinn* from *Eire*, whence Ireland), from ancient names given to Ireland and transferred by the Gaelic settlers to districts in Scotland. These names (*Elgin* would represent a form of *Elg*) were probably in origin the names of earth goddesses. They are strongly associated with water sources, rivers and streams. (See *Findhorn* below).

Forres (RM Forais) probably derives from *fo-ros* 'lesser wood' or 'lesser promontory' (*ros* has both these senses).

Inveravon probably represents *inbhir-abhainn*. *Inbhir* is, as we said above *(Cullen)*, 'confluence'; *abhain* is the Gaelic word for 'river'. The confluence is where the river *Livet (*from *liòmhaid,* 'shining') of whisky fame meets the river *Avon* (which is simply the word for 'river', so called because it is the major stream in the area).

Mortlach (RM Morthilloch) is probably G. *mòr-thulach*, 'large knoll'.

Rothes. The Gaelic form is *Rathais* probably from *rath-fhas*, 'fort settlement'.

Rothiemay, probably from *rath* 'fort' and *magh*, 'plain': 'fort on the plain'.

Spynie. This possibly derives from a Gaelic borrowing of British *spaith,* 'hawthorn' in the form of *spiathanaigh,* 'the place of the hawthorns'.

St Andrews and Lhanbryde. St Andrews is obvious. *Lhanbryde* raises interesting questions. In RM it is *Lamnabride* and *Lamanbride.* The second element is certainly Bride, Gaelic *Brighid*, the saint's name. The first element is probably Gaelic *lann*, 'enclosure', cognate with Welsh *llan*, which came to mean 'church'. (The spelling with 'lh' here is late and fanciful — though apposite). The RM forms point to an original *Lann-mo-Bhrighde* (with m/n metathesis) with *mo* 'my' showing the hypochoristic form commonly found with saints' names (*Kilmarnock* for example is *Cill-mo-Earnóig*, 'church of my Earnóg', and see *Marnoch* (BB). Here the meaning would probably be 'Brighid's enclosure' or 'church'.

Urquhart. We have a citation of this name in Adomnan's Latin *Life of St Columba* which dates from the end of the 7th century. The form is *Airchartdan* of which the first element is *ar* 'on' and the second the British *cardden*, 'copse'. The name means '(the place) on the copse'.

The names of some of the towns are:

Buckie. This name probably derives from *boc*, 'buck' either a stream name *bocaich* 'bucking, leaping' or the same form meaning 'the place of the bucks'.

Craigellachie (RM Elechyn). The first element is *creag* 'rock, cliff'; the second element, going on the RM form, is probably *ealachainn*, 'platform'.

Dufftown was founded in 1817 by James Duff, 4th Earl of Fife and derives its name from its founder.

Findhorn (RM Findaryn). This derives from the river of the same name at the mouth of which it is situated. The first element is early Gaelic *find*, 'white' the second is *Eirinn* (for which see under *Elgin* above). The name *Deveron* (BB) derives from *dubh*, 'black' compounded with the same generic element. These descriptive elements are common with different generic terms in river names: *Desk-* in *Deskford*, for example, is *dubh* compounded with a Celtic *esc*, 'water' (cf. Gaelic 'uisge'; the Gaelic for the River Dee, for example, is *Uisge Dé*). The element *find* (G. *fionn*) also occurs in settlement names, for example, *Fintry* (BB) and *Fintray* (GN) compounded with the British element *-treb* 'settlement' (cf. *Moray*). It also appears in

Findochty compounded with *ochtamh*, 'eighth', a land measure element. See also *The Ochts* where the Gaelic term is borrowed into English.

Garmouth. The early forms (mid 16th century) *Garmoch/Germoch* suggests a stream name *Gairmeach* 'the calling one'. (This type of name is discussed in Watson, Chap. XIV.)

Portgordon, founded in 1797 by the 4th Duke of Gordon — hence the name.

Portknockie probably derives from *port* and *cnocaich* 'hilly place'.

Tomintoul derives from Gaelic *Tom an t-Sabhail*, 'hillock of the barn'.

There are many settlement names in *bal-* G. *baile*, for example, *Balnabreich, baile na braich*, 'malting settlement'; *Balnagone, baile nan gobhan*, 'smiths' settlement'. Land division names are *Davoch, G. dabhach* 'a vat or tub', indicating the area of land that the tub's fill of grain would plant. Associated names are *Lettoch, leth-dabhach* 'half davoch' (cf. also the English version *Halfdavoch* (Dyke and Moy) and the equivalent *Haddo* (GN), with typical loss of final 'ch' in names of Gaelic origin). There are crop names; for example, *Lynachore: Loinn a' choirce*, enclosure of oats; domestic animal names, for example *Knocnagore: cnoc nan gobhar*, 'goat hill'; *Delnabo: dail nam bó*, 'cattle hollow'; 'activity names', for example, *Auchenhalrig: achadh na h-eilrig*, 'deer trap field'; *Maggieknockater: magh an fhucadair*, 'the fullers' plain'; water names *Aldavallie: allt a' bhealaidh*, 'broom stream'; *Bogentenie: bog an teine*, 'fire bog'; *Corskie: crasgaich*, 'place of the crossings'; names of high ground, for example, *Drummin: druimean* 'little ridge'; *Latternach: leitirneach*, 'place of the steep slopes'; *Tulloch: tulach*, 'hill(ock)'; and so on.

BANFF AND BUCHAN DISTRICT

On *Banff* see above under *Elgin*. *Buchan* is the ancient name of the area attested in 12th century sources but clearly going back to antiquity.

Some interesting parish names are

Aberdour, from *aber-dobhair*, 'confluence of the water'.

Aberchirder, aber-chiar-dobhair, 'confluence of the dark water'.

Alvah, all-mhagh, 'rock plain'.

Auchterless, from *uachdar* and *leas*, 'upper enclosure'.

Crimond (RMS Creichmont) is probably a combination of *crithich*, 'quagmire' and *monadh*, 'hill'.

Deer, New, Old. Site of Celtic Abbey (see above) and later religious centre.

Fordyce. The first element is probably *fothir*, steep terraced slope', the element *dyce* is obscure (cf. also *Dyce* (AB)).

Inverkeithney. *Inbhir* is compounded with an element which probably derives from Celtic *cèto-*, O.W. *coet*, 'wood' and so could mean 'confluence of the wooded place.'

Longside. The first element here is probably G. *lann, loinn* 'enclosure'. The second part may be English 'side' but is more likely to be something like G. *saighead*, 'arrow'.

Lonmay. G. *loinn* and *magh*, 'enclosure of the plain'.

Marnoch. G. *Marnoch*. The area is called after a saint Mo-Earnóg who was associated with it.

Ordiquill is *ord,* 'round shaped hill' and *coille,* 'wood', i.e. 'wood hill'.
Pitsligo, peit-sligeach, 'shelly portion'.
Rathen, probably G. *ràthan,* 'little fort'.
Strichen (RMS Straithechin, Streychin). The first element is G. *strath*, 'strath'; the second is obscure.
Turriff. The Book of Deer has *turbruad.* The name is obscure in origin.

Some town names here as in other districts coincide with parish names, for example (as well as some of the above),
Peterhead, called after the Church of St. Peter situated there, and *St Fergus,* called after a foundation dedicated to that saint.

There are other names associated with saints, such as, *St. Combs,* which is named after the church of St. Colm.

Other names are *Cairnbulg: cairn builg,* 'bag cairn', *Fetterangus: fothair Aonghais,* 'the terraced land of Angus' and *Maud,* derived from *Auldmaud* which looks like *allt nam bad,* 'stream of the clumps'.

River names are *Boyne* a name that recurs in Ireland and Scotland and originated in the name of *Boand,* the river goddess. *Boyndie* is clearly derived from it but the nature of the last element is obscure. The River *Ugie* joins the sea at *Inverugie* beside *Peterhead.* The origin of the name is not known.

GORDON DISTRICT

Some parish names are
Alford deriving from *ail-phort*, 'fort of the rock'.
Auchindoir, from *achadh an dobhair*, 'field of the rock'.
Belhelvie. This looks like *baile Shealbhaigh*, 'Sealbhach's steading'.
Cairnie (RM Cardeney) a locative form of *cardenach*, 'place of the copses' (see *Urquhart* (MY), *Kincardine* etc).
Chapel of Garioch. The chapel is of ancient origin. *Garioch* is G. *Garbhthach* (17th century), the meaning is obscure, but might mean 'rough lands'.
Cluny from *cluaineach*, 'place of the meadows'.
Drumblade. The first element is *druim*, 'ridge'; the second might be G. *blàith* cognate with W. *blawd*, 'meal' — giving us 'meal ridge'.
Fintray from *find-treb*, 'white settlement' (see above).
Glass is probably from G. *glas*, 'a stream'.
Huntly. The Gordons imported the name with them to the area from Berwickshire in the middle ages. Its wider application to the town and parish is modern.
Insch G. *innis*, plural *innse*, 'pasture land(s)'.

Inverurie from *inbhir-iubhraigh* 'the confluence of the yew wood or the yew river'; the *Urie* tributary joins the Don here.

Kemnay. The earliest form of the name is *Camnay* which indicates G. *camna(i)ich,* 'place of the bends or twists'.

Kennethmont. This is an interesting name. To begin with, it has nothing to do with a Kenneth. The earliest forms are *Kynalcmund, Kilalckmunith* showing different first elements: *ceann*, 'head, end' or *cill*, 'church'; the final element would appear to be a form of *monadh*, 'hill'; the rest and, indeed the whole name therefore, is obscure.

Kildrummy appears to represent *cill an droma*, 'the church of the ridge'.

Kintore seems to be a compound of *ceann*, 'end' and *torr*, 'hill' i.e. 'hill head'.

Meldrum. This is probably *maol-druim*, 'bare, or blunt, ridge'.

Midmar. This was originally *Migmarr*, the 'marsh of Marr'.

Monymusk is *mòn na musc,* 'the moss of the musk', the latter being a stream name meaning 'stinking'.

Rayne, perhaps from G. *raon*, 'plain, tilled land'.

Tough (RMS Tulich). This derives from G. *tulach*, 'a hill'.

Towie (RMS has both . . . *Towiis* . . . and . . . *Tolliis* . . . as Latin locative plurals of the name). It would appear to be the plural form of *tulach*, i.e. *tulaigh*, modern G. *tulaich*.

Tullynessle. The first element *Tully-* is the same as the last name in a different form; the rest of the name is obscure.

Many parish names are of ancient origin and thus present difficulties of interpretation. There are many other interesting names in this District but we are unable to discuss them here. Perhaps it should be mentioned that the river Don runs through Gordon district for most of its course (see *Aberdeen* below). The River Urie has been discussed above (see *Inverurie*). We might mention two other stream names briefly. The parish of *Foveran* derives its name from *Foveran Burn*. The name probably derives from *fogharan*, 'noisy one'. *Tarty* Burn (RMS Tawarty) is from G. *tabhartach*, 'productive'.

KINCARDINE AND DEESIDE DISTRICT

Aboyne and Glentanar. *Aboyne* (RMS Obeyn) possibly *ath Bhoinn* (Boyne ford); *Glentanar,* the glen of the river *Tanar* whose name is obscure.

Banchory Devenick. Banchory G. *beannchor* means 'bend' usually 'river bend'. This parish was that of St. Devenick's church distinguishing it from *Banchory Ternan* dedicated to St. Ternan. Both are ancient Celtic foundations as the saints' names show.

Bervie. The parish takes its name from the *Bervie* river. The name is probably derived from *bearbhach*, 'turbulent'. *Inverbervie* is the settlement at the confluence of the *Bervie* and the sea.

Coull G. *cùl*, 'back; backland'.

Crathie and Braemar. Crathie, G. *Craichidh* meaning 'quagmire place' from *craithich, crithich* (cf. *Craichie* (MY), *Crichie, Crathes,* etc).

Dunnottar has been discussed above: *dùn fhoithir*, 'fort of the slope' (cf. *Fordoun* with the same sense).

Durris. This is probably *dubh ros,* 'black wood'.

Fettercairn. The first element is G. *foithir*, 'terraced slope', the second one G. *càrn*, 'cairn'.

Fetteresso. G. *foithir easach*, 'slope with waterfalls'.

Fordoun is probably G. *foithir*, 'slope' and *dùn*, 'fort': 'fort of the slope'.

Garvoch. This is again a stream name: G. *garbhach*, 'rough water'.

Glen Muick, Tullich and Glen Gairn. Glen Muick is G. *gleann muic*, 'pig glen', the name is originally that of the river *Muick. Tullich* (see above *Tough, Towie*, also *Tilly-* all from *tulach*, 'hill(ock)'.

Kincardine O'Neil. Kincardine, as we have shown above, means 'end of copse', 'O'Neil' derives from the fact that the area was designated 'baronia de Neill' the 'barony of Neil'. The 'O'' therefore is, probably, simply 'of'.

Kinneff. The first element is from G. *ceann*. The second is obscure but may contain the second element in *Abernethy*, for example, with 'th' changing to 'f'.

Lumphanan. The first element is probably *lann, lonn,* 'enclosure, church'. For the second element *Finnán* has been suggested giving 'the church of St Finnan' but the early spellings are against this interpretation (for example, RMS Lumpquhannan). (cf. *Pannanich*, near *Dinnet* which might be related to Welsh *pant,* 'hollow'.)

Maryculter. Culter is from G. *cùltìr,* 'back land'. *Maryculter* and *Peterculter* are churches dedicated to St. Mary and St. Peter respectively.

St Cyrus. Named after the church of 'St. Cyric'; in Latin *Ecclesia Cyrici*; G. *Eaglais Giric*. This latter is the basis of the name *Ecclesgreig*.

Strachan G. *strathan*, 'straths'.

There are many interesting river and upland names in this district. We have touched on some above. Others are briefly, the River *Dee*, in Gaelic *Uisge Dé*. The name derives from the ancient word for 'goddess' *Déva* (the Don is from *Dévona*; see *Aberdeen* below). *Cowie Water* is from *collaich*, 'place of the hazels'. The *Water of Feugh* is probably from *foidhach,* 'place of the woods'. *Water of Aven* derives from Gaelic *abhainn,* 'river'. The *Burn of Canny* probably means the 'white burn'. The *Burn of Luchray* means the burn of the 'swamp'. *Lochnagar* derives its name from a neighbouring loch, the 'loch of the shouting'. *Socach,* the hill name, is G. *socach*, 'snouted'. The district name *Mearns* is Gaelic *Maoirne*, 'chamberlain's territory', from G. *maor,* Welsh (and Pictish) *maer*, ultimately from Latin *maior*, 'administrative official, chamberlain'. *Braemar* is *Bràigh Mhàr* the 'upper area of Marr'. *Ballater* and *Balmoral* are of uncertain origin.

ABERDEEN DISTRICT

Aberdeen, in Gaelic *Obar Dheathain,* 'confluence of the Don' derives its name from its original site at the mouth of the Don. The concentration at the Dee estuary is a later development.

Parish names are

Dyce. The name is obscure in origin.

Newhills is just what it says.

Nigg. This is probably G. *an eag*, 'the gap'.

Old Machar (cf. *Newmachar*). This name probably derives from the Gaelic word *machair* meaning 'a plain', cf. *Machair Rois*, 'the plain of Ross', *Machair Aonghais*, 'the plain of Angus' and *A' Mhachair Ghallda* applied to the *Lowlands* of Scotland. The name would have applied to the low land to the north of the lower Don.

Peterculter. See *Maryculter* (KD) above.

The nomenclature of lower Deeside (as well as Upper Deeside, see Watson and Allan, *Placenames of Upper Deeside*) shows a strong Gaelic element. If we travel out the Deeside Road from Aberdeen, for example, we find the following names

Mannofield. The first element is from G. *manach*, 'monk'.

Pitfodels G. *peit fodhail*, 'portion of the lesser fields'.

Cults. This is probably G. *coillte* 'woods'. (Note the English plural ending on this and the previous name).

Murtle, possibly *mòr tulach*, 'large(r) hillock' (cf. *Mortlach*) with loss of final *-ach.*

Milltimber. The first element is G. *meall*, 'round hill'; the second is not clear.

Binghill. This appears to be a Gaelic-English doublet name, the first part being from Gaelic *beinn*, 'peak, hill'.

Peterculter (see above).

These names continue beyond the Aberdeen District boundary with the *Leuchar Burn,* possibly *luathghàir,* 'joyful noise' and the *Gormack Burn,* possibly *gairmeag,* 'calling one', or *gormag,* 'green, verdant one', both of which meet and join the Dee west of Peterculter.

It has previously been stated that town and city nomenclature was often unjustly neglected. We may conclude by looking briefly at the names of Aberdeen Streets. They are a fascinating commemoration of the city's history both ancient and modern. They indicate its holy places: *St. Catherine's Wynd, St. Andrew's Street, St. Machar Place* (a doubtful saint, perhaps), *St. Fittock's Road, St. Paul's Street,* even *St. Peter's Gate*! They name its royal places: *King Street, Queen Street, Victoria Road, Albert Street.* They commemorate its worthies ancient and modern: *Elphinstone Road, Marischal Place, Provost Fraser Drive, Provost Rust Drive, Provost Watt Drive.* They name its places of beauty (one might think): *Hazledene Road, Heathryfold Circle, Primrosehill Gardens, Spring Garden;* they name its activities: *Market Street, Fish Street, Shiprow, Bank Street* (2), *Flourmill Brae, Wrights and Coopers Place.* Three of them, *Harlaw Place, Harlaw Road, Harlaw Terrace* celebrate its legendary victory of 1411. One of them (at least), *Wagril's Lane* is a mystery, for no-one in Aberdeen knows what a *Wagril* is.

Mystery is of course never far from the place name investigator, even, as has been shown above, when he seems at first sight to be on very safe ground. Here we have concentrated on name origins and on the names that are not of Scots or English origin as these are of easier access to the majority of those interested. We have also concentrated on district names and on some town and river names. Many of the suggested explanations are tentative. The great majority of names we have not been able to touch on at all.

Chapter twenty-two

DIALECT SPEECH

Mr J. Derrick McClure

"When he alighted from the Edinburgh coach at the canny twa and twae toun of Aberdeenawa, he had some doubts if the inhabitants spoke any Christian language."[1]

The experience of John Galt's traveller is not unique, nor could it only have happened in 1793. The most casual visitor to the North-east is bound to be impressed by the vigour of the local speech: by the extent of its difference from not only Scottish Standard English but the dialects of other parts of Scotland, by its internal differences — for there is not one North-eastern dialect but several, varying between city and country, farmers and fishers, young and old — and by the stubborn pride with which its users speak both in it and of it. There is no question of its "dying out" here: the Doric, as it is universally called, can be heard in any street or shop. Nor is the social stigma which often affects dialect speech at any rate quite as prominent as elsewhere in Scotland: members even of the professional classes do not consider it beneath them to use at least an occasional dialect word or morpheme, and many of them switch happily into the home speech when in company with friends or family. It is true that the speech of Aberdeen is often compared unfavourably to that of the smaller towns or the countryside — *coorse* is the word generally applied to it — but even the dialects of Aberdeen's most deprived areas are recognisably related to the traditional North-eastern Doric.

The Lowland Scots tongue, of which North-eastern speech is so distinctive and distinguished a branch, has its origin in the Anglo-Saxon dialect of the ancient Kingdom of Northumbria, the northern half of which was annexed by Malcolm II — like all Kings of Scots before him, and for several generations after, a Gaelic speaker — in 1018. Between then and (a convenient chronological landmark) the Reformation, the Northumbrian dialect in Scotland progressed triumphantly, for historical reasons beyond the scope of this essay, from the tongue of a language of the kingdom, spoken over an area as large as and more populous than the Gaeltacht and, unlike the Gaelic tongue, associated with the political, commercial and cultural developments which in the high Middle Ages had made of Scotland an integral and flourishing part of Western European Christendom.

When and by what stages it came to the North-east cannot be precisely ascertained; but since the spread of the Anglo-Saxon tongue is associated above all with the foundation and development of burghs, and the anciently-established and prosperous trading city of Aberdeen was granted the status of Royal Burgh by William the Lion in 1178, it was presumably about this time that Gaelic, which had long since superseded Pictish, began itself to suffer the long process of displacement from the North-east by Scots. By the end of William's reign, Kintore, Cullen and Banff were established as burghs and therefore centres of the new speech; and when in 1261 a new burgh was founded at the mouth of the Ythan, its name could not have been more simple or more Saxon — Newburgh. In a later and more troubled period, Robert I's Herschip of Buchan may well have contributed to the decline of Gaelic in the area, for the slaughtered tenants of the Comyn family were replaced by settlers from south of the Forth. And when, within living memory of Robert I and his achievements, Aberdeen's archdeacon John Barbour began his epic poetic tribute to the hero king, he used what was by then the language of his deaconry: Lowland Scots. Barbour's name for his language was "Inglis": another century was to pass before Scotsmen were to realise the appropriateness of calling it "Scottis". As to the name "Doric", that came to be applied to the Scots tongue only in the 19th century. Historically the word referred to a dialect of classical Greek, used in literature for comedy and pastoral poetry: the Scots of Allan Ramsay and his successors was often compared to Doric, and later commandeered the name for itself. However, even in Barbour's time the language was clearly distinct from the Southern English of his contemporary Chaucer: a fact which bears some relevance to a misconception still sadly prevalent in Scotland, even in the North-east. Among many people, respect and affection for the gweed aal spik o the fowk co-exist oddly with a notion that the local dialects are in some sense "bad English": that they represent the corrupt attempts at speaking English of people who are too simple, ignorant, vulgar or whatever to do it properly. The slightest trace of historical knowledge puts this notion out of court with no grounds of appeal. The Anglo-Saxon dialects of Scotland and England have been distinct for as long as their history can be traced: even Northumbrian Anglo-Saxon itself, which to an untrained reader would bear no resemblance to either modern Scots or modern English, small and loosely integrated corner of the King's domain to the principal was different in some respects from Mercian, the principal ancestor of the English of Chaucer, Shakespeare and Milton. The Doric is nobody's bad attempt at anything: it is itself, a regional speech distinct for centuries, and one of the badges of a populace which still vigorously maintains its local identity.

For obvious topographical reasons, communications between the North-east and other parts of Scotland have been slow and difficult until recent times; and therefore the dialects show many features not found elsewhere in Scotland. The characteristic *f-* for *wh-* was in being as early as the 16th century: the Aberdeen Burgh Records for 1539 bear witness to this with a spelling *for,* instead of the customary *quhar,* for the Scots cognate of *where. Far* is still the regular pronunciation; and similarly *what, who, when* are *fat* (when unstressed *fit*), *faa* and *fan.* This replacement of *wh-* by *f-* is in the southern part of our area — south of Aberdeen — restricted to pronouns and adverbs, but elsewhere it is general: *white* is heard as *fite, whin* as *funn, whaup* as *faap, whisky* as *fusky,* and so on. An exception is the word *wheel,* which is never pronounced *feel:* this is because wheeled carts were not introduced in the North-east until comparatively recently — the rugged terrain would have made them useless — and when the wheel eventually came to be part of everyday life in the region, the phonological change from *wh-* to *f-* had ceased to be operative, and the word was not affected. (It is also true, of course, that *wheel* pronounced *feel* would cause an awkward homophonic clash: *feel* in North-eastern Scots, besides the meanings which it has as a verb in both Scots and English, is as the local cognate of *fool* in frequent use as an insult term: "Awaa, ye're feel!")

This is far from the only feature of pronunciation which marks off the dialects of the North-east. A habit once considered typical of the region, and still to be heard among its older inhabitants, is the use of initial *vr-* in words of which the English cognates are spelt *wr-.* (Like other "silent letters" in English, the *w* in these words is not there for nothing: it was once pronounced, and had not fully disappeared from speech before the printing-press arrived to fossilise English spelling for, it seems, all time to come. In Scots, the approximant *w,* instead of vanishing, took the contrary course and became a strongly-articulated fricative *v.*) Thus *wrong* is *vrang* (the correspondence of Scots *a* with English *o* is not peculiarly North-eastern but general: cf. *aff, drap, Rab, Tam* and many other forms common to all Scots dialects), *write* is *vreit,* a joiner is a *vricht* (wright), a miserly person is a *vratch* (wretch), a snowdrift is a *vraith* or *vreyth* (wreath, in a peculiarly Scots semantic development of this word). "He vrocht awaa" — worked away — can still be heard, *vrocht* being cognate with *wrought,* an obsolete (in English) past tense of *work.*

Similarly, words written in English with *-aw,* where the *w* has long ago ceased to be pronounced as a consonant, appear in North-east Scots with a *-v;* thus *blow, sow, snow* — in Central Scots *blaw, saw, snaw* — are *blyaave, shaave, snyaave. Taw,* which originally meant to soften leather by beating it, appears as *tyaave,* generally with the sense of "toil or struggle at a difficult task" — "keep tyaavin awaa!" (This word used as a noun in its plural form is the once-notorious *tawse,* though in Aberdeen schools this implement was referred to rather as the *scudder.*) The extraneous *-y-* sound in these words appears before a long *a* in other words too: *bake* and *cake* are *byaak* and *cyaak*, the local word for a tinker is not *caird* but *cyaard,* and the Gaelic word *càrn,* meaning a pile of stones, appears not as *cairn,* as in other Scots dialects, but *cyaarn.*

A parallel case to *vr-* is the retention of *k* in the cluster *kn-*, as in *knee, knife, knot* and a few other words of local currency such as *kneef* (smart, alert, fit), *knip* (a mischievous child), *kneevlick* (a lump of bread, cheese or the like): this usage, however, probably now survives only in memory. Interestingly, a pronunciation traditionally associated with the area immediately south of ours, Angus, was *tn-:* a character named T'nowehead's Bell appears in J. M. Barrie's *Auld Licht Idylls.* The assimilation of the historical *kn-* to *tn-* represents a stage prior to its complete disappearance.

Father, mother and *brother* in the North-east are *fader, midder, breeder*; and this correspondence of medial *d* to English *th* is found in several other words of similar structure, such as *hedder* (heather), *idder* (other), *widder* (weather). *Daughter* is not *dochter,* as in most other parts of Scotland, but *dother*; similarly the auxiliary verb *might* is not *micht* but *mith.*

"Scotch was rubbish, all ee's and wee's," thought Ewan Tavendale in Grassic Gibbon's *Cloud Howe*[2]. It certainly appears to any listener that the *ee* vowel has an odd preponderance in the North-east dialects. One reason is that the normal change in Scots from the vowel of Anglo-Saxon *hām,* pronounced much as *harm* is today by a Southern Englishman but with a less retracted vowel, to Scots *hame* has in this area gone a stage further in the special case of words ending in *-n;* so that *bane, stane, nane* — in English *bone, stone, none,* the first two showing the regular and the third an irregular development of the Anglo-Saxon *ā*-vowel in the southern dialect — are *been, steen, neen. One* — *ane* in Eastern, *yin* in Western Scots dialect — is in the North-east *een. Taen,* the past participle of *tak* (take), becomes *teen*: "But Ah teen 'at een!", the author hears weekly in his capacity as mentor to an Aberdeen primary school chess club.

Another and more widespread source of *ee*'s is the development of Anglo-Saxon long *ō*, pronounced as in *go*, in words such as *mōna* (moon: the sound spelt *oo* in English is the normal reflex of this vowel in the Southern dialect). In medieval Scots — by Barbour's time — this had become a vowel like that of French *lune;* and the same vowel of course occurred in many words borrowed into Scots from French itself. Words formerly containing this vowel, whether of Saxon or French origin, are pronounced in various ways in different parts of Scotland: this is, in fact, one of the most conspicuous of the features which distinguish the regional dialects. Thus, the customary Scots spelling *muin* has to be associated in the West with the pronunciation *min,* in Fife *mane,* in Angus and some parts of the Eastern Borders *meun* (with a vowel like that of French *deux*) — and in the North-east, the result is *meen.* Similar cases are *bleed, breet* (same as *brute* but often used with a milder sense), *dee* (do) and its participle *deen, eese* (use), *fleer* (floor), *freet* (fruit), *peer* (poor), *seer* (sure), *speen* (spoon), *tee* (too). When the vowel follows a *k*-or *g*-, a preceding *w*-sound has developed; thus *good, cool, school* are *gweed, cweel, squeel.* This, perhaps, is the *wee* disdained by Ewan. The adjective *wee,* ubiquitous in the Scots of farther south, is decidedly less common here, its place being taken by what has become a stereotype of North-east speech, the diminutive suffix *-ie.* Mannies, wifies, lounies, quinies, sheepies, lammies, doggies, catties, beddies and the like abound in the region: the writer was once instructed, during a summer spent working with the Parks Department, to "fill up yon holie". The word *thingie,* used when the real name of something referred to is unknown or momentarily forgotten, occurs very frequently. If a greater degree of diminution (with possible overtones of affection or contempt) is required, the double diminutive *-ickie* can be used: *lassickie, housickie.* As a diminutive adjective, *little* is preferred to *wee,* its comparative and superlative forms *littler* and *littlest* being used freely. As a Glasgow mother speaks of her *weans* (from *wee yins*), an Aberdeen mother refers to the *littleens.*

Almost as prominent an auditory feature as *ee* in the dialect is a long open *aa. All, call, fall, salt* and similar words, pronounced with an *aw*-sound in Scotland south of the Mounth, are *aa, caa,* etc., in this region. (The loss of the *l* is a 15th century development, and the words should not be written *a', ca'* and so on, which gives the erroneous impression that they are simply their contemporary English cognates with the *l* omitted). "Going" is *gaan*, often palatalised in the Buchan and Banff areas to *gyaan* or even *jaan.* Words where the *aw* in other Scots dialects is derived from an early *aw* (then pronounced like *ow* in English *cow*) rather than *al* have the same sound, thus *craa, claa, draa* instead of *craw, claw, draw: blaa* and *snaa* have largely replaced *blyaave* and *snyaave.* (This last, incidentally, is a clear illustration of the inadequacy of a simple statement that a dialect, or certain dialect words or forms, are "dying out". It is certainly the case, and has been for a long time, that some Scots words are being used with diminishing frequency. But it does not necessarily follow that they are merely giving place to Scottish Standard English. The grandchildren of the Buchan farmers who said *blyaave* and *snyaave* probably no longer use these pronunciations; but it can hardly be denied that *blaa* and *snaa* sound perfectly convincing as samples of North-east dialect pronunciation: they are not the general Scots *blaw* and *snaw,* still less the English *blow* and *snow.*)

Another general feature of North-east dialect pronunciation is the prevalence of an *ey*-like diphthong in words which in most other Scots dialects have *ee-* or *ae*-like vowels. Thus, *chain, change, wait* and *rein* are *chyne, chynge, wyte* and *ryne.* The word for stomach, corresponding to general Scots *wame,* is *wyme. Quine,* the invariable local word for girl, is cognate with both *queen* and the obsolete English word *quean* meaning a disreputable woman. (The male counterpart of *quine, loun,* is peculiar to the North-east only in being used without pejorative overtones: in general Scots the word traditionally means a rascal.) *Speak, wheat, weak, seven* and *eleven* (in other dialects *seevin* and *eleevin*) are *spyke* though not often, in contemporary speech, in the vicinity of Aberdeen, where the pronunciation is *spik* — likewise *wik* (week), *briks* (breeks), etc. ,*fyte, wyke, seyven, aleyven. Weave* is *wyve,* and the local word for a spider is *wyver. Coal* and *coat* have as cognates *quyle* and *quyte,* though the meanings are more specific; a quyle is a burning or glowing ember — black coal is simply coal — and a quyte is a fisherman's oilskin jacket.

Finally, *few* and *new* appear as *fyowe* and *nyowe*, and the French-derived *beauty* and *duty* are likewise heard as *byowty* and *dyowty.* A splay-toed person is *skyow-fittit;* and in this expression at least this obsolescent usage certainly survives.

There are, of course, numerous other pronunciation features of the North-east dialects; but most of them are shared with all or most other forms of Scots. Thus throughout Scotland (and to some extent in Northern England too) such words as *toun* and *doun* retain the original Anglo-Saxon vowel instead of showing the diphthongisation that took place around Shakespeare's lifetime in the Southern English dialect; in all forms of Scots the Saxon $\bar{a}$ has generally become an *ae*-like vowel instead of the *o* of English, thus *gae, nae, mair, sair* and so on. *Nae* (the negative) provides one local shibboleth: in all parts of Scotland *no* in the sense of "not any" is *nae* — "There nae tatties the day" — but only in the North-east is the same form used with a verb, instead of the general Scots *no,* as the equivalent of *not* — "he's nae comin".

The Scots dialects are characterised not only by pronunciation but by vocabulary; and in this respect too, the North-eastern speech contains hundreds of words common to all dialects of Scots and many more that are peculiarly its own. This may be an appropriate context in which to dispose of another common misconception. It is of course true that many Scots words are borrowed from other languages. Gaelic, for example, has given numerous anciently-established topographical terms — *ben, glen, loch, strath, craig, inch* — several words, mostly borrowed at a much later date, referring to items of Highland culture — *clarsach, coronach, pibroch, philibeg, sporran, claymore* — and a number of words which once were in general use, though now most of us probably know them, if at all, only from Burns — *ingle, tocher, clachan, sonsie, cranreuch, messan.* North-eastern families still have their *shargers*, and fishermen from the Broch measure their herring in *crans.* Scandinavian has given us words in abundance: *kirk, kist, brig, big* (build), *gowk, graip, harns, lowe, meikle, nowt, rowp, tyne.* French, partly because of the Auld Alliance, is a prolific source of words in Scots: *ashet, aumrie, dour, fash, braw, gean, houlet, tassie;* Aberdeen's motto *Bon-Accord,* and the traditional name for a first-year University student *bejan* (from *bec jaune,* equivalent to "greenhorn") — now, alas, superseded by the uninspiring English term "fresher". And the Flemish, Dutch and Plattdeutsch of the Low Countries and the cities of the Hanseatic League, principal trading partners of Scotland in the Middle Ages and later, have given (for example) *bucht, crouse, dowp, haik, redd, swack, fozie* and *scaffie.* However, the ploy sometimes adopted by those who wish to denigrate the local speech of describing these words as "just Scandinavian" or "just French" — with, of course, the implication "and therefore not Scots" and the further implication "and how ridiculous of the Scots to take pride in them" — betrays a woeful lack of linguistic knowledge. A national tongue, the language of a people with a cosmopolitan outlook and extensive cultural and commercial relationships with other countries — such as Scots once was — may freely borrow and assimilate words from the languages of its partner states without thereby losing its identity or its integrity. When (let us say) a Dutch word comes to be used easily and naturally by Scots who could not begin to converse in Dutch, and to be pronounced by them with a Scots accent, inflected according to Scots grammatical rules, and incorporated into networks of meaning with other words in the Scots vocabulary, it is a fully-naturalised Scots word, its Dutch origins being of purely historical interest. There could be no more obvious illustration of this than English, which became so saturated with French borrowings in the Middle Ages, and with Latin- and Greek-derived learned words in the Renaissance, that it is virtually impossible to produce a sentence of any length in English using only the native Anglo-Saxon wordstock. This fact was recognised long ago by one of Northern Scotland's many remarkable personalities, the witty Cavalier scholar Sir Thomas Urquhart of Cromarty, who remarked of Western Europe's leading languages "Were [they] stript of what is not originally their own, we should not be able with them all in any part of the world to purchase so much as our breakfast in a market."[3] The abundance of loan words in the mither tongue should be recognised for what it is, a monument to the time when an independent-minded Scotland was a functioning member of the European comity of nations: the indictment which they embody lies not in the fact that they exist but in the fact that the historical and cultural heritage which they represent has been so ignominiously thrown away.

The copious and fascinating literature of the North-east (see Chapter 23) attests to the remarkable richness and distinctiveness of the local dialect vocabulary. Not only in the works of William Alexander, Charles Murray and their successors, but in the speech of rural and coastal Aberdeenshire until well within living memory, local words could be heard in abundance: a couple of dozen selected almost at random are *baillie* (cattleman), *boodie* (goblin, or scarecrow), *brodmill* (brood of chickens), *clossach* (hoard of money), *clyack-sheaf* (last sheaf cut at harvest), *dundeerie* or *dinnideer* (uproar), *feer* (plough the first guiding furrow), *galshach* (a delicacy), *gansey* or *maasey* (a thick woollen jersey), *gudge* (short thick-set person), *habber* (stutter), *hallach* (scatterbrained), *keb* (sheep tick), *kink-hoast* (whooping cough), *kysie* (cowrie shell), *mineer* (disturbance), *pyocher* (wheezing cough), *raeverie* (rumour), *squallach* (scream), *stamagaster* (unpleasant surprise), *thraaheuk* (instrument for twisting straw ropes), *yaavins* (bristles of barley), *yowies* (fir cones). Undoubtedly there are many people still alive in Aberdeenshire who have some or all of these words in their active vocabulary, and many more for whom they are at least a living memory.

It cannot be denied, however, that most of them would be puzzling to an average pupil at a primary school in the heart of Aberdeen. Yet here too, it would be wrong to conclude from this that the dialect is simply disappearing. If the word *thraaheuk* would perplex a boy from Footdee or Sandilands, so would the implement itself: never having seen one, he naturally would not know its name. The disappearance of a word need not be due simply to a change in the language, but to a change in the way of life of its users. And Aberdeen city speech, unquestionably, has a significant number of words of its own: those listed in the following paragraphs are all ones which the writer, an Ayrshireman, learned during his first few months of residence in Aberdeen.

Schoolboys play marbles with such diverse varieties as *dazzies, peezies, peebles* and *tattie-smashers,* using as targets *kypies* (depressions in the ground) or *fennies* (the action of standing with heels together and toes apart). A ride on somebody's back is a *coalie-bag* — a term which, without the diminutive, even finds its way into school sports-day programmes — and a ride on the shoulders is a *coxie-cusie* or *cockerty-hooie.* An ice-cream cone is a *cappie* — a peculiar local development of the general Scots word *cap* or *caup* meaning a wooden dish. Rubber-soled training shoes are *jimmies,* presumably from *gym-shoes:* if an Edinburgher in Aberdeen asked for them by his local word *gutties* he would be given golf balls. Boot polish is *blaik* and laces are *pynts.*

Aberdeen bakers deal in *rowies* (crisp flaky rolls: the word, of course, is the Scots cognate of *roll* with the usual diminutive suffix but its use is specifically restricted to this particular type of roll), *safties* (*softies* to the more genteel — soft rolls) and *stewie-baps* (floured rolls — hence the taunt "Ye couldna knock the stew aff a bap!" *Stew* is not generally used of flour except in this context: its usual meaning is dust). The amateur gardeners whose efforts are such an asset to Aberdeen fertilise their plots with *sharn* (manure) and water them from *roozers* (watering cans). Fractious children *wheenge* and *peenge*. To trip over your own feet is to *hyter,* to play aimlessly with something is to *ficher,* to work in an ineffectual, disorganised fashion is to *scutter. Bam, bampot* and *bamstick* are common insult terms denoting lack of intelligence.

All these words, and many others in daily use among Aberdonians of all ages, certainly qualify as North-eastern dialect words; and the fact that they flourish as such in a contemporary urban setting is evidence that the dialects are not simply disappearing but rather changing: adapting themselves, as living languages can and must do, to the changes which for good or ill have occurred in the life of the North-east.

All allowances being made, however, there is no question but that the pristine rural and coastal dialects of Aberdeenshire, used through many years by dozens of poets and fiction writers as well as by the generations of people for whom they were the normal daily means of communication, are losing their identity: if not necessarily by simply being submerged in central-belt Scots or Scottish Standard English — or, much more fearful to contemplate, in the gruesome babel of English and American accents and dialects emanating from the media and the pop scene — then through the social changes that consign the ways of life which they reflect to history. Johnny Gibb's modern counterpart no longer hires orra men at the feein mart and sets them to blaikin the mear's graith. And it need not be emphasised that those days cannot be brought back to life.

Yet they are enshrined in the region's abundant dialect literature and in the Doric itself; and in this form at least they can and must be preserved. The Doric is much more than merely a form of speech: it is the embodiment of a whole way of life, so intimately interrelated with the social and cultural history of the region that its loss would be nothing less than the abandonment of an entire folk-memory. Such a betrayal should be impossible even to contemplate; yet it could easily happen. By allowing our children to spend their entire schooldays in courses that make no reference whatever to the language, literature or social history of the North-east, and their entire leisure in pursuit of the English and American pop culture of the entertainment world, we connive at a process which will, if not checked, wipe out the North-east as a distinctive culture area in a few decades. The Doric and its associated literature are still capable of arousing enormous interest and affection among the middle-aged and elderly in Aberdeen and its environment. If this interest is not passed on to the younger generation, a cultural heritage of which any region should be proud will be irretrievably lost. The task is urgent.

Vol. III, Chap. xvi.

1. John Galt, *The Entail.* Oxford English Novels edition, ed. Ian A. Gordon, Oxford 1970, p. 305.
2. Lewis Grassic Gibbon, *Cloud Howe,* chap. iii. In *A Scots Quair,* Hutchinson (London) 1967, p. 277.
3. Sir Thomas Urquhart, *The Jewel,* ed. R.D.S. Jack and R. J. Lyall, Edinburgh (Scottish Academic Press) 1983, p. 65.

Chapter twenty-three

LITERATURE

Dr. Douglas Young

The North-east has made its greatest impact on the world of literature not through its writers, though they are many and talented, but through the achievements of people who could neither read nor write. These are the classic ballads which were created from the 14th century until the 18th century, and continually re-created with each performance as they were handed down orally from generation to generation (Buchan 1972).

Although the work of illiterate people, these great narrative songs are not primitive in any belittling sense. Unlike the later bothy songs of the 19th century they do not deal with the day-to-day routine of country life, but range further into the tragedy and the magic of existence, exploring the archetypal conflicts within families and between power groups.

Their world is a world of violence and sudden death in which plenty of opportunity is given for the exercise of the heroic virtues, and not only on the part of the men. Whether or not it be because women played an important part in the composition and the transmission of the ballads, they certainly play a prominent role in them. There is the stoic heroism of Margaret Forbes in "Edom of Gordon" matched by the treachery of Peggy Gordon in "The Baron of Brackley" and the awesome ruthlessness of Lady Crichton in "The Fire of Frendraught".

Nor are these songs primitive in any technical sense. They are very sophisticatedly wrought works of art with a command of narrative structure and patterning, of dialogue and imagery, and a facility to embody character which we mere literates can scarce imagine to be within the capacity of composers who needed no resort to writing.

By the middle of the 18th century the social conditions in Aberdeenshire which fostered and sustained this tradition of balladry were disappearing. The great agricultural improvements of the later 18th century produced a rural society which was less communal and more class conscious, a society of big farmers and farm labourers, in which respect for the ballads gradually fell down the social scale until in our own time they were left in the guardianship of the travelling folk and such a magnificent exponent as Jeannie Robertson. These social changes were at the same time being re-inforced by the spread of literacy, which inevitably leads to the devaluation and the enfeeblement of the oral tradition.

But memory of the ballads did not disappear overnight. In the 1900s, the greatest of all North-east folksong collectors, Gavin Greig, himself a considerable man of letters, poet, dramatist and novelist, was able to find those who still had the ballads, perhaps a little modified by time (Shuldham-Shaw and Lyle 1981).

But most of the collection made by Greig and his collaborator J. B. Duncan contains folksong of a different kind and produced by the new conditions of rural Aberdeenshire in the 19th century. The emergence of the bothy system provided a new impetus to song, very different from the classical ballad, with less "glamour", more rooted in day-to-day life, in which the farm servants responded to the hardness and privation of their existence sometimes with healthy ribaldry, sometimes with pungent satire of the oppressive system, with a love of their horses, and particularly a love of the land itself which is one of the touchstones of all North-east literature (Ord 1925).

Even when the oral tradition began in the 14th century, there were those who could read and write and for whom literature was something to be found in a book, and it is then that the great tradition of Scottish poetry begins, with the first major contribution coming from the North-east.

In 1375 John Barbour was Archdeacon at St. Machar's Cathedral in Old Aberdeen whilst he was writing his great epic poem *The Bruce.* This huge poem, over 13,000 lines in length, sets out to tell the true story — what Barbour calls the "suthfast tale" — of Bruce and the Scottish Wars of Independence that had taken place some 60 years earlier.

The Bruce is not only a chronicle of history, though as such it is remarkably reliable, it is also a great work of literature. Barbour has immense powers of description, particularly in conveying the wonder and also the terrible savagery of battle. He also has a power which a modern novelist might envy to convey character. There is a whole gallery of significant characters, but at the centre is Bruce himself, and we see him develop from a rather callow young adventurer to become the great leader, not only physically courageous but with a mature moral sense and an incomparable ability to win the devotion of his men.

One of the main questions which preoccupies Barbour is why the Scots, with their limited resources, were able to repulse the much more numerous and sophisticated English army. Principally, he concludes, it was a matter of motivation. The Scots were fighting for Freedom, for the independence of their nation, and nothing is more worth fighting for. The English on the other hand were fighting for imperial conquest. And the Scottish army was a democratic army, led by their consent, and in whose deliberations every man had a say. Even before Bannockburn Bruce consults his men; the choice is theirs.

> For if ye think spedful that we
> Fecht, we sall fecht; and if ye will
> We lieff, your liking to fulfill,
> I sall consent on alkyn wiss
> Till do richt as ye will deviss;
> Tharfor sais on your will planly.

This respect for the democratic spirit, the insistence that regardless of class structures every man is entitled to independence of mind and action, is another of the recurring features of the literature of the North-east.

In the centuries which followed Barbour, the North-east produced poets in considerable number. In his *The Bards of BonAccord* for the years between 1375 and 1860 William Walker mentions over 70 individuals most of whom are now quite forgotten (Walker 1887). Some, however, are still worth reading (Alison 1976).

Alexander Ross was born in Kincardine O'Neil in 1699 and spent most of his working life as schoolmaster at Lochlee in Glenesk. His best known poem "Helenore" tells the story of two country lovers who are separated when he is carried off by Highland raiders, and although the story may seem sentimental to the modern reader Ross does have the ability to place his tale in a real setting of local life and local speech.

John Skinner, the Episcopalian minister of Longside and friend of Burns, is still remembered for his songs, such as "Tullochgorum" and "The Ewie Wi The Crookit Horn", but perhaps makes most impact on a modern reader with his spirited account of a traditional ball game in "The Monymusk Christmas Ba'ing".

David Grant, author of *Lays and Legends of the North,* was born at Affrusk near Banchory in 1832 and in such poems as "The Sounin o The Kirk" and "The Muckle Spate o Twenty Nine" he shows a rare ability to capture comic character and action in a fine swinging rhythm.

In *The Bards of BonAccord,* which was published in 1887, Walker says that he has excluded all living authors. This is just as well for otherwise his volume would have been twice its already considerable size, there being a great upsurge in the vernacular poetry of the North-east around the turn of the century. Literacy had been spreading throughout the 19th century and with the 1872 Education Act became virtually universal, thus providing a much enlarged reading public. This also led to the development of local newspapers and the press of the region has been an important means of maintaining the local literary tradition from the time of William Alexander to the sterling efforts of Cuthbert Graham in our own time.

Life in the North-east was changing very markedly at this period. The spread of education, the much greater ease of communication outside the region, and the advance of "progress" generally, meant that people could see their traditional life disappearing. Nowhere was this more manifest than in the matter of language. Schooling meant standard English and a devaluation of the dialect. The North-east vernacular movement of the late 19th century and early 20th century can be seen as a reaction to this, as an attempt to evoke a traditional but disappearing way of life, and in so doing to demonstrate the poetic richness of the local language.

The most important of these poets is undoubtedly Charles Murray, who was born in Alford in 1864 (Murray 1979). He trained as a surveyor in Aberdeen and in 1888 emigrated to South Africa where he rose to become Secretary for Public Works. His poetry is therefore largely that of an emigrant looking back on the world of his childhood and couched in the Aberdeenshire speech which was current in the Vale of Alford when he was a boy.

Murray's work has always been popular — the tale is often told of how when his poem "There's Aye A Something" was published in *The Press and Journal* in 1933 the first printing was sold out by 9 a.m. — but, perhaps because of this popularity, he has not been held in very high esteem by the literati. In 1928 Hugh MacDiarmid wrote, "I say Charles Murray has not only never written a line of poetry in his life, but that he is constitutionally incapable of doing so".

Between these two extremes of popular adulation and critical rejection Murray remains a significant and able poet who wrote some very fine poems but also a fair amount of pretty terrible verse. There is a thread in his work of "home thoughts from abroad" which focuses not on the real life of the North-east but on some sentimental fantasy world. This is evident in a poem like "Hame" which begins,

> There's a wee, wee glen in the Hielan's
> Where I fain, fain would be. . . .

Murray is at his best when he has his eye very firmly focused on reality, observing the natural world and particularly the changes wrought by seasons, or describing character. The poems which impress me most are those in which he presents North-east types with a fine blend of understanding and sardonic humour. The protagonist of "The Packman" is superbly observed, an example of the new "upwardly mobile" self-made man, admirable in some ways, but ruthless and completely dedicated to that North-east dream of "getting on". He is not unrelated to John Watt of Dockenhill who, in that superb piece "Dockens Afore His Peers", reveals the same kind of hard practicality and ruthless self-interest, married to a kind of low cunning and insidious charm. Alongside these two in the gallery of North-east characters I would place the speaker in that other little masterpiece "Gin I was God" who carries the belief which we saw in Barbour that one man is as good as another to its logical end and sees himself as god. But still his feet are rooted in the clay and he can lament the wastrie of what has become of his creation — "A hale week's wark".

These are the characters who throughout the 19th century had been making the new and prosperous North-east, hard working, hard headed, and maybe just a little hard of heart. But in contrast we should place that other fine character "the wee herd" from the poem "The Whistle". He seems to come from an older world, a more traditional and carefree world of fun and enthusiasm, of music and romance. But his is a world that is disappearing in the name of "progress" and "education", and in the superb last stanza the changing season is used to evoke its replacement by harder, more practical but austere values, with the schoolmaster significantly dealing the final blow.

> But the snaw it stopped the herdin' an' the
> winter brocht him dool,
> When in spite o' hacks an' chilblains he was
> shod again for school;
> He couldna sough the catechis nor pipe the
> rule o' three,
> He was keepit in an' lickit when the ither
> loons got free;
> But he aften played the truant — 'twas the
> only thing he played,
> For the maister brunt the whistle that the wee
> herd made.

Colin Milton has described "The Whistle" as "a kind of cultural parable through which certain powerful contemporary fears were expressed" (Hewitt and Spiller 1983) and it is this awareness of the disappearance of the old life and of the old language which lies at the heart of Murray's work and that of several other poets of the time.

Following on from Charles Murray there is a considerable body of

41. The Crown Tower at King's College, University of Aberdeen. The building was completed in 1506 *(G. Stables)*

42. The Town House, Old Aberdeen. It was built in 1788 of hewn granite. It signified the civic independence of Old Aberdeen from 1489 to 1891, when the small burgh of barony was finally absorbed by its royal burgh neighbour *(G. Stables)*

43. The Shetland ferry, St. Clair, in Aberdeen harbour *(J. Livingstone)*

44. Provost Skene's House in Broad Street, Aberdeen. With Provost Ross's house in the nearby Shiprow, it forms two surviving 17th century houses in the centre of the city *(J. Livingstone)*

45. The planned settlement of Charlestown of Aboyne, on Deeside *(J. S. Smith)*

46. Strathisla Distillery *(G. Stables)*

47. The coastal settlements of Findochty, Portknockie and Cullen (background) *(J. S. Smith)*

48. Elgin, in the productive Laich o' Moray, with the cathedral in the centre of the picture *(Moray Aerial Archaeology Group)*

49. In Forres (like Elgin) the late medieval layout of the town is still distinguishable *(Moray Aerial Archaeology Group)*

50. The planned village of Burghead *(Moray Aerial Archaeology Group)*

51. The Strathspey King: James Scott Skinner
(Painted in 1913 by J. Young Hunter, City of Dundee District Council)

52. The first Labour Prime Minister: James Ramsay Macdonald
(Aberdeen Journals Limited)

53. The distinguished novelist James Leslie Mitchell, alias Lewis Grassic Gibbon
(Mrs R. Martin)

good vernacular verse from the North-east in the later years of last century and the early years of this one (Wheeler 1985). This work may not often touch the high seriousness of great poetry but at its best it is given a lasting quality because it is so firmly rooted in the genuinely felt experience of a distinctive way of life and commands such a firm mastery of local speech.

These men and women were not the full-time professionals of literature but people who had to work their way in life in some more mundane labour. Far from detracting from their writing, however, this often gives it its distinctive character and strength. J. M. Caie's work for the Board of Agriculture for Scotland gave him a first hand view of farming life that is evident in the totally unsentimental portrayal of such a poem as "The Auld Plooman". David Rorie likewise spent much of his working life as a general practitioner in Cults and this is reflected in his verse, not only in the obvious way of "The Auld Doctor" and "Isie", but more pervasively for it stimulates that wry, even sardonic view of human nature which is his hallmark (Donaldson 1983). As Rorie himself says,

As I gang roon' the kintra-side
Amang the young an' auld,
I marvel at the things I see
An' a' the lees I'm tauld.

What Rorie does for medicine, J. C. Milne does for education (Milne 1963). Murray's "wee herd" would have well appreciated the succinctness and the terrible truth of his poem called "Discipline":

As I gaed doon by kirk and toun
I heard the larkies singin',
And ilka burnie treetlin doon,
And wid and welkin ringin.

As I gaed doon by kirk and toun,
Quo I, "A skweel, gweed feth!"
And there I heard nae sang nor soun',
But bairns quaet as death!

But the dead hand of education can fall not only upon the bairns but also upon the teachers.

Fin first I sa' Jean Calder
A winsome lass was she,
Walkin doon the Spital
Wi' a lad I wished was me!

Fin neist I sa' Jean Calder
Wow! she lookit grim
Wi' twenty years o' teachin'
And drivin learnin in!

These poets speak directly of things that people understand and in a language which they recognise as their own, and therefore they have always been popular in a way that poetry elsewhere has long since ceased to be. The original edition of Mary Symon's *Deveron Days* published in 1933 was sold out within a week, and even in the 1970s there was a massive public enthusiasm for the work of Flora Garry (Garry 1975). And it is a tradition that persists, reaching a new high point in the contemporary work of Sheena Blackhall (Blackhall 1984).

In addition to this distinct tradition of local vernacular poetry, there are a number of North-east poets who have made their way in the wider world of Scottish literature who yet reveal their North-east origins in their work. In George Bruce's poetry the austere landscape of Buchan, the rocks and the sea, provide the setting, whilst the language itself, though usually English and not Scots, has a kind of spareness which derives from the speech of his native Fraserburgh which he described as "a community which required a spare, athletic language for survival's sake."

Alexander Scott's eschewal of sentimentality, his wry humour which often verges on the sardonic, betray his North-east origins, whilst his long poem "Heart Of Stone" gives a most sharp and astringent picture of his native city of Aberdeen.

Fowr-square til aa the elements, fine or foul,
She stares back straucht at the skimmeran scaud
o the sun
Or bares her brou til the bite o the brashy gale,
Riven frae raw rock, and rockie-rooted . . . .

Alistair Mackie was born into that world of granite tenements, and although his education and his work as a teacher have long since taken him out of that environment, it is back to that world of Aberdeen before the War that he comes again and again in his collection *Back Green Odyssey*.

A sma bit street that hirpled doun a brae.
Whitever roads I took since then I
began wi workin' fowk in granite tenements.
Aa the lave was superstructure.

The 19th century saw not only the emergence of a strong tradition in local poetry, but also a considerable prose tradition (Donaldson and Young 1981). From the 1850s onwards there has been a steady flow of novels reflecting the life of the region.

Our first significant novelist had in his own day a greater eminence in the world of literature than any other North-east writer before or since. George MacDonald was on friendly terms with the great names of Victorian literature such as Tennyson and Matthew Arnold, and was particularly close to Ruskin and Lewis Carroll.

His reputation was not confined to Britain. When he visited the United States in 1872 the great figures of American literature — Emerson, Longfellow, Mark Twain — turned out to meet him, and the editor of *Scribner's Magazine* could predict that "thousands of hearts would beat quicker and lean out to meet him as towards no other living man, with loving sympathy and reverence."

MacDonald was born in Huntly in 1824. He studied at King's College, Aberdeen, and then in London where he trained for the ministry. His church career came to an abrupt end, however, when he was dismissed from his charge because his religious views were too radical for the time. He therefore turned to the novel as a way of getting his ideas across and as a way of making a living.

These propagandist and commercial considerations account for the two weaknesses which modern readers will find in the 25 novels that he wrote, namely a tendency to preach and an unashamed pandering to popular Victorian taste. He has had a more lasting success with his children's books, such as *At The Back Of The North Wind,* and when he ventured to apply the conventions and techniques of the fairy story to an adult audience he produced in *Phantastes* and *Lilith* two of the most strange and disturbing fantasies in the whole of literature.

Several of his novels draw upon his North-east origins, most successfully *Alec Forbes of Howglen* which largely follows his own childhood in Huntly and his university days in Aberdeen. Its strengths lie in its masterly analysis of the Calvinist mentality, in its depiction of small town life, and the bold attempt to convey the real North-east speech of his characters, as can be seen in the following interchange:

> "I never saw sic widdiefows," chimed in a farmer's wife who was standing in the shop. "They had a tow across the Wast Wynd i' the snaw, an' doon I cam o' my niz, as sure's your name's Charlie Chapman — and mair o' my legs oot o' my coats, I doobt, than was a'thegither to my credit."

> "I'm sure ye can hae no rizzon to tak' shame o' your legs, gude wife," was the gallant rejoinder; to which their owner replied with a laugh:
>
> "They warna made for public inspection, ony gate."

But the great master of authentic North-east dialogue must surely be William Alexander in his classic novel *Johnny Gibb of Gushetneuk*. Alexander was born in Chapel of Garioch in 1826 and began life as a farm servant until an accident caused him to have a leg amputated and diverted him into a career in journalism where he rose to be editor of the *Aberdeen Free Press*.

Johnny Gibb first appeared as a serial in that newspaper in 1869-70, one indication of the importance of the local press in our literature. The novel gives a series of sketches of life in the parish of Pyketillim in the years 1839-1848, and provides an incomparable picture of Aberdeenshire life in a period of intense change, in the farm touns, in the kirk, and at the school, and of the relationship between tenant and laird. The realism comes from the absolutely authentic use of language. Nowhere else is there to be found so direct and undiluted a rendering of the distinctive speech of the region.

The novel also provides a vividly drawn gallery of characters. There is Mrs Birss, the classic social climber, who manipulates husband and children towards her goal of being "gentry" and in the end gets the just deserts of her folly and malice. Johnny himself is the archetypal North-easter, dour and forthright, honest and determined, and with a true love of the land. He is an embodiment of the spirit that made the North-east what it is, for he has virtually made his own farm out of wasteland and bog; as he says, "there's been grun made oot o' fat wisna grun ava."

But the book is more than a mere entertainment; it is a searching social study of a community in the process of change as the "improvements" establish themselves. It is set at the time of the Disruption when the Free Kirk broke away from the Church of Scotland, and this religious upheaval is seen as merely a reflection of a much deeper social conflict as the changes in agriculture produce a divided society with the new big farms pushing out the old peasantry into landless labour. There is no doubt that the author shares Johnny's commitment to the traditional values of the peasantry in the face of the new commercialism, and agrees with him when he says,

> Noo, this is fat I canna win at the boddom o' ava. I'm weel seer it was never the arreengement o' Providence that the man that tills the grun an' spen's the strength o's days upon't sud be at the merciment o' a man that never laid a han' till't . . . .

At the end of the 19th century we might mention Lorna Moon, born in Strichen in 1886, whose novel *Dark Star* may seem to many to be extravagantly romantic, but whose short stories in *Doorways in Drumorty* are much more tough-minded. Into the 20th century we find a continuing flow of good prose writers, Ian Macpherson, John R. Allan, Nan Shepherd, Hunter Diack, but the greatest is unquestionably the author who wrote under the name of Lewis Grassic Gibbon.

James Leslie Mitchell (Plate 53) was born in 1901 in Auchterless and was just eight when the family moved to Arbuthnott in the Mearns where he spent his formative years. Though he left the world of small farming when he was 16 never to return to it, going on to a life of journalism in Aberdeen and Glasgow, a career in the armed services which took him to the Middle East, and a few short years as a full-time writer in the south of England, it was to the Mearns that he returned in his imagination for his greatest work.

When *Sunset Song* was published in 1932, under the pseudonym of Gibbon, he had already published four novels under his own name. In these he had roamed the world from the battlefields of the First World War to the political conflicts of contemporary London, from Egyptian romance to science fiction. The pseudonym is significant because it reflects a change in his work which made him a great writer. What differentiates *Sunset Song* from these earlier novels is that it concentrates in a more sure and sustained way on his own most intense experience of life in the North-east, and most importantly of all leaves behind the uncertainties of his writing in English and moves on to his own distinctive and evocative exploitation of the language of his childhood.

Through the character of Chris Guthrie, Gibbon explores his own experience of growing up in the Mearns. Like the author she feels herself often at odds with her parents and the narrowness of the community in which she lives. Farm life with all its drudgery and crudeness sends her off to books to find a world that is more refined and exciting. She aspires to being a teacher and to lead a life of her own. And yet there is in her a strong love of the folk and of the land itself. Significantly Chris resolves this conflict in a way that differs from the author's own life. Despite all the attractions offered by a professional career, she decides that she cannot leave the land, and finds her future in marriage to Ewan Tavendale who "fair had the land in his bones", until the War comes and destroys their happiness.

This personal story is played out against a backdrop of the changing life of the Mearns in the early years of the century, and Gibbon gives a picture of what life was like in a traditional farming community that is more vivid and absorbing than anything else in our literature. But it is a life that is doomed by the growing mechanisation and commercialism. At the start Kinraddie is a community of small holdings, each supporting its own family, but by the end things are quite different, with the farms run into large units. And with these changes in agriculture come sweeping changes in lifestyle; the old ways of neighbourliness and co-operation have gone; the songs and the language are all different.

But it is the way that Gibbon himself uses that traditional language more than anything else that makes the novel great. In *Sunset Song* he tries to give the impression of the text being continually spoken by an ever-changing sequence of voices that are always authentically local. It is not just a matter of vocabulary, though there are a number of dialect words; it is much more a matter of trying to capture the distinctive tune, the idiom, the patterning of words. In *Sunset Song* we can say that the North-east finds its own distinctive voice in fiction.

As in poetry, the prose tradition is still alive today with distinguished living writers like David Toulmin and Jessie Kesson. Toulmin was born in Rathen in 1913 and after leaving school at 14 he spent the next 40 years as a farmservant. It is out of this experience that his writing comes with its distinctive documentary strength. He has written a large number of essays about the changing life on the farms of Buchan, many impressive short stories, but his only full length novel so far is *Blown Seed.* Here he follows on from Gibbon in several ways, particularly in the ease with which he is able to make the jump from his own male authorship into the life of a female central character. Helen MacKinnon resents the chauve and squalor of life on her father's farm and decides to go out on her own. She marries the kindly but ineffectual Audie Foubister and then leaves him when she is seduced by the tinker Meldrum Spark. But although Meldrum can arouse her passion, he is no provider, and she is forced back to the loveless and conventional life of a wife. She has made her bid for freedom and self-fulfilment but has to settle for compromise and a roof over her head.

This motif of the aspiring individual imprisoned by circumstance is the keynote of Jessie Kesson's fiction. She herself was brought up in an orphanage in Skene and worked the land until she made her escape to London and her writing. Her central characters, however, fail to break out of their imprisonment.

Experience has left Jessie Kesson with a far from romantic view of life in the North-east. She once said,

> North-east people are a race apart. They are
> tough and unsentimental and hardworking.
> But they lack . . . sweetness.

So her picture is of a community where life is hard, not only physically but also in terms of human relationships, particularly for those who aspire to something beyond the parks and the byres. There is a lack of charity and understanding which can make life a prison for such people.

Her first novel *The White Bird Passes* tells of how this prison falls about a sensitive and imaginative child as she grows up. Janie is brought up in the slums of Elgin but there is a marvellous sense of the child's magic view of the world despite all. Then she is placed in an Aberdeenshire orphanage and her horizons are forcibly narrowed. "And I don't want to work on a farm," she insists. "I want to write poetry," but farm work is all that there is. *Glitter of Mica* too emphasises the servitude of farm life. As a child Hugh Riddel is aware of this in his father's mean existence. "But it was all going to be different with him." Now a middle-aged man he is trapped in the aptly named farm of Darklands, bitter and frustrated. The heroine of *Another Time Another Place* is also caught, in a life of cold and wet and back-breaking work to save a few pennies for a dress from the mail order catalogue. She is a young wife but there is little romance for her, tied to a man who is decent enough but old and cold — lacking in "sweetness". And then the Italian prisoners of war come along and seem to offer an alternative, coming as they do from a land of sunshine and passion. But it is a dream. They are not interested in her, or interested only in casual sex. The war ends, they leave, and she is left in her prison.

With Jessie Kesson we may say that the tradition of North-east literature which began some 600 years ago with the anonymous composers of the great ballads, and which over the years has encapsulated the harshness as well as the beauty of this land, and the distinctive character of its folk, is still alive and well.

Chapter twenty-four

SOME FAMOUS LOCAL PEOPLE

Dr. Paul Dukes

Let us begin with some soldiers. There were many Scottish mercenaries throughout Europe in the early modern period. Several of them came from the region near "Krampius, very high and broad", as a Russian *Cosmography* of the 17th century called it. One of them, Patrick Gordon of Auchleuchries near Ellon was on leave from Moscow in Edinburgh in October 1669 when he wrote:

"I go into the country where wintering, I intend to return for Russia in the Spring and hoped to go by way of Poland. If in this journey I find no grounds for a settlement anywhere else, I intend to continue in Russia sometime longer, albeit God knoweth the pay there yields us but a very bare subsistence as things go now. Even in Scotland soldiers of fortune can attain no honourable employment for Nobles and persons of great quality. In England aliens are seldom employed, so that necessity (who was never yet a good pilot) constrained us to serve foreign Princes when notwithstanding if with honour we could be any ways steadable to our native country it would be some comfort."

Lack of alternative (a circumstance of much wider application then and later) took Patrick Gordon away to Russia, where he remained most of the time until his death in 1699. By that time, he had risen to the rank of General and had become renowned as one of the close associates of the young tsar who was to achieve greater fame as Peter the Great. The Scottish soldier's contribution to Peter's prosperity was threefold. Firstly, in the strictly military sense, he helped win battles, especially in the south against the Turks and their henchmen, the Crimean Tatars. He also played a leading rôle in the formation of modern regiments and their realistic peacetime battles as well as participating in Peter's naval exercises. Secondly, he aided Peter in a struggle to preserve the tsar's position on the throne in 1689 (at a time when he would rather have been with

James VII and II in an attempt to uphold the Stuart cause). Then, when Peter was away in Holland and England on his famous Great Embassy in 1698, he led the suppression of a revolt by the musketeers which could have toppled the tsar in his absence. Thirdly, but by no means least, Gordon exerted a cultural influence on Peter that helped to prepare him for the Great Embassy.

In 1717, the now celebrated tsar went on another of his travels westwards, as another outstanding military man from the Grampian Region tells us in his memoirs: ". . . the Emperor of Russia, Peter the First, arrived in Paris, and I resolved to try to get into his service; for having now nothing to trust but my sword, I thought it high time (being about 20 years old) to quit the Academy. . . ." James Keith, brother to George, the 10th and last hereditary Earl Marischal of Scotland, and originating from Inverugie just outside Peterhead, had begun his education in Aberdeen and participated in the '15, then in the '19 led by the Duke of Ormonde. He went on to fight for the King of Spain, but found his Protestantism a bar to promotion, and so, about ten years after his first thought of entering Russian service, he actually did so. Peter the Great was now dead, and a somewhat turbulent period in Russian politics had ensued. But Keith was able to ride the storm; indeed, he found himself promoted to the prestigious rank of Lieutenant-Colonel in the Imperial Guards. His career went from strength to strength as he performed valuable deeds in the Ukraine and along the Baltic coast. He received more advancement in rank, and other rewards, including a large estate in the Baltic province of Livonia, the title deed to which is now kept in the Aberdeen University Archive. After about twenty years in Russia, however, Keith became completely disillusioned with constant bickering at court, and left for a further period of military service with Frederick the Great of Prussia, until his death in battle in 1758. Brother George is said to have provided the epitaph which may be seen on the plinth to the statue of Keith in Peterhead: *Probus vixit, fortis obiit* — "He lived honestly and died bravely."

That statue was presented to the Burgh of Peterhead in 1868 by King William I of Prussia. It is the copy of one erected earlier in Prussia itself. Another foreign statue to a military hero from Grampian Region has not been matched by a copy in his native land. It stands on Laurel Hill, Philadelphia as a monument to Hugh Mercer, Brigadier in the American Revolutionary Army from 1776 until his death in an attack on Princeton. He had been born in Aberdeen, educated at Marischal College, and involved in the '45 as an army doctor. Emigrating to the colonies, he developed his military skills in the Indian Wars and made his first acquaintance with George Washington. It is difficult to say that Mercer's prowess as a soldier was in the same category as Gordon's and Keith's. There are probably others who deserve as much to be recorded, although we must be careful not to assign a Grampian association to some who appear to have it but in fact do not. For example, the statue of Gordon of Khartoum stands outside Gordon's College, but he was born in Woolwich.

It is high time we moved on from war to peace. As is only to be expected in a region with a university stretching back to the end of the 15th century, there have been many distinguished academics. Here, only a small selection can be mentioned. Duncan Liddel was Professor of Mathematics and Medicine at several German universities in the late 16th century. There is a monumental brass to him on the wall of the Church of St. Nicholas in Aberdeen and a stone to him standing in a field of his former estate near Dyce. He endowed a Chair at Marischal College, the first incumbent of which was William, younger brother of Arthur Johnston, who achieved wider fame not only as a writer of Latin verse (deemed by some to be the "Scottish Ovid") and a classical scholar, but also as a doctor (physician to Charles I in 1625).

As a vigorous outpost of the Scottish Enlightenment, Aberdeen made its mark in the 18th century. Most renowned at the time was James Beattie, born at Laurencekirk, and appointed to the Chair of Moral Philosophy at Marischal College in 1760. Ten years later he produced an *Essay on the Nature and Immutability of Truth,* which is said to have made him famous overnight. A further decade on, his fame was increased by the publication of *The Minstrel,* a long poem full of fine sentiments. Beattie was lionised in London and had his portrait painted by Sir Joshua Reynolds. That portrait has been his most lasting memorial, for his own work has now been largely forgotten.

Beattie's renown has long been overtaken by that of his contemporary as Professor of Moral Philosophy at King's College, Thomas Reid. Originating from Strachan (pronounced Strawn) near Banchory, Reid made his name through an attack on the philosophy of David Hume, *Inquiry into the Human Mind upon the Principles of Common Sense,* published in 1764. Hume himself was impressed, as have been many other philosophers since. Indeed, Reid's reputation as a metaphysician has recently risen to such heights that he must be looked upon as perhaps the greatest thinker to originate in Grampian Region, even if he did leave it in the later stages of his career for Glasgow.

In the earlier part of the century, a most deserved reputation as classical scholar was established by Thomas Blackwell, who was born in Aberdeen in 1701 and later became Principal of Marischal College as well as Professor of Greek like his father before him. In 1735 he brought out *An Inquiry into the Life and Writings of Homer,* in which he pointed out that the bard took his descriptions of ancient Greece from his close acquaintance with the traditional life of the people and related the events of the times in a manner strongly influenced by their epic and mythical traditions. In such a way, Blackwell laid claim to the title of father of modern folklore studies.

Contemporary to the Enlightenment, but not part of it, was Alexander Cruden, MA of Marischal College, but making his name in London through the mammoth task of the completion of a *Bible Concordance,* which was first published in 1737. Cruden attempted to improve the morals of the capital, a task even more formidable than the composition of the *Concordance.* He spent some time in an asylum, then escaped from it and took unsuccessful legal proceedings against his incarcerators. He died with the consolation of knowing that his major work had achieved wide fame.

Moving into the 19th century, let us begin with two remarkable Orientalists. James Legge, born in Huntly and MA of King's College in 1835, became Professor of Chinese at Oxford. His works were published in Hong Kong and Shanghai as well as in Britain. William Robertson Smith, born (and later buried) at Keig near Alford, studied theology at Edinburgh, Bonn and Göttingen after graduation from Aberdeen in 1865. Returning to become Professor of Hebrew and Old Testament Studies at Aberdeen Free College, he was later dismissed for contributing an article deemed heretical on the Hebrew language to the *Encyclopaedia Britannica.* He found consolation in the reputation of a martyr for truth and the post of Editor-in-Chief of the *Encyclopaedia Britannica,* and was later made Professor of Arabic at Cambridge. Another unfortunate dismissal was that of James Clerk Maxwell, who had to leave Aberdeen as the junior Professor of Natural Philosophy at the time of the fusion of the two colleges in 1860. His work on *Electricity and Magnetism,* produced in 1873, has been considered one of the outstanding scientific achievements of a single individual. Among renowned 19th century graduates of Aberdeen University were Robert Grant, who identified 8551 stars while Professor of Astronomy at Glasgow, and William MacGillivray, Professor of Natural History first at Edinburgh, then at Aberdeen, whose work was appreciated both by the American ornithologist Audubon and Queen Victoria, as well as by a more general public. In the early 20th century, J. Arthur Thomson, another Professor of Natural History, did much to popularise zoology and other branches of science.

So far, we have looked little at those achieving their fame through their efforts on behalf of the preservation of body and soul, the doctors and the divines. There have been so many of these that it is difficult to know where to begin, and we can therefore take only a small selection of each. Many medics came from the remarkable Gregory family, which stemmed from John, the minister at Drumoak, who died in the middle of the 17th century. Let us briefly consider two: first, another John, who studied at Leyden and Edinburgh as well as Aberdeen before becoming Professor of Medicine at King's College in 1755, then removing to Edinburgh as Professor of Physic in 1766. He wrote several works on a variety of subjects, including a comparison of human faculties with animal, a description of the duties of a physician and "A Father's Legacy to his Daughter". The last of these gave the advice: "If you happen to have any learning, keep it a profound secret, especially from the men." Hence perhaps, a contribution to the almost total absence of women from our Grampian Hall of Fame. Our second Gregory is James, son of the previous John, who followed the educational path of his father and then, also like him, occupied a medical chair at Edinburgh. He became famous, even notorious, as an advocate of blood-letting, blistering and vomiting and other harsh remedies, and was best remembered as the deviser of a rhubarb-based purgative bearing the family name. Sir James McGrigor was born at Cromdale, Strathspey, but educated at Aberdeen Grammar School and Marischal College. After studying medicine at Aberdeen and Edinburgh, he purchased a post as army surgeon, and rose to fame in the Peninsular Army under Wellington, who deemed him "one of the most industrious, able and successful public servants I have ever met." McGrigor may be considered the founder of the British Army Medical Corps. A contemporary of his, with a medical degree from King's College in 1794 but no other known Aberdeen connection, was Sir James Wylie, who did for the Russian army what McGrigor did for the British, and has a statue still standing in Leningrad as a testimony to the fact. A third knight was Sir Patrick Manson, born at Oldmeldrum in 1845, who contributed to the conquest of malaria, and a fourth was Sir Alexander Ogston, Professor of Surgery, who discovered the pus organism in 1881 and thus facilitated safer medical practice. J. J. R. Macleod, Professor of Physiology from 1928 to 1935, was associated with the development of insulin and has therefore been widely celebrated by diabetics.

We have given so much attention to the University of Aberdeen that it is appropriate to begin our selection of divines with its founder, William Elphinstone. Born in Stirlingshire and graduating from the University of Glasgow, he later became Bishop of Aberdeen and gained papal sanction for the foundation of a local university in 1495. His many-sided activities have been fully described by Dr. Leslie Macfarlane.

Gilbert Burnet, born in Edinburgh but educated at Marischal College, became a close associate of William of Orange and a passionate apologist for the "Glorious and Bloodless" Revolution of 1688. He was Bishop of Salisbury and author of many works, most notably his *History of My Own Time.*

Among well-known clerical emigrants, John Strachan, born and educated in Aberdeen before emigrating to Canada, became Bishop of Toronto and showed filial piety towards his *alma mater* when seeking in 1826 a Royal Charter for a university in his diocese by calling it King's College. He was its first president as well as founder (like James Blair, a Marischal graduate, at William and Mary College at the end of the 17th century, and William Smith, another King's graduate, at the University of Pennsylvania in the middle of the 18th century). Strachan is well commemorated at what became in 1849 the University of Toronto, where his name is pronounced (like the Deeside village) Strawn. The thousands of missionaries from the region will have to be represented by Mary Slessor. Born in Aberdeen, if growing up in Dundee, she was inspired to go off to Africa and to devote most of her life to the Calabar Mission of the Church of Scotland. Those faring abroad included explorers such as James Augustus Grant, born in Nairn and a graduate of Marischal College; journalists of whom the most famous was the King's College graduate and war correspondent Archibald Forbes; and engineers such as Thomas Blake Glover, who is said to have brought the railway to Japan; and many other administrators and entrepreneurs.

Foreign parts, of course, included England, and Grampian "aliens" often made their mark there. At the highest level of public life, two prime ministers can be claimed: Lord Aberdeen; and James Ramsay Macdonald (Plate 52). Outstanding lawyers have included Sir George Mackenzie of Rosehaugh, born in Dundee and a graduate of King's College, known as the "Bloody Advocate" because of some of his judgements in the troubled late 17th century, but also considered by one of his oppenents to be the "brightest Scotsman of his time". He wrote widely on legal and other subjects, including on reason and on solitude. Equally, even more wide-ranging was Sir James Mackintosh, who came from Fortrose on the Black Isle to King's College before being called to the English Bar in 1795. already, he had begun to make a name for himself with a defence of the French Revolution in response to the attack on it by Edmund Burke. He went on to cover a wide range of subjects linguistic, literary, historical and political as well as legal. Lord Byron considered him "the first man in England".

There seems to be something in the Grampian air promoting the spirit of invention. James Gregory, a member of that famous family, was known in the 17th century and after for his refinement of the telescope. In 1784, the son of a Kincardineshire clergyman James Tytler became in Edinburgh the first Briton to make an ascent in a balloon. And Robert William Thomson, born in Stonehaven in 1822, was the originator of, among many other devices, an early version of the pneumatic tyre. The quality of the local light was no doubt an inspiration for the portrait painter George Jamesone, the Scottish Van Dyck as he has been called, at the beginning of the 17th century, as it was for the pioneer photographer George Washington Wilson, towards the end of the 19th century. James Gibbs probably remembered some of the local stones as he left his native Aberdeen in 1703 with an MA from Marischal College to study architecture in Rome, and then returned to England to design such buildings as the Church of St. Martin's-in-the-Fields in London, King's College in Cambridge and the Radcliffe Library in Oxford. He also designed the West St. Nicholas Church in Aberdeen, and is said to have influenced the style of the White House in Washington. Finally, a long tradition of music-making has led to such varied performers as Mary Garden, *prima donna* at the Paris Opera in the late 19th century, and Scott Skinner (Plate 51), celebrated at about the same time as a fiddler throughout Britain and North America.

These, then, are just a few of the famous people connected through birth, education or adoption with Grampian Region in fields other than literature. Among the qualities essential to fame is a certain amount of durability, and for that reason nobody still alive has been included here, although in time his or her claim may be overwhelming.

Bibliography

GENERAL

Aberdeen Civic Society	Archibald Simpson - Architect of Aberdeen	Aberdeen	1978
Adam, J.	The Changing Face of Agriculture in the Parish of Peterculter - The Post War Years 1944 -1984	Unpub. B. Ed. dissertation, University of Aberdeen	1985
Alexander, W. M.	The Place-names of Aberdeenshire	Spalding Club, Aberdeen	1952
Alison, J. (ed.)	The Poetry of North-East Scotland	Heinemann	1976
Anderson, J.	A General View of the Agriculture of the County of Aberdeen	Edinburgh	1794
Andrews, A.	The Whisky Barons	Jupiter Books	1977
Anson, P. F.	Fishing Boats and Fisher Folk on the East Coast of Scotland	London	1930 & 1971
Antiquities of Aberdeen and Banff — Four Volumes		Spalding Club, Aberdeen	1847-1869
Barnard, A.	The Whisky Distilleries of the United Kingdom	David & Charles	1969
Bisset, D. R.	Group Marketing: Grampian Pigs Limited College Digest	North of Scotland College of Agriculture	1982
Blackhall, S.	The Cyard's Kist	Rainbow Books	1984
Bourne, W. R. P. *et al.*	The Loch of Strathbeg	Nature Vol. 242 No. 5293, 93-95	1973
Brander, M.	Guide of Scotch Whisky	Johnston & Bacon	1975
Brander, M.	The Original Scotch	Hutchinson	1974
Buchan, D.	The Ballad and The Folk	Routledge and Kegan Paul	1972
Carnegie, H.	Harnessing the Wind — Captain Thomas Mitchell of the Aberdeen White Star Line	Centre for Scottish Studies, University of Aberdeen	1984
Catt, D. C. & Rees, A. M. M.	Agriculture in the North East Chapter 9 of North East Scotland, A Survey of Its Development Potential	HMSO	1969
Chapman, K.	North Sea Oil and Gas: a geographical perspective	David & Charles	1976

Coull, J. R.	Salmon-Fishing in the North-East of Scotland before 1800	Aberdeen Univ. Review XLII, I, No. 137, 31-38	1967
Coull, J. R.	Fisheries in the North-East of Scotland before 1800	Scottish Studies 13, 17-32	1969
Crabtree, J. R.	Assessing Business Viability Using Gross Output Analysis in Farm Management Review. Issue No. 19	Agri. Econ. Div. School of Agriculture, Aberdeen	1984
Daiches, D.	Scotch Whisky	Collins	1978
Daw, M. E.	Group Marketing, Lesson for Group Marketing in College Digest	North of Scotland College of Agriculture	1982
Diack, W.	Rise and Progress of the Granite Industry of Aberdeen	Aberdeen	1950
Distillers Co. Ltd.	D.C.L. and Scotch Whisky	Distiller Co. Ltd., London	1978
Donaldson, W. (ed.)	David Rorie; Poems and Prose	Aberdeen University Press	1983
Donaldson, W. & Young, D. (eds.)	Grampian Hairst	Aberdeen University Press	1981
Edlin, H. L. (ed.)	The Forests of North-East Scotland in Forestry Commission Guide	HMSO	1976
Entwhistle, G. & Crabtree, J. R.	The Scope for Developing Deep-Water Port Facilities for Scottish Barley Exports in Economic Report No. 142	Agri. Econ. Div. School of Agriculture, Aberdeen	1985
Entwhistle, G. & Crabtree, J. R.	The Use of Wheat by Distillers in Economic Report No. 143	Agri. Econ. Div. School of Agriculture, Aberdeen	1985-86
Episcopal Register of Moray (Registrum Episcopatus Moraviensis)		Spalding Club, Aberdeen	1837
Federation of U.K. Milk Marketing Boards	United Kingdom Dairy Facts and Figures 1985	Aberdeen	1985
Fenton, A.	The Hearth in Scotland	SVBWG Dundee & Edinburgh	1981
Fenton, A., Walker, B., Stell, G. (eds.)	Building Construction in Scotland. Some Historical and Regional Aspects	SVBWG Dundee & Edinburgh	1976
Fenton, A.	Scottish Country Life	John Donald	1977
Fenton, A.	The Rural Architecture of Scotland	John Donald	1981
Financial Times	Oil and Gas Industry Yearbook	Longman	1986
Forestry Commission	Census of Woodlands and Trees — Conservancy of East Scotland	Forestry Commission	1984
Galt, J.	The Entail in Oxford English Novels edition, Vol. III Chap. xvi ed. I. A. Gordon, p. 305	Oxford	1970

Garry, F.	Bennygoak and Other Poems	Rainbow Books	1975
Gaskin, M. ***et al***	North East Scotland — a survey of its Development Potential	HMSO	1969
Gibbon, L. G.	Cloud Howe in A Scots Quair, chap. iii p. 277	Hutchinson	1967
Gordon, S.	The Cairngorm Hills of Scotland	London	1925
Graham, T. R.	Group Marketing. Caithness Livestock Breeders Ltd., in College Digest	North of Scotland College of Agriculture	1982
Grampian Regional Council/Banff & Buchan District Council	Contingency Plan for Petrochemical Industries	Aberdeen	1980
Grampian Regional Council	Grampian Quarterly Economic Review — Winter	Dept. of Physical Planning	1981/82
Grampian Regional Council	Future Oil and Gas prospects 1985 Update — August	Dept. of Physical Planning	1985
Grampian Regional Council	Grampian Quarterly Economic Review — Autumn	Dept. of Physical Planning	1985
Grampian Regional Council	Quarterly Focus: Forestry and Wood Processing	Dept. of Physical Planning	1984
Grampian Regional Council	Grampian Region Structure Plan Survey Report	Aberdeen	1984
Gray, M.	The Fishing Industries of Scotland 1790-1914	Oxford	1978
Gunn, N. M.	Whisky and Scotland	Routledge	1935
Haughs, M. A.	The Indebtedness and Profitability of Farms in the North of Scotland, 1981/82 and 1982/83 in Farm Management Review, Issue No. 20	Agri. Econ. Div. School of Agriculture, Aberdeen	1985
Hewitt, D., Spiller, M. (eds.)	Literature of the North	Aberdeen University Press	1983
Hunt, D. & Atkin, A.	Oil-related impact on the industrial infrastructures of Aberdeen	Unpub. Report to SSRC North Sea Oil Panel	1979
Jackson, K.	The Gaelic Notes in the Book of Deer	Cambridge University Press	1972
Johns, P. M. & Leat, P. M. K.	An Approach to Regional Economic Modelling: The Case of Grampian in Economic Report 144	Agri. Econ. Div. School of Agriculture Aberdeen	1986
Keith, A.	Eminent Aberdonians	Aberdeen	1984
Keith, J. S.	A General View of the Agriculture of Aberdeen	Edinburgh	1811
Leslie, W.	A General View of the Agriculture of the Counties of Nairn and Moray	London	1813

Locke, G. M. L.	The Place of Forestry in Scotland	Forestry Commission Research and Development Paper 113	1976
Lockhart, B. R. H.	Scotch	Putnam	1951
Machie, A. D.	The Scotch Whisky Drinker Companion	Ramsay Head Press	1973
Mackay, G. A. & Moir, A. C.	North Sea Oil and the Aberdeen economy	Social Science Research Council London	1980
Matthews, J. D.	Wood Conservation Strategy in the Grampian Region — Part C Forestry and Wood Products	Aberdeen	
McDowell, R. J. S.	The Whiskies of Scotland	Longmans	1967
McDowell, S. & Begg, H. M.	Industrial performance and prospects in areas affected by oil development in ESU Research Papers No. 3	Scott. Econ. Research Council, London	1981
Mellor, R. E. H.	Railways of Scotland — Papers of A. C. O'Dell	Centre for Scottish Studies University of Aberdeen	1984
Milne, J.	Celtic Place-names in Aberdeenshire	Aberdeen	1912
Milne, J. C.	Poems	Aberdeen University Press	1963
Moss, M. S. & Hume, J. R.	The Making of Scotch Whisky	James & James	1981
Murray, C.	Hamewith	Aberdeen University Press	1979
Naismith, R. J.	Buildings of the Scottish Countryside	Victor Gollancz	1985
Naylor, E. L.	Changes in Farm Structure — A Survey of Four Parishes in North East Scotland in Farm Management Review, Issue No. 17	Econ. Div. School of Agriculture Aberdeen	1982
NOSCA	Landlord/Tenant Partnerships. Bulletin 29, May	NOSCA	1984
Ord, J. (ed.)	Bothy Songs and Ballads	John Donald	1925
Revell, B. J.	A Market Share Analysis of Meat Demand 1968-1982 in Meat Demand Trends	MLC Economic Inf. Service 83/2. 2	1983
Revell, B. J. & Johns, P. M.	Monthly Livestock Slaughtering Statistics. Scottish and Regional Figures	Unpub. Reports Agri. Econ. Div. School of Agriculture Aberdeen	1985
Ritchie, W.	Environmental aspects of oil and gas pipeline landfalls in North East Scotland	Proc. of 17th International Coastal Eng. Conf. ASCE/ Sydney 2938-2954	1980

Robertson, G.	A General View of the Agriculture of Kincardineshire	London	1811
Rogie, A.	The North East Market for Grass Fed Lambs 1981 and 1982 in Farm Management Review, Issue No. 18	Agri. Econ. Div. School of Agriculture Aberdeen	1983
Ross, J.	Whisky	Routledge	1970
Scottish Mountaineering Club	Scottish Mountaineering Club Journal. Various issues		
Scottish Mountaineering Trust	SMC Climbers' Guides — various editions and titles		
Scottish Tourist Board	Royal Grampian Country	Dept. of Geography University of Aberdeen/ Scottish Tourist Board	1969
Scott Morton, R.	Traditional Farm Architecture in Scotland	Edinburgh	1976
Shuldham-Shaw, P. & Lyle, E. (eds.)	The Greig-Duncan Folk Song Collection. Vols I and II	Aberdeen University Press	1981 1983
Smith, J. S.	George Washington Wilson's Aberdeen	Keighley	1982
Smith, J. S. (ed.)	New Light on Medieval Aberdeen	Aberdeen	1985
Sutherland, I.	From Herring to Seine Net Fishing on the East Coast of Scotland	Wick	1986
Sutherland, R. M.	Recent Trends in the Movement of Cattle into North-East Scotland Farm Management Review. Issue No. 19	Agri. Econ. Div. School of Agriculture Aberdeen	1984
Thomson, J. M. *et al.* (eds.)	Register of the Great Seal (Registrum Magni Sigilii Regum Scotorum)	Edinburgh	1882-1914
Urquhart, G. A.	The Amalgamation of Agricultural Holdings: A Study of Two Parishes in Western Aberdeenshire	Jour. of Agri. Economics Vol. XVI, No. 3	1965
Urquhart, Sir T.	The Jewel (eds.) R. D. S. Jack and R. J. Lyall	Scottish Academic Press	1983
Walker, W.	The Bards of Bon Accord	Edmund and Spark	1887
Warren, R. W.	Group Marketing, Harlaw Fruit Limited College Digest 1982	NOSCA	1982
Waterman, J. J.	Aberdeen and the Fishing Industry in the 1870s	Centre for Scottish Studies University of Aberdeen	1979
Watson, A.	The Cairngorms, SMC District Guide	Scottish Mountaineering Trust	1975
Watson, A. & Allan, E.	The Place Names of Upper Deeside	Aberdeen	1984

Watson, R. D.	Amenity and Recreation on the River Dee in Biology and Management of the River Dee	NERC	1985
Watson, W. J.	The History of the Celtic Place-Names of Scotland	Wm Blackwood & Son, Edinburgh	1926
Wheeler, L. (ed.)	Ten Northeast Poets	Aberdeen University Press	1985
Wilson, R.	Scotch made easy	Hutchison	1959
Wilson, R.	Scotch: the formative years	Constable	1970
Wilson, R.	Scotch: Its History and Romance	David & Charles	1973
Wise, M.	The Common Fisheries Policy of the European Community	London	1984
Wyness, F.	Aberdeen — Century of Change	Aberdeen	1975

PRE-HISTORY AND HISTORY

Allan, J. R.	North East Lowlands of Scotland	London	1952
Adair, E.	North-East Folk: from College to Castle	Edinburgh	1982
Allardyce, J.	Bygone Days in Aberdeenshire	Aberdeen	1913
Anderson, G.	Kingston on Spey	Edinburgh	1957
Anderson, M. L.	A History of Scottish Forestry	Nelson, London	1967
Anderson, R.	Aberdeen in Bygone Days	Aberdeen	1910
Anderson, R.	Deeside	London	1911
Aspinall, A., Warren, S. E., Crummet, J. G. & Newton, R. G.	Neutron activation analysis of faience beads	*Archaeometry* 14, 1, 27-40	1972
Atkinson, R. J. C.	Fishermen and farmers In: Piggott, S. (ed) The Prehistoric Peoples of Scotland, 1-38	London	1962
Barnes, I. C. M.	The Aberdeen stocking trade	Textile History 8, 77-98	1977
Barrow, G. W. S.	Kingship and Unity — Scotland 1000-1306	Edward Arnold	1981
Beaton, H.	At the back of Bennachie or Life in the Garioch in the Nineteenth Century	Aberdeen	1915
Berry, J.	James Dunbar 1742-1798: a study of his thought and of his contribution to the Scottish Enlightenment	Ph.D. Thesis University of London	1970
Blundell, Dom. Odo.	The Catholic Highlands of Scotland Vol 1. The Central Highlands	Edinburgh	1909
Bradley, R.	The social foundations of prehistoric Britain	London	1984
Breeze, D. J.	The Northern Frontiers of Roman Britain	Batsford London	1982
Brereton, H. L.	Gordonstoun: Ancient Estate Modern School	Chambers	1968
Brown, I.	Balmoral — The History of a Home	Glasgow	1955
Brown, J.	The New Deeside Guide	Aberdeen	1860

Buchan, J.	A School History of Aberdeenshire	Aberdeen	1961
Buchan Watt, V. J.	The Book of Banchory	Edinburgh	1947
Burl, H. A. W.	The Stone Circles of the British Isles	Yale	1976a
Burl, H. A. W.	Berrybrae recumbent stone circle	*Discovery Excav. Scot* 1976, 6	1976b
Burl, H. A. W.	Rites of the Gods	London	1981
Burl, H. A. W.	Report on the excavation of a Neolithic mound at Boghead, Speymouth Forest, Fochabers, Moray, 1972 and 1974	*Proc. Soc. Antiq. Scot.* 114 (1984), 35-73, fiche 1: A2-C10	1984
Cairnorrie, W. R. I.	The Book of Methlick	Aberdeen	1939
Callander, J. G.	Notice of the discovery of two drinking-cup urns in a short cist at Mains of Leslie, Aberdeenshire	*Proc. Soc. Antiq. Scot.* 46 (1911-12) 344-348	1912
Cameron, A. C.	The History of Fettercairn	L. & R. Parlane Paisley	1899
Campbell, R. H.	The Scottish improvers and the course of agrarian change in the 18th century: L. M. Cullen & T. C. Smouth (eds.). Comparative aspects of Scottish and Irish social and economic History	Donald Edinburgh 204-215	1977
Cant, R.	Old Moray	Elgin Society	1948
Cant, R.	Moray in Scottish History	Elgin Society	1952
Cant, R.	Historic Elgin and its Cathedral	Elgin Society	1974
Cant, R.	The Middle Ages In: The Moray Book D. Omand (ed.)	Paul Harris Edinburgh	1976
Carter, I.	Farmlife in Northeast Scotland 1840-1914 — The Poor Man's Country	Edinburgh	1975
Champion, T., Gamble, C., Shennan, S., & Whittle, A.	Prehistoric Europe	London	1984
Childe, V. G.	Trial excavations at the Old Keig stone circle, Aberdeenshire	*Proc. Soc. Antiq. Scot.* 67 (1932-33) 37-53	1933
Childe, V. G.	Scotland before the Scots	London	1946
Clark, R. W.	Balmoral — Queen Victoria's Highland Home	London	1981
Clark, V. E.	The Port of Aberdeen	Aberdeen	1921
Clarke, D. V., Cowie, T. G. & Foxon, A.	Symbols of Power at the time of Stonehenge	Edinburgh	1985
Coles, F. R.	Report of the stone circles in Aberdeenshire (Inverurie, eastern parishes, and Insch district)	*Proc. Soc. Antiq. Scot.* 36 (1901-02), 488-581	1902
Coles J. M., Taylor, J. J.	The excavation of a midden in the Culbin Sands, Morayshire	*Proc. Soc. Antiq. Scot.* 102 (1969-70), 87-100	1970

Coull, J. R.	The historical geography of Aberdeen	*Scottish Geographical Magazine* 79, 80-94	1963
Coull, J. R.	Salmon fishing in the northeast of Scotland before 1800	*Aberdeen University Review* 42, 31-38	1967
Coull, J. R.	Fisheries in northeast Scotland before 1800	*Scottish Studies,* 13 17-32	1969
Coull, J. R.	Fisheries in Scotland: evidence in Macfarlane's Geographical Collections	*Scottish Geographical Magazine 93* 5-16	1977
Coull, J. R.	The evolution of settlement in the Buchan District of Aberdeenshire since the late 16th century. O'Dell Memorial Monograph 17	University of Abedeen	1984
Cramond, W.	The Making of a Banffshire Burgh	Banff	1893
Cramond, W.	The Annals of Cullen	W. F. Johnston	1888
Cranna, J.	Fraserburgh, Past and Present	Aberdeen	1914
Cruden, S.	The Scottish Castle	Nelson	1960
Cumine, J.	The burgh of Rattray	*Trans. of the Buchan Field Club,* 1, 114-121	1887-90
Daiches, D.	The paradox of Scottish culture: the 18th century experience	Oxford University Press	1964
Dalrymple, C. E.	Notes of the excavation of the stone circle at Crichie, Aberdeenshire	*Proc. Soc. Antiq. Scot.* 18 *(1883-84),* 319-325	1884
Davidson, J.	Inverurie and the Earldom of the Garioch	Edinburgh	1878
Devine, T. M.	The rise and fall of illicit whisky working in North Scotland 1780-1840	*Scottish Historical Review,* 54 155-177	1975
Dodgshon, R. A.	The nature and development of infield-outfield in Scotland	*Trans. Instit. of British Geographers,* 59, 1-23	1973
Dodgshon, R. A.	Land and society in early Scotland	Clarendon Press Oxford	1981
Douglas, R.	The Annals of Forres	Elgin	1934
Duff, D. (ed.)	Queen Victoria's Highland Journals	Exeter	1980
Duffus, H. G.	A History of Monquhitter	Galashiels	1985
Durie, A. J.	Linen spinning in the north of Scotland 1746-1773	*Northern Scotland,* 2, 13-36	1974
Edwards, K. J.	Aspects of the archaeology of the Howe of Cromar In: Gemmell, A. M. D. (ed.) Quaternary Studies in North East Scotland, 82-87	Aberdeen	1975
Edwards, K. J.	Environmental impact in the prehistoric period	*Scot. Archaeol. Forum,* 9 (1979), 27-42	1979

Edwards, K. J. & Ralston, I. B. M.	Postglacial hunter-gatherers and vegetational history in Scotland	*Proc. Soc. Antiq. Scot.* 114 (1984), 15-34	1984
Emerson, R.	The Building of Fyvie Castle In: Treasures of Fyvie	Trustees of the National Galleries of Scotland	1985
Emery, F. V.	The geography of Sir Robert Gordon 1580-1661 and Sir Robert Sibbald 1641-1722	*Scottish Geographical Magazine,* 74, 3-12	1958
Findlay, J. T.	A History of Peterhead	Aberdeen	1933
Forbes, A. H.	Forres — A Royal Burgh 1150-1975	Moray & Nairn County Library	1975
Fraser, D.	Portrait of a parish	Standard Press Montrose	1970
Fraser, G. M.	The Bridge of Dee	Smith, Aberdeen	1913
Fraser, G. M.	The Mounth passes over the Grampians	*Scottish Geographical Magazine,* 36, 116-122; 169-180	1920
Fraser, G. M.	The Old Deeside road	R. Callander Finzean	1980
Friell, J. G. P. Watson, W. G. (ed.)	Pictish Studies	British Arch. Reports British Series, vol. 125 Oxford	1984
Gaffney, V.	Lordship of Strathavon	Third Spalding Club, Aberdeen	1960
Gaffney, V.	Tomintoul: its glens and its people	Sutherland Press Golspie	1976
Gaskin, M.	North East Scotland — A Survey of its Development Potential	HMSO Edinburgh	1969
Geddes, A.	Burghs of laich and brae	*Scottish Geographical Magazine,* 61, 38-45	1945
Gibb, A. & Paddison, R.	The rise and fall of burghal monopolies in Scotland: the case of North East Scotland	*Scottish Geographical Magazine,* 99, 130-140	1983
Giles, J.	Drawings of Aberdeenshire Castles	Third Spalding Club, Aberdeen	1936
Godsman, J.	A history of the burgh and parish of Ellon, Aberdeenshire	W. & W. Lindsay, Aberdeen	1958
Godsman, J.	Glass, Aberdeenshire: the story of a parish	A. P. Reid & Son Aberdeen	1970
Gourlay, R. & Barrett, J.	Dail na Cairaidh	*Curr. Archaeol.* 8 (1983-84), 347-349	1984

Graham, A.	The military road from Braemar to Spittal of Glenshee	*Proc. Soc. Antiq. Scot.* 97, 226-236	1963-4
Graham, A.	Two canals in Aberdeenshire	*Proc. Soc. Antiq. Scot.* 100, 170-178	1967-8
Graham, A.	Old harbours and landing places on the east coast of Scotland	*Proc. Soc. Antiq. Scot.* 108, 322-365	1976-7
Graham, C. & Todd, S.	Old Aberdeen — Burgh: Cathedral: University	Aberdeen	1978
Graham, C.	Historical Walk-about Aberdeen	Aberdeen	1974
Graham, C.	Portrait of Aberdeen and Deeside	Hale	1972
Graham, C.	Portrait of the Moray Firth	Hale	1977
Graham Smith, G. S.	Anvil stones: with special reference to those from Skelmuir, Aberdeenshire	*Proc. Prehist. Soc. East Anglia* 3, 1 (1918-19), 33-59	1919
Grampian Regional Council	Various Structure and District Plans		
Grant, A.	Independence and Nationhood — Scotland 1306-1469	Edward Arnold	1984
Grant, I. F.	An old Scottish handicraft industry	*Scottish Historical Review,* 18, 277-289	1921
Haldane, A. R. B.	The drove roads of Scotland	Nelson, London	1952
Haldane, A. R. B.	New ways through the glens	Nelson, London	1962
Hamilton, H. (ed.)	Selections from the Monymusk Papers	Scottish History Society, Edinburgh	1945
Hamilton, H. (ed.)	Life and labour on an Aberdeenshire estate	Third Spalding Club, Aberdeen	1946
Hamilton, H. (ed.)	The Third Statistical Account of Scotland, the County of Aberdeen	Glasgow	1960
Hamilton, H. (ed.)	The Third Statistical Account of Scotland, the County of Banff	Glasgow	1961
Hamilton, H. (ed.)	The Third Statistical Account of Scotland, the Counties of Nairn and Moray	Glasgow	1965
Hamilton, H.	An economic history of Scotland in the 18th century	Clarendon Press Oxford	1963
Hamilton, R.	The Pluscarden Story	Pluscarden Abbey	1977
Hampsher-Monk, I. & Ambramson, P.	Strichen	*Curr. Archaeol.* 7 (1982), 16-19	1982
Handley, J. E.	Scottish farming in the 18th century	Faber, London	1953
Hanson, W. S. & Maxwell, G. S.	Rome's North West Frontier	Edinburgh University Press Edinburgh	1983

Hawke-Smith, C. F.	Two Mesolithic sites near Newburgh, Aberdeenshire	*Proc. Soc. Antiq. Scot.* 110 (1978-80) 497-502	1980
Henderson, J. A.	History of the Parish of Banchory Devenick	Aberdeen	1890
Henderson, J. A.	Annals of Lower Deeside	Aberdeen	1892
Henshall, A. S.	The Chambered Tombs of Scotland Vol. 1	Edinburgh University Press	1963
Henshall, A. S.	The Chambered Tombs of Scotland Vol. 2	Edinburgh University Press	1972
Henshall, A. S.	The Early Peoples In: Omand D. (ed.) The Moray Book, 95-112	Edinburgh	1976
Henshall, A. S.	The Neolithic pottery from Easterton of Roseisle, Moray, In: O'Connor, A. & Clarke, D. V. (eds.) From the Stone Age to the '45, 19-44	Edinburgh	1983
Hill, O.	Scottish castles of the 16th and 17th centuries	Country Life London	1943
Hunter, J.	The church of St. Nicholas, Aberdeen	*Proc. Soc. Antiq. Scot.* 105, 236-247	1972-4
Imlach, J.	History of Banff	R. Leask, Banff	1868
Inglis, J. C. & Inglis, R. B.	An early metalworker's mould from Corsegight, New Deer	*Proc. Soc. Antiq. Scot.* 113 (1983), 634-646	1983
Jackson, K.	The Gaelic Notes in the Book of Deer	Cambridge	1972
Jenkins, D. (ed.)	The biology and management of the River Dee	NERC, Lavenham Press, Suffolk	1985
Kay, G.	The Landscape of Improvement: a case study of agricultural change in North East Scotland	*Scottish Geographical Magazine,* 78, 100-111	1962
Keillar, A.	Megalithic monuments of N.E. Scotland	London	1934
Keith, A.	A Thousand Years of Aberdeen	Aberdeen University Press	1972
Keith, A.	The Parishes of Drainie and Lossiemouth	Private Publication Lossiemouth	1975
Kellas-Johnstone J. F.	A Concise Bibliography of the History, Topography and Institutions of the shires of Aberdeen, Banff and Kincardine	Aberdeen	1914
Kenworthy, J. B.	The prehistory of north east Scotland In: Gemmell, A. M. D. (ed.) Quaternary Studies in North East Scotland, 74-81	Aberdeen	1975
Kenworthy, J. B.	Nethermills Farms, Crathes: Excavations, 1978-80, Interim Report	St. Andrews	1981

Kenworthy, J. B.	The Flint In: Murray, J. C. (ed.) Excavations in the medieval burgh of Aberdeen 1973-81, 200-215	Edinburgh	1982
Keppie, L. J. F.	Mons Graupius: the search for a battlefield, Scottish Archaeol. Forum, vol. 12, 79-88	Edinburgh University Press	1981
Kilbride-Jones, H. E.	An account of the excavation of the stone circle at Loanhead of Daviot, and of the standing stones of Cullerlie, Echt, both in Aberdeenshire, on behalf of HM Office of Works	*Proc. Soc. Antiq. Scot.* 69 (1934-35), 168-223	1935
Kilbride-Jones, H. E.	A late Bronze Age cemetery: being an account of the excavation of 1935 at Loanhead of Daviot, Aberdeenshire, on behalf of HM Office of Works	*Proc. Soc. Antiq. Scot.* 70 (1935-36), 278-314	1936
Kinnes, I.	Circumstance not context: the Neolithic of Scotland as seen from outside	*Proc. Soc. Antiq. Scot.* 115 (1985)	1985
Kyd, J. G.	The drove roads and bridle paths around Braemar	Oliver & Boyd Edinburgh	1958
Lacaille, A. D.	Unrecorded microliths from Tentsmuir, Deeside and Cromar	*Proc. Soc. Antiq, Scot.* 78 (1943-44), 5-16	1944
Lindsay, I. G.	The Cathedrals of Scotland	Chambers London	1926
Lindsay, J.	Aberdeenshire Canal 1805-1854	*Journal of Transport History,* 6, 158-165	1963-4
Lindsay, J.	The Scottish Poor Law: its operation in the North East from 1745 to 1845	A. H. Stockwell Ilfracombe	1976
Lockhart, D.	The evolution of the planned village in north east Scotland	Ph.D. thesis University of Dundee	1975
Lynch, F. & Ritchie, J. N. G.	Kerb cairns, In: Ritchie, J. N. G. *et al.* Small cairns in Argyll: some recent work	*Proc. Soc. Antiq. Scot.* 106 (1974-75), 14-38	1975
Macdonald, D. F.	Scotland's shifting population 1770-1850	Jackson Glasgow	1937
Macfarlane, L. J.	King's College, Old Aberdeen — a guide and history	University of Aberdeen	
Macfarlane, L. J.	William Elphinstone and the Kingdom of Scotland	Aberdeen	1985
D. Macgibbon & T. Ross	The Castellated and Domestic Architecture of Scotland 5 volumes	Edinburgh	1887-92
Macintosh, J.	History of the Valley of the Dee	Aberdeen	1895
Macintosh, H. B.	Elgin Past and Present	Elgin	1914
Mackenzie, H.	The Third Statistical Account of Scotland, the City of Aberdeen	Edinburgh	1953
Mackinnon, L.	Recollections of an old lawyer	Aberdeen	1935
Mathieson, J.	General Wade and his military roads in the Highlands	*Scottish Geographical Magazine,* 40 193-213	1924

McConnochie, A. I.	Deeside	Aberdeen	1985
McConnochie, A. I.	Donside	Aberdeen	1985
McConnochie, A. I.	Bennachie	Aberdeen	1986
McLynn, F.	The Jacobites	Routledge & Kegan Paul London	1985
McNeill, P. & Nicholson, R. (ed.)	An Historical Atlas of Scotland c.400 - c.1600	Atlas Committee of Conference of Scottish Medievalists, University of St. Andrews	1975
Meldrum, E.	Sir George Skene's house in the Guestrow, Aberdeen	*Proc. Soc. Antiq. Scot.* 92, 85-103	1958-9
Mellor, R. E. H. & Smith, J. S.	A Visitor's Guide to Aberdeen	Centre for Scottish Studies University of Aberdeen	1986
Mercer, R. J.	The excavation of a late Neolithic henge-type enclosure at Balfarg, Markinch, Fife, Scotland, 1977-78	*Proc. Soc. Antiq. Scot.* 111 (1981), 63-171	1981
Milne, J.	Traces of early man in Buchan	*Trans. Buchan Fld Club* (1891-92) 97-108	1892
Milne, J.	Aberdeen — Topographic, Antiquarian and Historical Papers	Aberdeen	1911
Morgan, V.	The first statistical account for studying the agrarian geography of late 18th century Scotland	Ph.D. Thesis University of Cambridge	1968
Morrison, A.	Early man in Britain and Ireland	London	1980
Muir, R.	The political geography of North East Scotland	Ph.D. Thesis University of Aberdeen	1970
Nicol, A.	The story of the West Church of St. Nicholas, Aberdeen	Church Publishers Ramsgate	
O'Dell, A. C.	A century of coal transport in Scotland 1742-1942. L. D. Stamp and S. W. Wooldridge (eds.) London essays in Geography 229-240	Longman London	1951
O'Dell, A. C.	A view of Scotland in the middle of the 18th century	*Scottish Geographical Magazine,* 69, 58-63	1953
O'Dell, A. C. & Mackintosh, J. (eds.)	The North East of Scotland	British Association Central Press Aberdeen	1963
Ogilvie, R. M. & Richmond, I. A. (eds.)	Cornelii Taciti, de vita Agricolae	Clarendon Press Oxford	1967
Omand, D. (ed.)	The Moray Book	Paul Harris Edinburgh	1976

Paddison, R.	The evolution and present structure of central places in North East Scotland	Ph.D. Thesis University of Aberdeen	1969
Paterson, H. M. L. & Lacaille, A. D.	Banchory microliths	*Proc. Soc. Antiq. Scot.* 70 (1935-36), 419-484	1936
Patrick, J.	The Coming of Turnpikes to Aberdeen	Centre for Scottish Studies University of Aberdeen	
Piggott, S.	Traders and metalworkers, In: Piggott, S. (ed.) The Prehistoric Peoples of Scotland, 73-104		1962
Piggott, S.	Excavation of the Dalladies long barrow Fettercairn, Kincardineshire	*Proc. Soc. Antiq. Scot.* 104 (1971-72), 23-47	1972
Piggott, S. & Simpson, D. D. A.	Excavation of a stone circle at Croft Moraig, Perthshire, Scotland	*Proc. Prehist. Soc.*, 37, 1 (1971), 1-15	1971
Pratt, J. B.	Buchan	Aberdeen	1859
Prentice, R. J.	Pitmedden and its great garden	National Trust for Scotland Edinburgh	1965
Price, G.	Pictish, in idem, The Languages of Britain	Edward Arnold London, pp 20-28	1984
Rait, R. S.	The Universities of Aberdeen	J. G. Bisset Aberdeen	1895
Ralston, I. B. M.	Sands of Forvie settlement and burial site	*Discovery Excav. Scot.* 1980, 10-11	1980
Ralston, I. B. M.	A timber hall at Balbridie Farm	*Aberdeen Univ. Rev.*, 168 (1982), 238-249	1982
Ralston, I. B. M.	Notes on the archaeology of Kincardine and Deeside District	*Deeside Fld.* 18 (1984), 73-83	1984
Ralston, I. B. M., Sabine, K. A. & Watt, W. G.	'Later prehistoric settlements in North-east Scotland: a preliminary assessment', In: (eds.) Chapman, J. C. and Mytum, H. C. Settlement in North Britain 1000BC - AD1000 — British Archaeological Reports British Series, vol. 118, pp 149-173	Oxford	1983
Ralston, I. B. M. & Inglis, J. C.	Foul Hordes: the Picts in the North-east and their Background	Anthropological Museum, University of Aberdeen	1984
Rampini, C.	A History of Moray and Nairn	Blackwood	1897
Ritchie, G. & Ritchie, A.	Scotland: archaeology and early history	London	1981
Rolt, L. T. C.	Thomas Telford	Longmans	1958

Ruggles, C. L. N. & Burl, H. A. W.	A new study of the Aberdeenshire recumbent stone circles, 2: interpretation	*Archaeoastronomy 8* (1985), S25-S60 (= J. Hist. Astron, 16)	1985
Sangster, A. H.	The Story and Tales of the Buchan Line	Oxford	1983
Shaw, J.	Water Power in Scotland 1550-1870	Edinburgh	1984
Shaw, L.	History of the Province of Moray (3 vols)	London	1882
Shepherd, I. A. G.	'Pictish settlement problems in North-east Scotland', In: (eds.) Chapman, J. C. and Mytum, H. C. (See Ralston *et al.* supra), 327-56	British Archaeological Reports Vol. 118	1983
Shepherd, A.	Excavation of a Neolithic mound at Midtown of Pitglassie, Auchterless	*Proc. Soc. Antiq. Scot.* 116 (1986)	1986
Shepherd, I. A. G.	Beattie Lodge, Laurencekirk	*Disc. Excav. Scot.* 1984, 10	1984
Shepherd, I. A. G.	Powerful Pots: Beakers the north-east prehistory	Anthropological Museum University of Aberdeen	1986a
Shepherd, I. A. G.	Exploring Scotland's Heritage: Grampian	Edinburgh	1986b
Shepherd, I. A. G. & Cowie, T. G.	An enlarged food vessel urn and associated artefacts from Kiltry Knock, Alvah, Banff & Buchan	*Proc. Soc. Antiq. Scot.* 108 (1976-77), 114-123	1977
Shepherd, I. A. G. & Ralston, I. B. M.	Early Grampian: a guide to the archaeology	Aberdeen	1979
Sillett, S.	Illicit Scotch	Impulse Publications	1965
Simpson, W. D.	The Castle at Kildrummy	D. Wyllie	1923
Simpson, W. D.	Midmar Castle	Deeside Field	1937
Simpson, W. D. (ed.)	The book of Glenbuchat	Third Spalding Club	1942
Simpson, W. D.	The Province of Mar	Aberdeen	1943
Simpson, W. D.	The Earldom of Mar	Aberdeen	1948
Simpson, W. D. (ed.)	The region before 1700: A. C. O'Dell ed., The North-East of Scotland	British Association, Aberdeen	1963
Simpson, W. D.	Scottish Castles	HMSO	1959
Simpson, W. D.	The Development of Castle Fraser	Third Spalding Club	1960
Simpson, W. D.	Craigievar Castle	N.T.S. Guide	1966
Slade, H. G.	Castle Fraser: a seat of the ancient family of Fraser	*Proc. Soc. Antiq. Scot.* 109, 233-300	1977-8
Slater, T. R. (eds.)	The Mansion and policy. M. L. Parry & T. R. Slater (eds.) The Making of the Scottish Countryside, pp 223-247	Croom Helm	1980
Small, A.	The villages of the Howe of the Mearns	*Folk Life* 4 22-29	1966

Small, A. (ed.)	Publication of proceedings of conference "The Picts, a new look at old problems", held at Dundee University, September 1985 (forthcoming)		
Smith, A. (ed.)	A New History of Aberdeenshire (2 vols.)	Aberdeen	1875
Smith, A.	The History and Antiquities of New and Old Aberdeen	Aberdeen	1882
Smith, J. H.	The Gordon's Mill Farming Club 1758-1764	Oliver & Boyd	1962
Smith, J. S.	War and Peace in the Braes of Mar	*Aberdeen University Review,* 161, 36-43	1979
Smith, J. S.	The Development of Aberdeen Harbour	*Aberdeen University Review,* 164, 397-403	1980
Smith, J. S.	The Rise and Fall of Aberdeen's Granite Industry	*Aberdeen University Review,* 167, 163-167	1982
Smith, J. S.	George Washington Wilson's Aberdeen	Keighley	1982
Smith, J. S.	George Washington Wilson's Royal Deeside	Keighley	1984
Smith, R.	Grampian Ways: Journey over the Mounth	Melven Press	1980
Smout, T. C.	Scottish landowners and economic growth	*Scottish Journal of Political Economy,* 11, 218-231	1964
Smout, T. C.	A history of the Scottish People 1560-1830	Collins	1969
Smout, T. C.	The landowners and the planned village In: N. T. Phillipson & N. Mitchison (eds.), Scotland in the age of improvement pp 74-106.	Edinburgh University Press	1970
Smout, T. C. & Fenton, A.	Scottish agriculture before the improvers:	*Agricultural History Review,* 13, 73-93	1965
Smyth, A. P.	'Picts: "The Last Men on Earth, the Last of the Free" ' in idem, Warlords and Holy Men. Scotland AD80-1000 = The New History of Scotland, vol. 1, pp 36-83	Edward Arnold London	1984
Stevenson, R. B. K.	Notes on some prehistoric objects	*Proc. Soc. Antiq. Scot.* 82 (1947-48), 292-295	1948
Stirling, A. M. W.	Fyvie Castle	John Murray	1928
Stirton, J.	Crathie and Braemar — A History of the United Parish	Aberdeen	1925
Stuart, J. (ed.)	Lists of pollable persons within the shire of Aberdeen 1696	Third Spalding Club	1884
Symon, J. A.	Scottish farming past and present	Oliver & Boyd	1959

Taylor, W.	The military roads in Scotland	David & Charles	1976
Thom, A. & Burl, H. A. W.	Megalithic Rings	Brit. Archaeol. Rep. 81, Oxford	1980
Trail, K. E.	The story of Old Aberdeen	D. Wyllie & Son	1930
Tranter, N.	The Fortified House in Scotland — Aberdeenshire, Angus and Kincardine	Edinburgh	1966
Tranter, N.	The Fortified House in Scotland — North and West Scotland	Edinburgh	1970
Tranter, N.	The Queen's Scotland — The North East	London	1974
Tocher, J. F. (ed.)	The Book of Buchan	Peterhead	1910
Turner, W. H.	Flax cultivation in Scotland	*Trans. Inst. Brit. Geographers,* 55, 127-144	1972
Turnock, D.	Small farms in North Scotland: an exploration in historical geography	*Scottish Geographical Magazine,* 92, 164-181	1976
Turnock, D.	Stages of agricultural improvement in the uplands of Scotland's Grampian Region	*Journal of Historical Geography,* 3, 327-347	1977
Turnock, D.	Glenlivet: two centuries of rural planning in the Grampian Uplands	*Scottish Geographical Magazine,* 96, 165-181	1980
Walker, G.	Aberdeen awa': sketches of its men, manners and customs	A. Brown	1897
Walker, I. C.	A cinerary urn cemetery at Easter Culbeuchly, near Banff	*Proc. Soc. Antiq. Scot.* 94 (1960-61), 317-320	1961
Walker, I. C.	Easterton of Roseisle: a forgotten site in Moray In: Coles, J. M. and and Simpson, D. D. A. (eds.) Studies in Ancient Europe, 95-115	Leicester	1968a
Walker, I. C.	Beakers from Easter Gollachy, near Buckie, Banffshire	*Proc. Soc. Antiq. Scot.* 100 (1976-78), 188-190	1968b
Walton, K.	The distribution of population in Aberdeenshire 1696	*Scottish Geographical Magazine,* 66, 17-26	1950
Walton, K.	Rattray: a study on coastal evolution	*Scottish Geographical Magazine,* 72, 85-96	1956
Walton, K.	Population changes in North East Scotland 1 69-1951	*Scottish Studies,* 5, 149-180	1961

Walton, K.	Regional settlement: A. C. O'Dell, ed. The north-east of Scotland	British Association, Aberdeen	1963
Waterman, J. J.	The Coming of the Railway to Aberdeen in the 1840s	Centre for Scottish Studies, University of Aberdeen	1978
Watson, A. & Allan, E.	Papers relating to game poaching on Deeside	*North Scotland,* 7, 39-45	1986
Watson, W. H.	A. Marshall Mackenzie — Architect in Aberdeen	Centre for Scottish Studies, University of Aberdeen	1985
Watt, A.	Highways and Byways round Stonehaven	Aberdeen	1984
Watt, A.	Highways and Byways round Kincardine	Aberdeen	1985
Watt, W.	A History of Aberdeen and Banff	Edinburgh	1900
White, A.	The reformation in Aberdeen: J. S. Smith ed., New Light on Medieval Aberdeen	Aberdeen University Press	1985
Whiteley, A. W. M. (ed.)	The Book of Bennachie	Coupar Angus	1976
Whiteley, A. W. M. (ed.)	Bennachie Again	Coupar Angus	1983
Whittington, G.	Scotland: In A. R. H. Baker & R. A. Butlin, (eds.), Studies of field systems in the British Isles 530-579	Cambridge University Press	1973
Whyte, I.	Agriculture and society in 17th century Scotland	John Donald	1979
Wickham-Jones, C. R. & Collins, G. H.	The sources of flint and chert in Northern Britain	*Proc. Soc. Antiq. Scot.* 109 (1977-78), 7-21	1978
Winram, R. & Cluer, A.	Walking the Mat — past impressions of Aberdeen	Aberdeen	1984
Withers, C. W. J.	The Scottish Highlands outlined: cartographic evidence for the position of the Highland-Lowland boundary	*Scottish Geographical Magazine* 98, 143-157	1982
Wood, S.	The shaping of 19th century Aberdeenshire	Spa Books	1985
Wood, S. & Patrick, J.	History in the Grampian Landscape	Robin Callander Finzean	1982
Wyness, F.	City by the Grey North Sea	Aberdeen	1966
Wyness, F.	Royal Valley — the story of the Aberdeenshire Dee	Aberdeen	1968
Wyness, F.	Spots from the Leopard	Aberdeen	1971
Wyness, F.	More Spots from the Leopard	Aberdeen	1973
Youngson, A. J.	Alexander Webster and his "Account of the Number of People in Scotland in the year 1755"	*Population Studies,* 15, 198-200	1961-62

THE ENVIRONMENT

Allan, J. R.	North East Lowlands of Scotland	Hale	1952
Anderton, R.	Dalradian deposition and the late Precambrian - Cambrian history of the N. Atlantic region: a review of the Iapetus Ocean	*J. Geol. Soc.,* 139, 423-431	1982
Anderton, R.	Sedimentation and tectonics in the Scottish Dalradian	*Scott. J. Geol.,*	1986
Ashcroft, W. A. & Munro, M.	The structure of the eastern part of the Insch mafic intrusion, Aberdeenshire	*Scott. J. Geol.,* 14, 55-79	1984
Ashworth, J. R.	The sillimanite zones of the Huntly-Portsoy area in the north-east Dalradian, Scotland	*Geol. Mag.,* 112, 113-134	1975
Avery, M. I.	Winter activity of pipistrelle bats	*J. Anim. Ecol.,* 54, 721-738	1985
Baird, P.D.	Weather and Snow on Ben Macdhui	*Cairngorm Club Journal,* 17, 147-149	1957
Barclay, W.	Banffshire	Cambridge	1922
Barr, D.	3-D Palinspastic restoration of normal faults in the Inner Moray Firth: implications for extensional basin development	*Earth Planet Sci.* Letters 75, 191-203	1985
Barrow, G.	On the intrusion of muscovite-biotite gneiss in the south-eastern Highlands of Scotland, and its accompanying metamorphism	*Q. J. Geol. Soc.,* London, 49, 330-358	1893
Barrow, G., Hinxman, L. W. & Cunningham Craig, E.H.	The geology of Upper Strathspey, Gaick and the Forest of Atholl	Mem. Geol. Surv. Scotland	1913
Barton, J. S.	Wind and weather on Cairngorm summit	*Scottish Mountaineering Club Journal,* 33, 52-56	1984
Barton, J. S. & Borthwick, A. S.	August weather on a mountain summit	*Weather* 37,8, 228-233	1982
Barton, R. & Wright, B.	A Chance in a Million — Scottish Avalanches	Scottish Mountaineering Trust	1985
Beach, A.	Structural evolution of the Witch Ground Graben	*J. Geol. Soc.,* 141, 621-628	1984
Birse, E. L.	Assessment of Climatic Conditions in Scotland. 3 The Bioclimatic Sub-regions	Macaulay Institute	1971
Birse, E. L. & Dry, F. T.	Assessment of Climatic Conditions in Scotland	Aberdeen, Macaulay Inst. for Soil Research	1970
Bowes, D. R. & Leake, B. E. (eds.)	Crustal Evolution in North-western Britain and Adjacent Regions. Spec. Issue Geol. J. 10	Seel House Press Liverpool	1978
Bremner, A.	The glacial epoch in the north-east. In J. F. Tocher (ed.) The Book of Buchan, Jubilee Volume	Aberdeen	1943

Bremner, A.	Further problems in the glacial geology of North-eastern Scotland	*Trans. Edin. Geol. Soc.* 12 147-164	1932
British Association	Scientific Survey of Aberdeen and District	London	1934
Brown, A. *et al.*	Botanists Guide to the Counties of Aberdeen, Banff and Kincardine		
Brown, P. E.	Caledonian and earlier magmatism. In: Craig 1983, 167-204		1983
Burgess, J. J.	Flora of Moray	Courant & Courier, Elgin	1935
Chesher, J. A. & Lawson, D.	The Geology of the Moray Firth. Rep. Inst. Geol. Sci. No. 83/5	HMSO Edinburgh	1983
Connell, E. R., Edwards, K. J. & Hall, A. M.	Evidence for two pre-Flandrian paleosols in Buchan, north-east Scotland pp 570-572	*Nature,* 297	1982
Craib, W. G.	Flora of Banffshire	Aberdeen University Studies No. 40	1912
Craig, G. Y. (ed.)	Geology of Scotland (2nd ed.) Edinburgh	Scottish Academic Press	1983
Curran, J. C. *et al.*	Cairngorm Summit Automatic Weather Station	*Weather* 32, 2, 60-63	1977
Curry, G. B.	Fossils and tectonics along the Highland Boundary Fault	*J. Geol. Soc.,* 143, 193-198	1986
Curry, G. B., Ingham, J. K., Bluck, B. J. & Williams, A.	The significance of a reliable Ordovician age for some Highland Border rocks in Central Scotland	*J. Geol. Soc.,* 139, 451-454	1982
Curry, G. B., Bluck, B. J., Burton, C. J., Ingham, J. K., Siveter, D. J. & Williams, A.	Age, evolution and tectonic history of the Highland Border complex, Scotland	*Trans. Roy. Soc., Edinb.* Earth Sci., 75, 113-133	1984
Dickie, G.	Botanist's Guide to the Counties of Aberdeen, Banff and Kincardine	Aberdeen	1860
Doornkamp, J. C.	Atlas of Drought in Britain 1975-76	Institute of British Geographers	1980
Downie, C., Lister, T. R., Harris, A. L. & Fettes, D. J.	A palynological investigation of the Dalradian rocks of Scotland. Rep. Inst. Geol. Sci. No. 71/9	HMSO Edinburgh	1971
Duff, P. McL.D.	Economic geology, In Craig 1983 425-454		1983
Dybeck, M. W. & Green, F. H. W.	The Cairngorms Weather Survey	*Weather,* 10, 41-48	1955
Ferguson, R. I.	High Densities, Water Equivalent and Melt Rates of Snow in the Cairngorm Mountains, Scotland	*Weather,* 40,9, 272-276	1985
Fettes, D. J.	The structural and metamorphic state of the Dalradian rocks and their bearing on the age of emplacement of the basic sheet	*Scott. J. Geol.* 6, 108-118	1970

Fleet, H.	Erosion surfaces in the Grampian Highlands of Scotland. Rapport de la Commission pour la Cartographie des Surfaces d'Applanissement Tertiaires	Int. Geog. Union, 91-94 Paris	1938
Francis, P. E.	The climate of the agricultural areas of Scotland	Climatological Memorandum, 108, Met. Office	1981
Gemmell, A.M.D. & Ralston, I. B. M.	Some recent discoveries of ice-wedge cast networks in north-east Scotland	*Scott. J. Geol.* 20(1), 115-118	1984
Gibbs, A. D.	Structural evolution of extensional basin margins	*J. Geol. Soc.*, 141, 609-620	1984
Gillen, C.	Excursions to Cullen and Portsoy, In Trewin *et al* 1986		1986
Gillen, C.	Excursion to Huntly, Elgin and Lossiemouth, In: Trewin *et al* 1986		1986
Gillen, C. & Trewin, N. H.	Dunnottar to Stonehaven and the Highland Boundary Fault	Edinburgh	1986
Glennie, K. W.	Introduction to the Petroleum Geology of the North Sea 2nd ed.		1986
Glennie, K.	Petroleum Geology of the North Sea	Oxford Blackwell	1986
Green, F. H. W.	History Repeats Itself — Flooding in Moray in August 1970	*Scottish Geographical Magazine* 87, 2, 150-152	1971
Green, F. W. H.	Climate and Weather In: The Cairngorms, Nethersole-Thompson, D. & Watson, A. (eds.)	Collins	1974
Gunn, D. M. & Furmage, D. F.	The effect of topography on surface wind	*Meteorological Magazine,* 105, 8-23	1976
Hall, A. M.	The 'Pliocene' gravels of Buchan: a reappraisal: Discussion	*Scott. J. Geol.,* 18, 336-338	1982
Hall, A. M.	Weathering and landform evolution in North-east Scotland	Unpub., Ph.D. Thesis, Univ. of St. Andrews 572 pp	1983
Hall, A. M. (ed.)	Buchan Field Guide	Quaternary Research Association Cambridge	1984
Hall, A. M.	Cenozoic weathering covers in Buchan, Scotland and their significance	*Nature* 315 (6018) 392-395	1985
Hall, A.	Deep weathering patterns in North-east Scotland and their geomorphological significance	*Zeitschrift für Geomorph-ologie*	In Press
Hall, J.	Geophysical constraints on crustal structure in the Dalradian region of Scotland	*J. Geol. Soc.* 142, 149-155	1985
Hallam, A.	Jurassic, Cretaceous and Tertiary sediments, In: Craig 1983, 343-356		1983
Hamilton, H.	The granite industry, In: The North-east of Scotland, British Association for the advancement of Science	Central Press Aberdeen	1963

Hamilton, P.	The Climate of Aberdeen	*Scottish Geographical Magazine*, 79, 2, 74-79	1963
Harris, A. L.,	The growth and structure of Scotland. In: Craig, 1983, 1-22		1983
Harris, A. L. Baldwin, C. T., Bradbury, H. J., Johnson, H. D. & Smith, R. A.	Ensialic basin sedimentation: the Dalradian Supergroup, In: Bowes and Leake, 1978		1978
Harrison, S. J.	Register of Weather Stations	*Roy. Met. Soc.*	1983
Harry, W. T.	The form of the Cairngorm granite pluton	*Scott. J. Geol.* 1, 1-8	1965
Harte, B. Booth, J. E. Deptster, T. J. Fettes, D. J. Mendum, J. R. & Watts, D.	Aspects of the post-depositional evolution of Dalradian and Highland Border Complex rocks in the Southern Highlands of Scotland	*Trans. Roy. Soc. Edinb.* Earth Sci., 75, 151-163	1984
Harte, B.	Glen Esk Dalradian and Barrovian metamorphic zones, In: Trewin *et al.* 1986		1986
Harte, B. Booth, J. Fettes, D. J.	Excursion to the Dalradian of Stonehaven to Portlethen, In: Trewin *et al.* 1986.		1986
Henderson, W. G. & Robertson, A. H. F.	The Highland Border rocks and their relation to marginal basin development in the Scottish Caledonides	*J. Geol. Soc.*, 193, 433-450	1982
Hudson, N. F. C.	Banff-Whitehills Excursion In: Trewin *et al.* 1986		1986
Hutton, D. W. H.	Tectonic slides: a review and reappraisal	*Earth Science Reviews* 15, 151-172	1979
Innes, J. L.	Lichenometric dating of debris flow deposits in the Scottish Highlands	Earth Surfaces Processes and Landforms 8(6), 579-588	1983
Jamieson, T. F.	The Glacial period in Aberdeenshire and the southern border of The Moray Firth	*Q. J. Geol. Soc.* London 62, 13-39	1906
Jenkins, D. (ed.)	The Biology and Management of the River Dee	N.E.R.C. Suffolk	1985
John, J. I.	A sea-breeze front near Aberdeen 7 July 1979	*Weather,* 35, 10, 284-287	1980
Johnson, M. R. W.	Dalradian. In: Craig, 1983 77-104		1983
Jones, R. J. A. *et al.*	Mesoclimate Studies in the Upper Don Basin, Aberdeenshire	*Meteorological Magazine* 108, 289-308	1979
Karllsen, W., Vollset, J., Bjorlykke, K. & Jorgensen, P.	Changes in the mineralogical composition of Tertiary sediments from North Sea wells	*Proc. 6th Int. Clay Conf. 27*	1979
Kesel, R. H. & Gemmell, A. M. D.	The Pliocene gravels of Buchan: a reappraisal	*Scott. J. Geol.* 17(3), 185-203	1981

Kneller, B.	Introduction, In: Trewin *et al.* 1986		1986
Kneller, B.	Fraserburgh-Cairnbulg Excursion, In: Trewin *et al.* 1986		1986
Kneller, B. C. and Leslie, A. G.	Amphibolite facies metamorphism in shear zones in the Buchan area of NE Scotland	*J. Metamorphic Geol.*, 2, 83-94	1984
Lambert, R. St. J., Holland, J. G., & Winchester, J.A.	A geochemical comparison of the Dalradian Leven Schists and the Grampian Division Monadhliadh Schists of Scotland	*J. Geol. Soc.*, 139, 71-81	1982
Leslie, A. G.	Excursion to Belhelvie and Insch, In: Trewin *et al.* 1986		1986
Linton, D. L.	Problems of Scottish scenery	*Scottish Geographical Magazine* 67. 65-85	1951
Lovell, J. P. B.	Permian and Triassic, In: Craig 1983, 325-342		1983
Macgillivray, W.	The Natural History of Dee side and Braemar	Bradbury & Evans, London	1855
Macgregor, R.	Fife and Angus Geology; an Excursion Guide	Blackwood Edinburgh	1968
Macpherson, A.	Climate In: The County of Aberdeen	Third Statistical Account of Scotland	1960
Maitland, P. S. & East, K.	The freshwater fish fauna of south-west Scotland	*Trans. J. Proc. Dumfries Galloway Nat. Hist. Soc.* 47, 49-62	1970
Maitland, P. S.	The freshwater fish fauna of the Forth area	*Forth Nat. & Hist.* 4, 33-47	1980
Maitland, P. S.	The freshwater fish fauna of the Outer Hebrides	*Hebrid. Nat. 4* 36-45	1981
Maitland, P. S. & East, K.	The freshwater fish fauna of Shetland	*Glasg. Nat. 19* 321-324	1976
C. C. Wallen(ed.)			
Manley, G.	The Climate of Britain In: The Climates of Northern and Western Europe	Elsevier	1970
Manley, G.	Meteorological Observations on Royal Deeside	*Weather* 33,12 457-459	1978
Marren, P.	A Natural History of Aberdeen	Callander	1982
McBoyle, G. R.	Some deductions on the effect of the local environment on the climate of Aberdeen	Unpub. Ph.D. thesis, University of Aberdeen	1969
Mckerrow, W. S.	The northwest margin of the Iapetus Ocean during the early Palaeozoic	*Mem. Am. Assoc. Petrol.Geol.*, 34, 521-533	1982
McVean, D. N. & Ratcliffe, D. A.	Plant Communities of the Scottish Highlands	HMSO London	1962
Met. Office	Frequencies of snow depths and days with snow lying at stations in Scotland for periods ending Winter 1981/82	Climatological Memorandum 144	1983

Mossman, R. C.	The Climate of Braemar	*Journal Scottish Meteorological Society,* 3rd series, 10, 25-41	1896
Munro, M.	Cumulate relations in the "Younger Basic" masses of the Huntly-Portsoy area, Grampian Region	*Scott. J. Geol.* 20, 343-360	1984
Munro, M. & Gallacher, J. W.	Disruption of the "Younger Basic" masses in the Huntly-Portsoy area, Grampian Region	*Scott. J. Geol.* 20, 361-382	1984
Mykura, W.	Old Red Sandstone, In: Craig 1983, 205-252		1983
N.E. Scotland Bird Club	N. E. Scotland Bird Report	Published annually by N. E. Scotland Bird Club	
Nethersole-Thompson, D. & Watson, A.	The Cairngorms	Collins London	1981
Nethersole-Thompson, D.	Crossbill taxonomy. Knox A. G. in "Pine Crossbills"	Poyser	1975
O'Dell, A. C. Macintosh, J.	The North-east of Scotland	British Association, Aberdeen.	1963
Oldershaw, W.	The Lochnagar granitic ring complex, Aberdeenshire	*Scott. J. Geol.* 10, 297-310	1974
Omand, D. (ed.)	The Moray Book	Edinburgh	1976
Pankhurst, R. J. Sutherland, D. S.	Caledonian granites and diorites of Scotland and Ireland, In: Igneous Rocks of the British Isles, 149-180	Wiley, Chichester	1982
Parker, J.	The hazards of Scotland's climate In: S. Harrison (ed.) Climatic Hazards of Scotland	Norwich	1985
Peacock, J. D., Berridge, N. C., Harris, A. L. & May, F.	The Geology of the Elgin District	*Mem. Geol. Survey. Edinb.* HMSO	1968
Pearson, M. G.	Snowstorms in Scotland, 1782-1786	*Weather,* 28, 5, 195-201	1973
Peck, E.	North East Scotland	Edinburgh	1981
Perring, F. H. & Walters, S. M.	Atlas of the British Flora, 2nd edition	EP Publishing Ltd. Wakefield	1976
Piasecki, M. A. J.	New light on the Moine rocks of the Central Highlands of Scotland	*J. Geol. Soc.,* 137, 41-59	1980
Piasecki, M. A. J. & Van Breemen, O.	The "Central Highland Granulites": cover-basement tectonics in the Moine, In: Harris, A. L., Holland, C. H. and Leake, B. E. (eds.) The Caledonides of the British Isles -Reviewed	Spec. Publ. Geol. Soc., 8 139-144	1979
Plant, J. A.	The Climate of the Coastal Region of the Moray Firth	Climatological Memorandum 62 Met. Office	1969

Plant, J. A.	The Climate of Aberdeen	Climatological Memorandum 66 Met. Office	1970
Plant, J. A., Watson, J. V. & Green, P. M.	Moine-Dalradian relationships and their palaeotectonic significance	*Proc. Roy. Soc.* London, 395A, 185-202	1984
Racey, P. A., & Swift, S. M.	Feeding ecology of Pipistrellus pipstrellus (Chiroptera: Vespertilionidae) during pregnancy and lactation. 1. Foraging behaviour	*J. Anim. Ecol.* 54, 205-215	1985
Racey, P. A. & Swift, S. M.	The residual effects of remedial timber treatments in bats	Biological Conservation 35, 205-214	1986
Rapson, S.	The age of corrie moraines and post-glacial environmental change in the Cairngorm Mountains, Scotland	Unpub. Ph.D. Thesis, University of Aberdeen	1983
Rapson, S.	Minimum age of corrie moraine ridges in Cairngorm Mountains, Scotland	*Boreas,* 14 155-159	1985
Read, H. H.	The Geology of the Country round Banff, Huntly and Turriff. (Expl. Sheets 86, 96)	*Mem. Geol. Surv. Scot.* Edinburgh HMSO	1923
Read, H. H.	Metamorphism and migmatization in the Ythan Valley, Aberdeenshire	*Trans. Edin. Geol. Soc.,* 15 265-279	1952
Richter, A.	Other Wild Life in: The Moray Book	Paul Harris Edinburgh	1976
Ritchie, J.	The influence of man on animal life in Scotland	Cambridge University Press	1920
Ross, S. M.	The physical background and climate In: The Moray Book, Omand, D.	Paul Harris Edinburgh	1976
Scottish Ornithologists' Club	Scottish Birds	Published by Scottish Ornithologists' Club	
Singleton, F.	Weather Data for Schools — Part One	*Weather,* 40, 9, 267-271	1985
Sim, G.	The vertebrate fauna of "Dee"	Wyllie, Aberdeen	1903
Sissons, J. B.	Scotland	Methuen London	1976
Smithson, P. A.	Regional Variations in the Synoptic Origin of Rainfall across Scotland	*Scottish Geographical Magazine,* 85, 3, 182-195	1969
Soper, J. & Hutton, D. H. W.	Late Caledonian sinistral displacements in Britain: implications for a three-plate collision model	*Tectonics,* 3 781-794	1984
Spink, P. C.	Scottish Snow Beds in Summer 1972	*Weather,* 28, 4, 162-163	1973
Spink, P. C.	Scottish Snow Beds in Summer: 1979 Survey and some comments on the Last Thirty Years	*Weather,* 35 9, 256-259	1980

Stebbings, R. E. & Griffith, F.	Distribution and status of bats in Europe. Report prepared for the NCC for inclusion in the EEC threatened species list	Nature Conservancy Council Banbury	1984
Sugden, D. E.	The age and form of corries in the Cairngorms	*Scottish Geographical Magazine,* 85(1) 34-46	1969
Sugden, D. E.	The selectivity of glacial erosion in the Cairngorm Mountains, Scotland	*Trans. Inst. Brit. Geogr.* 45, 79-92	1968
Sugden, D. E.	The Cairngorm Tors and their significance	Scottish Mountaineering Club Journal 32, 327-334	1982
Sutherland, D. G.	The Quaternary deposits and landforms of Scotland and the neighbouring shelves: a review	*Quat. Science Reviews* 3 157-254	1984
Swift, S. M., Racey, P. A. & Avery, M. I.	Feeding ecology of Pipistrellus pipistrellus (Chiroptera: Vespertilionidae) during pregnancy and lactation. 11. Diet	*J. Anim. Ecol.* 54 217-225	1985
Swift, S. M. & Racey, P. A.	Resource partitioning in two species of Vespertilionid bats (Chiroptera) occupying the same roost	*J. Zool.* London 200, 249-259	1983
Synge, F. M.	The glaciation of North-east Scotland	*Scottish Geographical Magazine* 72, 129-143	1956
Thomas, M. F.	Tropical geomorphology	Macmillan	1974
Townshend, G. K.	Some micro-climatic aspects of the Aberdeen area	*Scottish Geographical Magazine* 64, 2 66-70	1948
Trail, J. W. H.	The Flora of Buchan	P. Scrogie Peterhead	1902
Trail, J. W. H.	Flora of the City Parish of Aberdeen The Trail Memorial Volume	Aberdeen University Press	1923
Treagus, J. E. & Roberts, J. L.	The Boyndie Syncline, a D1 structure in the Dalradian of Scotland	*Geol. J.* 16, 125-135	1981
Trewin, N. H.	Orcadian Basin issue. Editorial introduction	*Scott. J. Geol.,* 21, Part 3, 225-226 (and 227-383 for other papers)	1985
Trewin, N. H.	Excursion to Crawton, In: Trewin *et al.*		1986
Trewin, N. H. Kneller, B. Gillen, C.	Guide to the Geology of the Aberdeen Area	Scottish Academic Press, Edin- burgh	1986
Vann, I. R.	The siting of Tertiary vulcanicity, In: Bowes and Leake 1978, 393-414		1978

Walker, A. D. Campbell, C.G.B. Heslop, R. E. G. Gauld, J. H. Laing, D. Shipley, B. M. & Wright, G. G.	Eastern Scotland. Soil and land capability for Agriculture, Soil Survey of Scotland, Sheet 5, 1:250,000 scale	Macaulay Institute for Soil Research Aberdeen	1982
Walton, K.	Climate, In: The North-east of Scotland	British Association for the Advancement of Science	1963
Ward, R. G. W.	Snow avalanches in Scotland with particular reference to the Cairngorm Mountains	Unpub. Ph.D. Thesis, University of Aberdeen	1981
Watson, A. & Hewson, R.	Population densities of mountain hares (Lepus timidus) on western Scottish and Irish moors and on Scottish hills	*Journ of Zoology,* 170, 151-159	1973
Webster, M. M.	Flora of Moray, Nairn and East Inverness	Aberdeen University Press	1978
Woodland, A. W. (ed.)	Petroleum and the Continental Shelf of Northwest Europe. Vol. 1 Geology	Applied Science Publishers, Barking	1975

Index